ACS SYMPOSIUM SERIES **327**

Photochemistry of Environmental Aquatic Systems

Rod G. Zika, EDITOR
University of Miami

William J. Cooper, EDITOR
Florida International University

Developed from a symposium sponsored by
the Divisions of Geochemistry and Environmental Chemistry
at the 189th Meeting
of the American Chemical Society,
Miami Beach, Florida,
April 28–May 3, 1985

American Chemical Society, Washington, DC 1987

Library of Congress Cataloging-in-Publication Data

Photochemistry of environmental aquatic systems.
  (ACS symposium series, ISSN 0097-6156; 327)

  "Developed from a symposium sponsored by the
Divisions of Geochemistry and Environmental
Chemistry at the 189th Meeting of the American
Chemical Society, Miami Beach, Florida, April 28–
May 3, 1985."

  Bibliography: p.
  Includes index.

  1. Environmental chemistry—Congresses.
2. Photochemistry—Congresses. 3. Water chemistry—
Congresses. 4. Aquatic ecology—Congresses.

  I. Cooper, William J. II. Zika, Rodney G., 1940–
III. American Chemical Society. Division of
Geochemistry. IV. American Chemical Society.
Division of Environmental Chemistry. V. American
Chemical Society. Meeting (189th: 1985: Miami
Beach, Fla.) VI. Series.

TD193.P48   1987   628.1'61   86-26489
ISBN 0-8412-1008-X

SP₂/2/87

ACS Symposium Series

M. Joan Comstock, *Series Editor*

Advisory Board

Foreword

The ACS SYMPOSIUM SERIES was founded in 1974 to provide a medium for publishing symposia quickly in book form. The format of the Series parallels that of the continuing ADVANCES IN CHEMISTRY SERIES except that, in order to save time, the papers are not typeset but are reproduced as they are submitted by the authors in camera-ready form. Papers are reviewed under the supervision of the Editors with the assistance of the Series Advisory Board and are selected to maintain the integrity of the symposia; however, verbatim reproductions of previously published papers are not accepted. Both reviews and reports of research are acceptable, because symposia may embrace both types of presentation.

Contents

Preface

Photochemistry is not a new field, and numerous books exist that cover the basic areas of photochemistry. The study of photochemistry in aqueous solutions, and in particular its application to environmental processes, is relatively new.

The field of aquatic photochemistry encompasses a wide diversity of areas within environmental science. Natural waters receiving solar radiation are active photochemical reactors. Within these reactors, primary and secondary processes are occurring. Heterogeneous reactions are associated with both living and nonliving particulate matter. Naturally occurring humic substances are relatively efficient initiators of photochemical reactions. Many xenobiotic chemicals in natural waters undergo either direct or indirect photochemical transformations.

Within the areas of water and waste water, photochemistry may be the result of open contact chambers or it may be used as a treatment process to control organic compounds or for disinfection. Within atmospheric studies, numerous photochemically induced reactions occur in cloud droplets.

Studies that are presently being conducted in the field range from purely phenomenological descriptions of photoproducts in the environment to time-resolved laser spectroscopic studies of primary photoprocesses. This book is a first attempt to compile chapters dealing with this complex and rapidly evolving field of environmental science.

Rod G. Zika
Rosenstiel School of Marine and Atmospheric Sciences
Division of Marine and Atmospheric Chemistry
University of Miami
Miami, FL 33149

William J. Cooper
Drinking Water Research Center
Florida International University
Tamiami Campus
Miami, FL 33199

August 23, 1986

Chapter 1

Introduction and Overview

William J. Cooper[1] and Frank L. Herr[2]

[1]**Drinking Water Research Center, Florida International University, Miami, FL 33199**
[2]**Office of Naval Research, Code 422CB, Arlington, VA 22217**

Sunlight that arrives at the surface of the earth contains substantial amounts of energy. When surface waters, which contain either natural or anthropogenic chromophores, are exposed to sunlight, light initiated chemical reactions often occur.

Sunlight induced photochemical reactions in surface waters may broadly be defined as environmental aquatic photochemistry. Within aquatic photochemistry, it is possible to envision reactions involving either inorganic and/or organic molecules. These chemicals could be either natural or anthropogenic and may participate in either homogeneous or heterogeneous reactions. Very often in these environments, a complex array of primary and secondary photoprocesses are occurring simultaneously.

Surface waters are diverse in nature. They might be near shore or inland wetland environments or mid-oceanic oligotrophic water. Until recently, sunlight induced photochemistry was not recognized as an important pathway for the transformation of natural and anthropogenic chemicals in surface waters. It is now well established that photochemically mediated processes are important in most, if not all, areas of aqueous phase environmental chemistry. Both direct, primary, and indirect photoprocesses have been documented in natural waters.

The fact that all of these possibilities exist is exciting. There are a seemingly endless number of combinations and permutations to study; however, caution should be used. The potential factors affecting any one study are so complex that extreme care must be taken when interpreting data obtained from natural systems. On the other hand, extrapolating data obtained in laboratory studies to natural environments generally requires the use of many assumptions.

Numerous reviews have been published that detail various aspects of aquatic photochemistry (1-11). This book brings together a group of papers representing a number of topics, in order to provide the reader with an appreciation of the complexity of the field and, at the same time, a glimpse of various areas

0097–6156/87/0327–0001$06.00/0

within the relatively young field of environmental aquatic photochemisty. This book is not an exhaustive compilation of the field of environmental aquatic photochemistry.

Direct Photoreactions

A wide variety of substances with active chromophores at wavelengths found in the surface solar spectrum occur in natural waters. Some of these substances undergo direct photolysis, that is a chemical change that results as a direct consequence of the absorption of photons by the substance. Conceptually, direct photoreactions are the simplest and usually the easiest type of process to study in natural waters. Since the reaction proceeds rapidly to products from the primary excited state manifold, the physical characteristics of the reactant's environment usually have only small effects on the reaction. Such reactions can often be studied in pure and/or relatively high concentrations of the reactant.

Comparatively few natural molecules fit into this category (5), and most of these exhibit only weak absorbances at the high energy threshold of the surface solar spectrum. Most naturally occurring compounds are therefore quite transparent to incident solar radiation and reactions of these compounds which proceed via direct photolysis are the exception rather than the rule. Most examples of direct photochemical reactions are found among the numerous studies done on xenobiotic substances (1,6), where the environmental rate is often derived from laboratory measurements which are carried out in organic solvents because of the limited solubility of the compounds. If the electronic absorption spectra and the quantum yield for the compound are determined in water or in an organic solvent system which gives a good approximation to water, then the calculation of an environmental rate is a relatively simple matter. For more complex molecules, the reaction quantum yield is generally wavelength independent (12) and the direct photolysis rate constant can be computed for a specific location and time from the electronic absorption spectra, the quantum yield, and the solar spectral irradiance.

Indirect Photoreactions

The high light transparencies of most compounds in natural water to solar radiation dictate that direct photo-reactions of these compounds are either not possible or represent only a minor reaction pathway. Indirect photochemical reactions for such compounds can only occur either through reaction with reactive molecules in ground or excited states that are themselves products of primary photochemistry, or through photosensitized reactions in which the excited state species of some chromophore transfers an electron or energy to the compound. The importance of both of these indirect reaction pathways in natural water systems is now recognized. A substantial amount of evidence exists in the literature implicating indirect reaction mechanisms in the photochemistry of both xenobiotic and natural compounds (4,5,6,10). The complexity of natural water systems and the host of simultaneous photo-reactions which are occurring frequently make a clear mechanistic interpretation of the data difficult.

Secondary photo-oxidants. There are three recognized primary sources of secondary oxidants in natural aquatic environments. The first of these arises from in situ primary photo-reactions which often produce free radicals and other reactive products. The range of reactivity for free radicals varies from the very strong oxidizing species like OH to weakly oxidizing and more selective species like CO_3^-, NO, and O_2^-. Subsequent reactions of these radicals can lead to other reactive products. For example, OH in seawater and other halide containing waters will rapidly convert to dihalide anion radicals like Br_2^- and I_2^- (5, 13). Hydrogen abstraction reactions from organic compounds by such inorganic radicals can produce radicals which in turn might react with oxygen to form organo-peroxy radicals and possibly peroxides. Reactive non-radical products can also be formed. Hydrogen peroxide for example is believed to result from the disproportionation of O_2^-, which in turn is generated primarily from dissolved humic substances (HS) (14-16). The compexity of the reaction sequence is shown in the following equations:

$$HS + hr \longrightarrow HS^* \qquad [1]$$

$$HS^* + O_2 \longrightarrow HS^{+\cdot} + O_2^{-\cdot} \qquad [2]$$

$$2O_2^{-\cdot} + 2H^+ \longrightarrow H_2O_2 + O_2 \qquad [3]$$

$$HS^{+\cdot} + O_2 \longrightarrow HSO_2^{\cdot+} \qquad [4]$$

$$HSO_2^{\cdot+} + RH \longrightarrow HSO_2H + R^{\cdot+} \qquad [5]$$

$$H_2O_2 \longrightarrow 2OH^\cdot \qquad [6]$$

$$HSO_2H \longrightarrow HSO^\cdot + OH^\cdot \qquad [7]$$

$$OH^\cdot + X^- \longrightarrow HOX^{-\cdot} \qquad [8]$$

$$HOX^{-\cdot} + X^- \longrightarrow OH^- + X_2^{-\cdot} \qquad [9]$$

(where X is a halide)

Although this set of reactions does not indicate all of the possible steps involved, it is interesting to note that the initial primary photoprocesses resulted in 10 secondary products. In addition, the two peroxide molecules (i.e. H_2O_2 and HSO_2H) are new chromophores and function as reservoirs for further radical production.

A second source for secondary oxidants comes from thermal reactions when reactive photo-products such as H_2O_2 react with other constituents of the water. Reactions of peroxides with various transition metals, for instance, will produce O_2 or OH radicals and often the metal ion is converted to a new reactive oxidation state. This sort of process has been demonstrated for the Cu(II)/Cu(I) couple in seawater (17). Reactions such as these may be far removed from the initial photochemical process; however, they are a consequence of it and may have the important function of acting as a redox buffer in environmental water systems.

The third source of secondary photo-oxidants arises from fluxes of atmospheric oxidants through the surface of natural water bodies. Although these products do not originate from aquatic photo-reactions, they nevertheless augment the in situ reaction sources of seconday reactive products and must be taken into account, especially when attempting to quantify reaction processes in the steep gradient region near the air-water interface. Thompson and Zafiriou (18) have examined the chemical impact on natural waters and have calculated air-water fluxes for many of the diverse atmospheric oxidants.

Photosensitized Processes. One of the most studied indirect photoreactions is the formation of singlet oxygen ($^1\Delta g$ O_2) by energy transfer from the triplet excited state of natural organic chromophores in environmental waters. This process has been observed in both seawater (19) and freshwater (20,21). The evidence suggests that singlet oxygen is a common product in natural water systems, but its importance relative to other secondary photo-products in affecting the chemistry is uncertain. Its limited significance is a function of its selective reactivity, low rate constants and its rapid relaxation to the ground state in aqueous media.

Photosensitization via energy transfer in dilute solutions of sensitizer and receptor is in general a low efficiency process. This will probably hold true for most environmental aquatic systems. Much higher efficiencies might, however, be obtained in heterogeneous reaction environments such as micelles, particles, or other interfaces where sensitizer and reactant are concentrated.

Photosensitization by electron transfer, as shown in equation 2 above, has also been observed (22,23). The occurrence of O_2^- (14,16) in natural waters is good evidence that these processes are occurring, at least for oxygen reduction. With electron acceptors other than oxygen, this process is probably similar to energy transfer in that there is a low probability for other electron acceptors to be involved except in heterogeneous environments.

Heterogeneous Reactions

Surface mediated processes are also an important consideration in natural water photochemistry. In aqueous media, two different surface/interfaces may occur that result in heterogeneous reactions. The two interfaces considered here are liquid-solid and liquid-liquid. Surface processes in geochemistry and aquatic enviroments have been covered in more detail in two recent books and the reader is referred to these volumes for more details (24,25).

Natural water systems often contain particulate matter. The particulate matter may be either living or non-living. Algae are the predominant component of the living particulate matter. The non-living particulate matter is primarily inorganic in composition, but may have organic matter associated with it. Particulate-liquid interfaces are known to participate in thermally and/or photochemically mediated reactions.

Surface microlayers are implicated in many chemical processes. They are exposed to the full solar spectrum of light arriving at the surface, and are often important in photochemically mediated reactions. The microlayer, associated with most natural waters, is considerably different in chemical composition from the underlying water column (26). Hence, the photochemically mediated reactions that take place in this layer may differ substantially from those in the water column. The differences in the reactions may be one of kinetics (rates of the reaction), or maybe mechanistic in nature and the reaction(s) proceed(s) via different pathways resulting in different reaction products.

One extreme case of the liquid-liquid interface is the oil spill (slick) problem. The field of oil-water photochemistry has recently been reviewed (27-29). It has been shown that numerous processes may and do occur simultaneously, and that the chemistry associated with studies of this type are extremely complex .

Natural microlayers form on most water surfaces. There are numerous difficulties encountered when studying them. One of the most perplexing problems centers around the collection of natural samples of microlayers. Another difficulty is that processes occurring in the microlayer are often not well characterized (26). Thus, innovative approaches are required to study processes similar to those in natural waters.

In the case of particulate matter, different types of reactions may be involved. Reactions that occur on the surfaces of the non-living particulate matter may involve direct photochemically mediated reactions in surface complexes. Another possibility is surface semiconductor redox reactions. In the case of the living algal particulate matter, a third process would be photosensitized reaction on the surface of algae.

The particulate surface heterogeneous reactions may result in primary and/or secondary processes. Most of the examples of algal associated processes suggest secondary reactions resulting from exudates in the aqueous phase.

Quantifying Environmental Photoprocesses

As in many areas of environmental science, one of the most difficult aspects of environmental photochemistry is extrapolating laboratory based experiments to the natural environment. One tool that is becoming used more frequently is that of mathematical models to predict the distribution of photoproducts in the environment (12). Modeling aquatic photoprocesses is complex, for in order to describe in detail the observed products, it is necessary to understand quantum yields throughout the solar spectrum, formation rates, in many cases decomposition rates (the photoproducts are rarely conservative), absorbance characteristics of the aquatic system, and physical mixing of the water masses.

The simplest modeling situation exists for those cases where
the quantum yield is a constant or can be assumed to be a constant
over the solar spectrum (12).   In cases where the quantum yield
varies as a function of wavelength the case is substantially more
complex.   This is true in the case of H_2O_2 formation from humic
substances (30) and is probably true for many other environmental
photoprocesses where multiple chromophores or reaction mechanisms
are involved.

Providing accurate model calculations requires that quantum
yields be carefully determined. New approaches are needed in
actinometry and in the measurement of the absorbance of active
chromophores in dilute solutions that absorb only a small fraction
of the total incident polychromatic radiation.   Quantum yields can
be obtained that are wavelength-averaged in the near UV (310 - 410
nm) and these are applicable to existing models (31). The use of
wavelength-averaged quantum yields is quite simple and in
particular, useful when single wavelength measurements are not
possible. Provided that good quantum yield and absorbance values
can be obtained for photoprocesses in natural aquatic systems, it
is possible to provide a good photochemical model approximation for
reaction rates in the environment (12).   To obtain a realistic
distribution of photochemically derived property, it is necessary
to consider properties such as decay rates of the species of
interest and physical mixing of the water column (32).

Summary

It is quite apparent from this introduction and the chapters to
follow, that the field of environmental aquatic photochemistry is
quite large. For the most part, it is a very young field and one
in which a considerable effort remains in order to obtain a
quantitative understanding of the significance to environmental
processes. This book is a first attempt to bring together a series
of papers discussing various aspects of this field.

References

1. Choudhry, G.G. Toxicol. Environ. Chem., 1981, 4, 261-295.

2. Sundstrom, G.; Ruzo, L.O.   In "Aquatic Pollutants:
    Transformation and Biological Effects"; Hutzinger, O.; van
    Lelyveld, L.H.; Zoeteman, B.C.J., Eds.; Pergamon Press, N.Y.,
    1978, 205-222.

3. Zafiriou, O.C. Mar. Chem., 1977, 5, 497-522.

4. Zafiriou, O.C. In "Chemical Oceanography" Vol. 8, 2nd ed.;
    Riley, J.P.; Chester, R., Eds.; Academic Press, London, 1983,
    339-379.

5. Zafiriou, O.C.; Joussot-Dubien, J.; Zepp, R.G.; Zika, R.G.
    Environ. Sci. Technol., 1984, 18, 358A–371A.

6. Zepp, R.G.; Baughman, G.L. In "Aquatic Pollutants:
    Transformations and Biological Effects"; Hutzinger, O.; van
    Lelyveld, L.H.; Zoeteman, B.C.J., Eds.; Pergamon Press, N.Y.,
    1978, 237–263.

7. Zepp, R.G. In "Dynamics, Exposure and Hazard Assessment of
    Toxic Chemicals"; Haque, R., Ed.; Ann Arbor Sci. Pub., Ann
    Arbor, MI, 1980, 69–110.

8. Zepp, R.G. In "The Handbook of Environmental Chemistry. Vol.
    2, Part B, Reactions and Processes"; Hutzinger, O., Ed.;
    Springer-Verlag, N.Y., 1980, 19–41.

9. Zepp, R.G. In "The Role of Solar Ultraviolet Radiation in
    Marine Ecosystems"; Calkins, J., Ed.; Plenum Press, N.Y.,
    1982, 293–307.

10. Zika, R.G. In "Marine Organic Chemistry: Evolution,
    Composition, Interactions and Chemistry of Organic Matter in
    Seawater"; Duursma, E.K.; Dawson, R., Eds.; Elsevier Sci.
    Publ. Co., Amsterdam, 1981, 299–325.

11. Mill, T. In "The Handbook of Environmental Chemistry. Vol. 2.
    Part A, Reactions and Processes"; Hutzinger, O., Ed.,
    Springer-Verlag, N.Y., 1980, 77–105.

12. Zepp, R.G.; Cline, D.M. Environ. Sci. Technol., 1977, 11,
    359–366.

13. Zafiriou, O.C.; True, M.B.; Hayon, E. In "Photochemistry of
    Environmental Aquatic Systems"; Zika, R.G.; Cooper, W.J.,
    Eds., ACS Symposium Series, Washington, D.C., this volume.

14. Cooper, W.J.; Zika, R.G. Science, 1983, 220, 711–712.

15. Draper, W.M.; Crosby, D.G. Arch. Environ. Contam. Toxicol.,
    1983, 12, 121–126.

16. Baxter, R.M.; Carey, J. Nature (London), 1983, 306, 575–576.

17. Moffet, J.W.; Zika, R.G. Mar. Chem., 1983, 13, 239–251.

18. Thompson, A.M.; Zafiriou, O.C. J. Geophys. Res., 1983, 88,
    6696–6708.

19. Momzikoff, A.; Santos, R. Mar. Chem., 1983, 12, 1–14.

20. Hagg, W.R.; Hoigne, J. Environ. Sci. Technol., 1986, 20,
    341–348.

21. Zepp, R.G.; Baughman, G.L.; Schlotzhauer, P.F. Chemosphere, 1981, 10, 109-117.

22. Fisher, A.M.; Winterle, J.S.; Mill, T. In "Photochemistry of Environmental Aquatic Systems"; Zika, R.G.; Cooper, W.J., Eds., ACS Symposium Series, Washington, D.C., this volume.

23. Powers, J.F.; Sharma, D.K.; Lanford, C.H.; Bonneau, R.; Joussot-Dubien, J. In "Photochemistry of Environmental Aquatic Systems"; Zika, R.G.; Cooper, W.J., Eds., ACS Symposium Series, Washington, D.C. this volume.

24. Davis, J.A., Ed. "Surface Processes in Aqueous Geochemistry." American Chemical Society, Washington, D.C., 1986.

25. Stumm, W., Ed. "Aquatic Surface Chemistry." Wiley-Interscience, 1986.

26. Williams, P.M.; Carlucci, A.F.; Henrichs, S.M.; Van Vleet, E.S.; Horrigan, S.G.; Reid, F.M.H; Robertson, K.J. Mar. Chem., 1986, 19, 17-98.

27. Payne, J.R.; McNabb, G.D. Mar. Technol. Soc. J., 1984, 18(3), 24-42; Payne, J.R.; Phillips, C.R. Environ. Sci. Technol., 1985, 19, 569-579.

28. Patton, J.S.; Rigter, U.W.; Boehm, P.D.; Feist, D.L. Nature, 1981, 290, 235-238.

29. Larson, R.A., Hunt, L.L.; Ablankenship, D.W. Environ. Sci. Technol., 1977, 11, 492-496.

30. Cooper, W.J.; Zika, R.G.; Petasne, R.G.; Plane, J.M.C. Environ. Sci. Technol., submitted.

31. Draper, W.M. In "Photochemistry of Environmental Aquatic Systems"; Zika, R.G.; Cooper, W.J., Eds. ACS Symposium Series, Washington, D.C., this volume.

32. Plane, J.M.C.; Zika, R.G.; Zepp, R.G.; Burns, L.A. In "Photochemistry of Environmental Aquatic Systems"; Zika, R.G.; Cooper, W.J. Eds., ACS Symposium Series, Washington D.C., this volume.

RECEIVED August 26, 1986

TRANSFORMATION OF XENOBIOTIC COMPOUNDS

Chapter 2

Specific Phototransformation of Xenobiotic Compounds: Chlorobenzenes and Halophenols

Pierre Boule[1], Claude Guyon[2], Annie Tissot[1], and Jacques Lemaire[1]

[1]Laboratoire de Photochimie Moléculaire et Macromoléculaire, U.A. C.N.R.S. 433, University of Clermont II, B.P. 45, 63170 Aubière, France
[2]Rhône Poulenc Santé, Centre de Recherches de Vitry, 13, Quai J. Guesde, 94400 Vitry-sur-Seine, France

An original aspect of aqueous photochemistry related to the anticipated fact that water would favour photochemical processes implying polarized or ionic excited
states, is emphasized in the class of chlorobenzenes and
halogenophenols. Such photoprocesses would be more specific than homolytic photodissociation leading to radicals.

In chlorobenzenes, a photohydrolysis mechanism is
observed. The monochlorobenzene is quantitatively transformed into phenol in aqueous solution, even in acidic
media (1<pH<13). In polychlorobenzenes, the polarization
of the C-Cl bond, which controls the photohydrolysis
process, is more affected by substituents in ortho- or
para-position than by meta substitution.

The phototransformation of halogenophenols largely
depends on the position of the halogen substituents
(i.e. Cl, Br or I). In 2-halogenophenols, a ring photocontraction accounts for the conversion into cyclopentadienic carboxylic acids. The conversion of 2-chloro-
and 2-bromo-phenolate into cyclopentadiene carboxylate
occurs with high quantum yields and excellent specificity. For 3-chlorophenol, a photohydrolysis mechanism
accounts for the specific transformation into resorcinol.
As opposite, the primary photoscission which is occuring
in 4-chlorophenol is essentially homolytic and many photoproducts are observed.

Laws and regulations, for example the European Communities 6th
Amendment to the 1967 Directive on the Classification, Labelling and
Packaging of Dangerous Substances require, a better knowledge on the
fate of xenobiotic chemical compounds in the three compartments of
the environment. In the aquatic media, biodegradation will be the
most likely pathway for the elimination of chemicals. Nevertheless,
phototransformation is a potential pathway for disappearance of many
chemicals. Up to now, the law requirements make a clear distinction
between identification and evaluation of concentration independent
photolability and determination of the photochemical mechanism. The

first properties are characterized by the disappearance quantum yield
and the corresponding lifetime in environmental conditions, assuming
phototransformation is the rate determining mechanism for removal.
The second aspect, generally more complex, is related to the indenti-
fication of the main photoproducts. It is known from experience that
phototransformations in aqueous media imply complicated stoichiome-
tries. Many primary photoproducts can be formed and secondary photoreactions can occur even at low conversion degree. These general features are specially true in phototransformation occuring through radical processes. In such mechanisms, loss of specificity is generally
observed and, in most cases, a material balance is impossible.

A new trend is now appearing in environmental aqueous photochemistry. Water as a polar solvent, can favor photochemical processes
which imply polarized (zwitterionic) or ionic excited states. In
such processes, a better specificity is expected. Water is indeed a
very unusual solvent in organic photochemistry, and very few examples
of specific photoreactivities in water has been reported before 1980
(1,2). Such isolated examples underlined, nevertheless, the special
role of the aquatic media. It is the purpose of this presentation to
emphasize this aspect through the report of some recent examples of
original phototransformations in water. Two specific photoreactions,
i.e. photohydrolysis and ring photocontraction have been observed in
chlorobenzene and halogenophenols. They will be described with some
details in the next section. Another specific reaction, i.e. photo-
cyclization, has been observed in diphenylamine and derivatives. This
reaction has been thoroughly studied several years ago (3 - 8) and
detailed studies have been previously reported (2,7,8).

Materials and Methods

All the reactants were commercial products. The purity of most of
them was higher than 99%, the purity of the others was higher than
98%. They were used without further purification, except for chlorobenzene distilled before use.

Irradiations at 296, 313 and 334 nm were carried out with a monochromator Bausch et Lomb equipped with a 200 W high pressure mercury arc. For irradiations at 254 nm, a low pressure mercury arc located in a cylindrical reflector with an elliptic base was used. Light
intensity was evaluated using chemical actinometers (potassium
ferrioxalate and uranyl oxalate). When necessary, the solutions had
been thoroughly degassed through conventional freeze-thaw cycles in
a vacuum line.

Absorption and emission measurements were carried out in quartz
cuvettes respectively with spectrophotometers Cary 118 C and Perkin-
Elmer MPF 3 L.

Chloride concentrations were determined using nephelometric measurements after addition of silver nitrate (for 4-chlorophenol) or
specific electrode potentiometry (electrode Orion 94-17 B).

For qualitative and quantitative analyses of products, high performance liquid chromatography (HPLC) was used on a Du Pont chromatograph type 850 equipped with a column Hibar C8 (5 μm) 250×4 mm.

Mass spectra (MS) were recorded in Centre National de la Recherche Scientifique (C.N.R.S.).

High resolution nuclear magnetic resonance spectra (350 MHz [1]H
NMR) were recorded on Cameca in the Rhône Poulenc Research Center.

Quenching effects were linearized using the classical Stern-Volmer plot: ϕ_0 /ϕ vs c_q, where ϕ and ϕ_0 are the quantum yields with and without quencher, c_q the concentration of quencher.
If the plot is a straight line, the slope of it gives the product $k_q \times \tau$, where k_q is the rate constant of the quenching process (in water when the process is controlled by diffusion $k_q \simeq 10^{10} 1.mol^{-1}.s^{-1}$) and τ the lifetime of the excited state quenched.

For sensitization reactions, another Stern-Volmer plot is classically used: $\frac{1}{\phi_s}$ vs $\frac{1}{c}$, where ϕ_s is the quantum yield of the sensitized reaction, c the concentration of the sensitized substrat. If the plot is a straight line, the ratio: $\frac{intercept}{slope}$ gives the product $k \times \tau$, where k is the rate constant of the sensitizing process, τ the lifetime of sensitizer triplet state.

Specific photohydrolysis of chlorobenzenes

Until the last years, the photochemical behavior of chloroaromatics was investigated only in organic solvents, because of their low solubilities in water. The main reaction observed was the photoreduction (9 — 13) in competition with a photosubstitution, when the solvent was an alcohol (14,15). Sometimes methanol/water (16) or acetonitrile /water mixtures (17) were used, but no specific reaction was induced by water and no formation of phenol was observed.

When monochlorobenzene was irradiated in aqueous solution at 253.7 nm, the formation of phenol was pointed out using fluorimetric measurements (emission at 295 nm). The quantitative titrations were carried out by HPLC. The formation of an equivalent quantity of hydrogen chloride was demonstrated using potentiometric measurements (18).

$$C_6H_5Cl + H_2O \xrightarrow{h\upsilon} C_6H_5OH + H^+ Cl^-$$

The reaction was specific. Neither biphenyl, nor polychlorinated derivatives were detected. The transformation quantum yield was 0.10 ± 0.02 in aerated or degassed solutions. It is important to stress the fact that the pH has no influence on the phototransformation quantum yield between pH= 1 and pH= 12; the reaction cannot be a photosubstitution by OH^- ions. Water must be directly involved in this reaction, called for this reason photohydrolysis.

The phosphorescence of biacetyl (2,3-butadione) can be sensitized by chlorobenzene in the aqueous media and biacetyl inhibits the photohydrolysis of chlorobenzene (19). Biacetyl in water is hydrated in the proportion of 73.5% (20) according to the reaction:

$$CH_3 - CO - CO - CH_3 + H_2O \rightleftharpoons CH_3 - CO - \underset{\underset{OH}{|}}{\overset{\overset{OH}{|}}{C}} - CH_3$$

Assuming, only, free biacetyl have inhibiting properties, a value of 320 ± 20 $mol^{-1}.l$ was obtained for the slope of the Stern-Volmer plot. The photohydrolysis of monochlorobenzene in degassed solution can be sensitized by acetone and hexadeuterated acetone with similar quantum yields (see table I).

Table I - Quantum yield of the photohydrolysis of chlorobenzene into phenol sensitized by acetone and hexadeuterated acetone, in degassed solution (18,19)

Acetone 5×10^{-2} mol.l^{-1} excitation at 296 nm		Acetone-D6 5×10^{-2} mol.l^{-1} excitation at 296 nm	
chlorobenzene ($\times 10^{-3}$ mol.l^{-1})	ϕ(phenol)	chlorobenzene ($\times 10^{-3}$ mol.l^{-1})	ϕ(phenol)
1.15	< 0.01	0.22	< 0.01
1.88	0.01-0.02	0.58	0.01
1.97	0.02	0.75	0.01 -0.015
4.06	0.02-0.03	0.87	0.02 -0.03
9.87	0.04-0.05	1.10	0.04
		2.93	0.04 -0.05
		3.65	0.055-0.06
		4.25	0.06
		4.40	0.06

With acetone many by-products are formed, whereas the sensitization is very selective with acetone-D6; for acetone-D6 concentration up to 10^{-1} mol.l^{-1}, phenol was the only product detected by HPLC. When acetone is irradiated in water a self-quenching mechanism occurs:

$$CH_3-CO-CH_3 \xrightarrow{h\nu} (CH_3-CO-CH_3)_{S_1} \xrightarrow{\phi \simeq 1} (CH_3-CO-CH_3)_{T_1}$$

$$(CH_3-CO-CH_3)_{T_1} \longrightarrow CH_3-CO^{\cdot} + CH_3^{\cdot}$$

$$(CH_3-CO-CH_3)_{T_1} + CH_3-CO-CH_3 \longrightarrow CH_3-CO-CH_2^{\cdot} + CH_3-COH-CH_3$$

$$CH_3-CO-CH_2^{\cdot} + CH_3CO^{\cdot} \longrightarrow CH_3-CO-CH_2-CO-CH_3 \quad \text{(acetylacetone)}$$

$$2 \ CH_3-CO^{\cdot} \longrightarrow CH_3-CO-CO-CH_3 \quad \text{(biacetyl)}$$

Acetylacetone is one of the major products of the photolysis of acetone (20). In the presence of chlorobenzene, the self-quenching reaction competes with the energy transfer and the radicals induce the formation of by-products. This self-quenching reaction is much reduced with hexadeuterated acetone. Up to 0.1 mol.l^{-1}, the major photoproduct from $CD_3-CO-CD_3$ in water is $CD_3-CO-CO-CD_3$. In the presence of chlorobenzene, the formation of biacetyl-D6 is inhibited through an energy transfer and the photohydrolysis is sensitized.

The active vibration mode associated with CD_3 group favors the non-radiative transition $T_1 \rightarrow S_0$ and shortens the intrinsic lifetime of the triplet state. This accounts for the lack of self-quenching reaction. Thus hexadeuterated acetone appears to be a more specific photosensitizer than acetone in water (19).

The specificity of the photohydrolysis allows to rule out a mechanism involving an homolytic scission of the C-Cl bond with formation of radicals. A direct photohydrolysis probably occurs from a polarized excited state. It is suggested this excited state would be the first triplet state to account for the sensitization and inhibition experiments (19).

From the sensitized phosphorescence of biacetyl, the quantum yield of inter-system crossing (ϕisc) was found to be 0.6 ± 0.1. From the slope of the Stern-Volmer plot it can be concluded that the lifetime of the triplet state is about 30 ns (figure 1). This result is in good agreement with the absence of inhibition by oxygen of dissolved air. The heterolytical scission of the C-Cl bond may be concerted (or not) with the heterolysis of the H-OH bond (18,19).

A similar photohydrolysis occurs with bromobenzene and polychlorobenzenes (18,19), but experiments were limited to di- and trichlorobenzenes (for solubility reasons). As shown by HPLC, the primary products in the photoreaction of dichlorobenzenes and trichlorobenzenes were respectively chlorophenols and dichlorophenols. The accumulation of the primary products was much smaller with trichlorobenzenes than with monochlorobenzene, because photochemical secondary processes occurred even at a very low rate of conversion. The following photohydrolysis quantum yields were obtained (18,21).

	ϕ		ϕ
bromobenzene	0.06 ± 0.01		
chlorobenzene	0.10 ± 0.01	1,4- dichlorobenzene	0.010 ± 0.002
1,3-dichlorobenzene	0.06 ± 0.01	1,3,5-trichlorobenzene	0.006 ± 0.001
1,2-dichlorobenzene	0.02 ± 0.01	1,2,4-trichlorobenzene	0.002 ± 0.001

It should be noted that the quantum yield of photohydrolysis decreased as the number of atoms of chlorine on the ring increased. This quantum yield depends too on the positions of the substituents. The influence of substituents can be rationalized as follows: chlorine is an electro-attracting substituent and the spin density on the ring decreases by increasing the number of chlorines (the same reason accounts for the decrease of the pK_a of chlorophenols). This electronic polarization antagonists the negative polarization of chlorine and makes more difficult the heterolytic scission. This phenomenon becomes clearly marked with 1-chloro-4-nitrobenzene. The very low quantum yield for photohydrolysis ($<3\times10^{-4}$) can be attributed to the high electro-attracting effect of $-NO_2$ group (21). The photohydrolysis of chlorobenzenes appears to be more difficult when substituents are located on conjugated sites: the polarisation is then delocalized on the whole molecule and the photohydrolysis is unfavored.

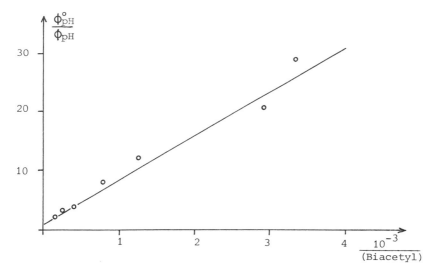

Figure 1.   Stern-Volmer plot for sensitization of phosphorescence
of biacetyl by chlorobenzene (2×10^{-3} mol.l^{-1}).   (Reproduced
with permission from ref. 19.   Copyright 1984 Pergamon.)
ϕ_{ph}^{o} and ϕ_{ph} : phosphorescence quantum yields of biacetyl respectively unsensitized and sensitized by chlorobenzene.

The effect of substituents is drastically different in organic solvents: in hexane, the main photoreaction of chlorobenzenes is photoreduction via a radical process. It was shown recently (13) that the rate of dehalogenation increases remarkably as the number of halogen atoms as substituents increases. In the particular case of dichlorobenzenes, the reactivity reaches a maximum with the *ortho*-derivative. The mechanism is then surely different from the mechanism of photohydrolysis.

Specific photocontraction and photohydrolysis in halogenophenols

Phototransformation of chlorophenols in water has received more attention than photochemical behavior of chlorobenzenes because these compounds are largely used in the field of herbicides (2-chlorophenol, 2,4-dichlorophenol, 2,4,5-trichlorophenol) and fungicides (4-chlorophenol, pentachlorophenol). It was shown several years ago that the irradiation of 3-chlorophenol produces resorcinol (22). According to Omura and Matsuura (22) the major photoproducts of 4-chlorophenol are 5-chloro-2,4'-dihydroxybiphenyl, 2,4'-dihydroxybiphenyl and hydroquinone according to the conditions. Grabowski (23) suggested the formation of catechol when 2-chlorophenol was irradiated in basic solution. Joschek and Miller (24) observed the formation of diphenols and *sym*-dihydroxybiphenyls from bromophenols irradiated at 254 nm. In the class of polychlorophenols, the mechanism of phototransformation in water was only described for 2,4-dichlorophenol (25), 2,4,5-trichlorophenol (26) and pentachlorophenol (27,28). The substitution of a chlorine atom by an hydroxyl group was the major process but duplications produce more complex products (29).

According to our own work, the photochemical behavior depends much on the position of the chlorine atoms on the ring. Specific reactions were observed with 2- and 3-chlorophenol, and an heterolytic mechanism was assumed. As opposite, for 4-chlorophenol, the reaction was much less specific and was explained by radical mechanism (30).

Photocontraction of 2-halogenophenols

When 2-chlorophenol in the anionic form (pH>9) was irradiated at 296 nm in aerated or degassed solution (10^{-5} to 10^{-3} mol.l^{-1}), a new band appeared on the uv spectrum at 270 nm. This band shifted to 276 nm in acidic solution (31), but after isolation, the photoproducts absorbed around 220 nm. The following structures of the isolated products were established from MS and NMR 350 MHz after esterification.

The product I (NMR spectrum on figure 2) accounted for about 70% of the 2-chlorophenol transformed and the product II for about 20%.

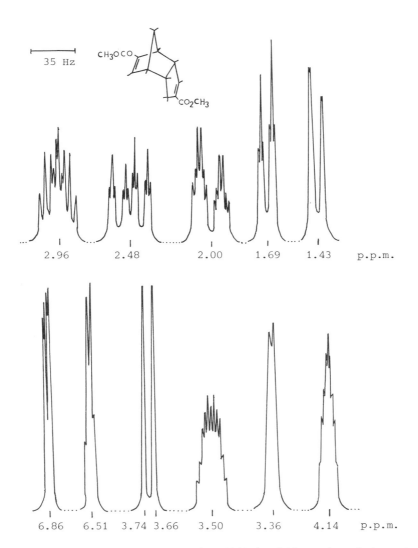

Figure 2. NMR 350-MHz spectrum (in CDCl$_3$) of the major photoproduct of 2-chlorophenolate (31). (Reproduced with permission from ref. 34. Copyright 1984 CDR.)

I   II

From these structures, it can be concluded that the primary photoproduct is a mixture of two cyclopentadienic acids (in the anionic form).

These acids dimerize during the isolation according to a Diels-Alder addition. The uv spectrum observed agrees with the spectrum obtained by Peters (32).

The reaction is very specific and the quantum yield is 0.30±0.03 in aerated or degassed solution (no influence of oxygen observed). Chlorine is quantitatively transformed into chloride ion as shown by potentiometric and nephelometric measurements (after addition of $AgNO_3$ for the latter).

In aerated solution, the primary products were partially photo-oxidized and accumulated less than in degassed solution.

When a methanolic solution of 2-chlorophenol was irradiated in the presence of sodium methylate, the esters of the cyclopentadienic acids were obtained. The uv spectrum observed agrees with the spectrum obtained by Peters (32) for 1-carbomethoxy-1,3-cyclopentadiene. A mechanism involving a Wolff rearrangement is suggested (30).

This scheme is similar to the mechanism proposed for the phototransformation of 2-diazophenol (33).

When the molecular form of 2-chlorophenol is excited at 296 nm
or 253.7 nm in aerated or degassed solution, the quantum of conversion
is 0.03 ±0.01. No influence of pH is noticed between pH= 1 and pH=5.5.
HPLC analysis indicated that two different products are formed - catechol and cyclopentadienic acids - with similar efficiencies (37).

It was not possible to sensitize the reaction by using acetone or
phenol (37).

The reaction of photocontraction of the aromatic ring appears
to be a characteristic of ortho-halogenated phenols. In any case, the
quantum yield is much higher with the anionic form than with the molecular one (34). The irradiation of 2-bromo- and 2-fluorophenolate
produces also a mixture of cyclopentadienic acids. The quantum yield
is 0.40±0.05 with 2-bromophenolate. A detailed study was carried out
with 2,4-dichlorophenol (35). When a solution of $1.65×10^{-4}$ mol.l^{-1}
at pH= 10 was irradiated at 313 nm, a new band appeared at 285 nm
on the uv spectrum (figure 3); the quantum yield of the transformation was evaluated to be 0.10±0.02 in both aerated and degassed solutions. The crude photoproduct was a mixture of chlorocyclopentadienic
acids (for about 70% of the chlorophenol converted) and a dimer of
these acids (for about 30%). On the NMR spectrum of the crude product, it was possible to identify a small amount of chlorohydroquino-
ne (<5%). The structures of the products were established by NMR
350 MHz. It was possible to identify three chlorocyclopentadienic
acids (III, IV, V) in the approximative proportion 6:3:1.

The dimer is formed from a Diels-Alder reaction between the isomers
IV and V.

When the molecular form of 2,4-dichlorophenol was irradiated,
the same photoproducts were formed but the quantum yield was only
0.01-0.02. No formation of diphenol was detected.

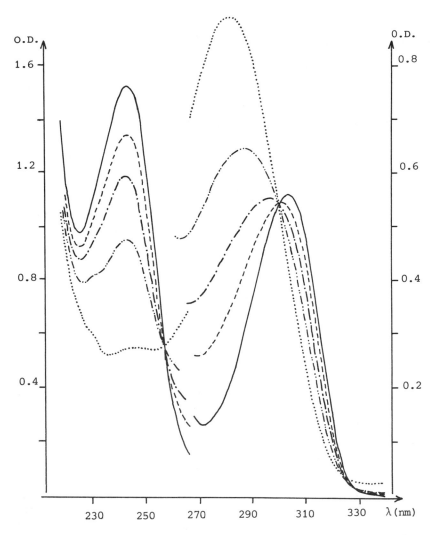

Figure 3.   Absorption spectra of a degassed solution 1.65×10^{-4}
$mol.l^{-1}$ of 2,4-dichlorophenol irradiated at 313 nm (pH= 10.8)

——————— t= 0   – – – – – – t= 3 min
— – — – · t= 6 min   —··—··— t= 12 min
············· t= 31 min

(Reproduced with permission from ref. 35.   Copyright 1984 Pergamon.)

The photocontraction of 2-halogenated phenolates could be extend ed to many derivatives studied (36,37). The quantum yield was evaluated to be 0.26 with 2-chloro-6-methylphenol in basic solution, and to be 0.10 with 2,4-dichloro-6-methylphenol (pH= 8 to 13), without any influence of oxygen. The specificity decreased with increasing number of chlorine atoms on the ring: with 2,5-dichlorophenolate, photocontraction competed with photohydrolysis. With 2,3- and 2,6-dichlorophenolates, the accumulation of cyclopentadienic acids was not quantitative.

Photohydrolysis of 3-chlorophenol, 3,5- and 3,4-dichlorophenol
Our previous work (30) indicated that when 3-chlorophenol in anionic or molecular form was irradiated at 254 nm or 296 nm (in aerated or degassed solution ($5\times10^{-5}-5\times10^{-3}$ mol.l^{-1})), a specific conversion into resorcinol was observed. For a conversion rate of 5%, about 80% of the chlorophenol transformed were converted into resorcinol according to the HPLC analysis. Chlorine was quantitatively converted into Cl$^-$ with an equal formation of H$^+$. The quantum yield of photoconversion of 3-chlorophenol was significantly higher with the anionic form (0.13±0.02) than with the molecular form (0.09±0.01). The photochemical behavior of 3-chlorophenol is similar to the behavior of chlorobenzene.

Only one difference appears: with 3-chlorophenol the photohydrolysis could be sensitized by phenol (37), whereas this reaction did not occur with chlorobenzene. The quantum yield of the sensitized photohydrolysis depended on the concentration of the acceptor and increased from 0.24 to 0.45 when the concentration of 3-chlorophenol increased from 4.4×10^{-5} to 6×10^{-3} mol.l^{-1}.
Both 3,5-dichlorophenol and 3,4-dichlorophenol behaved like 3-chlorophenol (35). A quantitative photohydrolysis was observed from both anionic and molecular forms: 3,5-dichlorophenol was converted into 5-chlororesorcinol (VI) and 3,4-dichlorophenol into 4-chlororesorcinol (VII). The quantum yields were higher with anionic forms (0.11±0.02 for both derivatives) than with molecular forms (respectively 0.03±0.01 and 0.020±0.005 for 3,5-dichloro- and 3,4-dichlorophenols).

With 3,5-dichlorophenol, the photohydrolysis could be sensitized by phenol with a specific formation of 5-chlororesorcinol (35). But the irradiation of a mixture phenol/ 3,4-dichlorophenol produced a complex mixture of products (including 4-chlororesorcinol). A competition between sensitization and radical induction appeared.

Radical photochemistry in 4-chlorophenol

The photochemical behavior of 4-chlorophenol differs from those of 2-chlorophenol and 3-chlorophenol. When an aerated or degassed solution ($2 \times 10^{-4} - 10^{-2}$ mol.l^{-1}) was irradiated at 254 nm or 296 nm, a mixture of products was formed as shown on HPLC analysis (Figure 4).

The formation of Cl$^-$ and H$^+$ was generally lower than the disappearance of 4-chlorophenol. At a low rate of conversion, the major product, in aerated solution as well as in degassed solution, was 5-chloro-2,4'-dihydroxybiphenyl (VIII), which was identified by MS and NMR spectra (37).

VIII

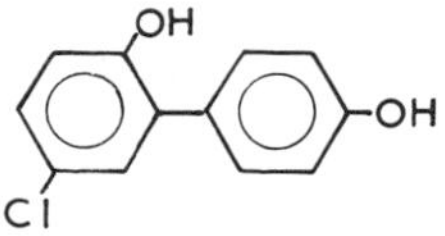

This product was reported by Kuwahara *et al.* (29). Hydroquinone was formed in degassed solution (for 12 to 15% of the chlorophenol converted). Dihydroxybiphenyls were also identified (mainly 4,4'-dihydroxybiphenyl (IX))(30).

IX

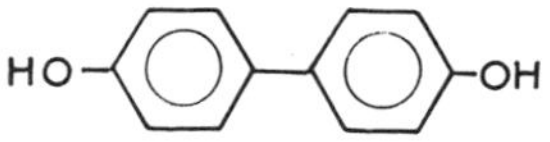

Polyphenolic oligomers (X) were formed when the rate of conversion exceeded 10% and at high initial concentration of 4-chlorophenol. These oligomers were identified by MS (30).

X

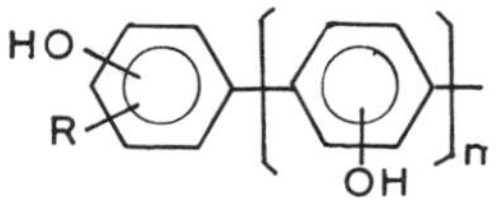

$R = H, OH, Cl$
$n = 1, 2, 3, 4$

The quantum yield of conversion of 4-chlorophenol was not measured with high accuracy (0.4±0.1). At low conversion rate (<0.1), the relative error on the conversion of 4-chlorophenol determined by HPLC measurement is about 25%. Moreover, the optical density at 254 nm increased much with the progress of the reaction (about a factor of 5 for 15% of transformation). At conversion rates higher than 0.1, secondary reactions are not negligible when the solution was irradiated at 296 nm. Nevertheless, the initial quantum yield of formation of Cl$^-$ (0.25±0.05) appeared to be significantly lower than the quantum yield of conversion of 4-chlorophenol (37).

When the irradiation was carried out in aerated solution, the formation of hydroquinone was enhanced,   p-benzoquinone and hydroxy p-benzoquinone were also formed. The products detected involve radical intermediates. Radicals can react either with chlorophenol or with other radicals and many products can be formed. The reaction is not specific. The photohydrolysis exists (formation of hydroquinone in degassed acidic solution) but it is only a minor pathway.

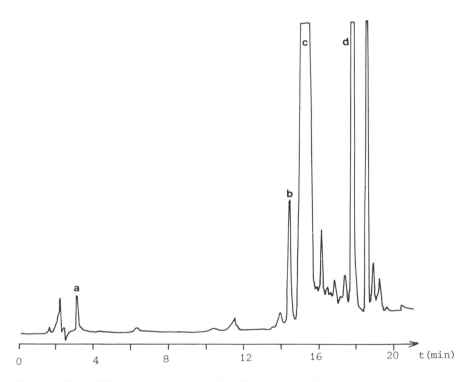

Figure 4. HPLC chromatogram of a degassed solution of 4-chlorophe-
nol (1.8×10^{-2} mol.1^{-1} irradiated at 253.7 nm) ([38])
HPLC conditions: H_2O/ MeOH gradient, detection at 254 nm
  a) hydroquinone   c) 4-chlorophenol
  b) 4,4'-dihydroxybiphenyl   d) 5-chloro-2,4'-dihydroxybiphenyl

Influence of chlorine substituents on the photochemistry

The position of chlorine atoms on the ring has a major effect on the orientation of the reaction. With dichlorophenols, the effect of a chlorine atom on positions 2 or 3 is prevalent and the reaction is specific and heterolytical scission of C-Cl bond is involved. When positions 2 and 3 are both chlorinated (2,3-dichlorophenol or 2,5-dichlorophenol) photocontraction and photohydrolysis are both observed, but photocontraction (i.e. orientation by position 2) is the major pathway of transformation.

   If the photohydrolysis does not compete with other routes of transformation, the quantum yield decreases with increasing number of chlorine atoms on the ring. The same phenomenon was observed with chlorobenzenes. The quantum yield was generally higher with anionic forms than with molecular forms. This can be explained by the increase in the spin density on the ring which enhances the negative polarization of chlorine atom(s).

Conclusions

Up to now, heterolytic photochemical processes in aqueous solution have been identified with a limited number of simple molecules. However, these molecules are good models for large classes of organic compounds appearing as xenobiotics in the aquatic media. It is again emphasized that ionic photochemical processes are characterized by high specificities. The phototransformation of chemical compounds, which involves polarised or ionic excited states, would be therefore easier to analyse, as opposite to the complex analytical situation met with compounds which are converted through radicalar mechanisms. Phototransformations in the aquatic environment must still be considered as occuring through complex reactions. Nevertheless, it might be anticipated that in favourable cases, complete analysis of the photoproducts would be possible. In such examples, the toxicity of the photoproducts would be directly assessed. Phototransformation could appear as an efficient depollution technique each time the toxicity of the photoproducts would be lower than that of the parent initial compounds.

Acknowledgments
The authors gratefully acknowledge the financial support of Centre National de la Recherche Scientifique (C.N.R.S.), Ministère de l'Environnement and Rhône Poulenc Industries.

Literature Cited

1. Joussot-Dubien, J.; Houdard, J. Tetrahedron Lett. 1967, 44, 4389
2. Lopez, D.; Boule, P.; Lemaire, J. Nouveau J. Chimie 1980, 4, 615
3. Grellmann, K.H.; Sherman, G.M.; Linschitz, H. J. Am. Chem. Soc. 1963, 85, 1881
4. Chapman O.L.; Eian, G.L.; Bloom, A.; Clardy, J. J.Am. Chem. Soc. 1971, 93, 2918
5. Förster, E.W.; Grellmann, K.H. J. Am. Chem. Soc. 1972, 94, 634
6. Fischer, G.; Fischer, E.; Grellmann, K.H.; Linschitz, H.; Temizer, A. J. Am. Chem. Soc. 1974, 96, 6267
7. Förster, E.W.; Grellmann, K.H.; Linschitz, H. J. Am. Chem. Soc. 1973, 95, 3108
8. Grellmann, K.H.; Kühnle, W.; Weller, H.; Wolff, T. J. Am. Chem. Soc. 1981, 103, 6889
9. Pinhey, J.T.; Rigby, R.D.G. Tetrahedron Lett.1969, 16, 1267
10. Crosby, D.G.; Hamadmad, N. J. Agr. Food Chem. 1971, 19(6), 1171
11. Arnold, D.R.; Wong, P.C. J. Am. Chem. Soc. 1977, 99(10), 3361
12. Parlar, H.; Steven, P.G.W.; Baumann, R.; Korte, F. Z. Naturforsch. 1979, 34b, 113
13. Nakada, M.; Fukushi, S.; Nishiyama, H.; Okubo, K.; Kume, K.; Hirota, M.; Ishii, T. Bull. Chem. Soc. Japan 1983, 56, 2447
14. Soumillion, J.P.; De Wolf, B. Chem. Comm. 1981, 436
15. Siegmann, J.R.; Houser, J.J. J. Org. Chem. 1982, 47, 2773
16. Mansour, M.; Wawrik, S.; Parlar, M.; Korte, F. Chem. Ztg.1980 104(11), 339
17. Choudhry, G.G.; Roof, A.A.M.; Hutzinger, O. Tetrahedron Lett. 1979, 22, 2059
18. Tissot, A.; Boule, P.; Lemaire, J. Chemosphere 1983, 12, 859 Tissot, A. Docteur-Ingénieur Thesis, University of Clermont II, Clermont-Ferrand, France, 1984
19. Tissot, A.; Boule, P.; Lemaire, J. Chemosphere 1984, 13, 381
20. Bouchy, M. Doctorat d'Etat Thesis, University of Nancy, Nancy, France, 1973
21. Boule, P.; Tissot, A.; Lemaire, J. Chemosphere 1985, 14, 1789

22. Omura, K.; Matsuura, T. Chem. Comm. 1969, 1394
    Omura, K.; Matsuura, T. Tetrahedron 1971, 27, 3101
23. Grabowski, Z. Z. Physik Chem. 1961, 27, 239
24. Joschek, H.I.; Miller, I. J. Am. Chem. Soc. 1966, 88, 3269
25. Crosby, D.G.; Tutass, H.O. J. Agric. Food Chem. 1966, 14,596
26. Crosby D.G.; Wong, A.S. J. Agric. Food Chem. 1973, 21, 1052
27. Hamadmad, N. Ph. D. Thesis, University of California, Davis, 1967
28. Wong, A.S.; Crosby, D.G. "Pentachlorophenol, Chemistry, Pharmacology and Environmental Toxicology"; Ranga Rao, K. Ed.; Plenum Press; New York 1978, pp 19-25
    Wong, A.S.; Crosby, D.G. J. Agric. Food Chem. 1981, 29, 125
29. Kuwahara, M.; Kato, N.; Munakata, K. Agric. Biol. Chem. (Tokyo) 1965, 29, 880
30. Boule, P.; Guyon, C.; Lemaire, J. Chemosphere 1982, 11, 1179
31. Guyon, C.; Boule, P.; Lemaire, J. Tetrahedron Lett. 1982, 23 1581
32. Peters, D. J. Chem. Soc. 1959, 1761 and 1961, 1042
33. Yagihara, M.; Kitahara, Y.; Asao, T. Chem. Lett. 1974, 1015
34. Guyon, C.; Boule, P.; Lemaire, J. Nouveau J. Chimie 1984, 8, 685
35. Boule, P.; Guyon, C.; Lemaire, J. Chemosphere 1984, 13, 603
36. Guyon, C. Docteur-Ingénieur Thesis, University of Clermont II. Clermont-Ferrand, France. 1983
37. Boule. P.; Guyon. C.; Lemaire. J. Toxic. and Environ. Chem. 1984, 7, 97
38. Boule, P. unpublished results.

RECEIVED June 9, 1986

Chapter 3

Photolysis of Phenol and Chlorophenols in Estuarine Water

Huey-Min Hwang[1], R. E. Hodson[1], and R. F. Lee[2]

[1]Department of Microbiology and Institute of Ecology, University of Georgia, Athens, GA 30602
[2]Skidaway Institute of Oceanography, P.O. Box 13687, Savannah, GA 31416

Phenol and a number of chlorophenols at a concentration of 25 μg L^{-1} in estuarine water were exposed to sunlight. The relative rates of photolysis decreased in the order 2,4,5-trichlorophenol, 2,4-dichlorophenol, pentachlorophenol, p-chlorophenol, and phenol. The photo-transformation rate constants for dichlorophenol, trichlorophenol and pentachlorophenol ranged from 0.3 to 1.2 hr^{-1} with half-lives ranging from 0.6 to 3 hr (light hours). Phenol and chlorophenol had half-lives ranging from 43 to 118 hr. Similar differences were observed for photo-mineralization with half-lives ranging from 6 to 14 days for dichlorophenol, trichlorophenol, and pentachlorophenol and 16 to 334 days for phenol and p-chlorophenol.
        Changes in pH, season, and cloud cover were among the factors to affect photolysis rates. At a pH below the pK$_a$ the photolysis rate was much lower due to a higher rate of photolysis for the phenoxide ion relative to the nonionized form. A decrease in the midday irradiance from 5.4 to 2.6 Einsteins/m^2/hr, due to cloud cover, resulted in photolysis rate constants of trichlorophenol decreasing from 1.07 to 0.30 hr^{-1}. Highest photolysis rates for all compounds were found in the summer, presumably due to the surface irradiance increase with much of this increase due to a shift in short wavelength light. Higher concentrations of suspended particulates in the summer resulted in a 4-fold higher diffuse attenuation coefficient at 330 nm in the summer compared with the winter. Thus, while surface irradiance increased in the summer the attenuation of this light in the water increased during this season due to higher levels of particulates. For surface waters the increase in summer irradiance affected photolysis rates more than the attenuation by particulates.
        With the exception of dichlorophenol and pentachlorophenol, the photolysis rate of the compounds was

0097-6156/87/0327-0027$06.00/0

similar in both distilled and estuarine water when the
screening factor, i.e., attenuation of light, of estuarine water was taken into account. The higher photolysis rate of 2,4-dichlorophenol in estuarine water
relative to distilled water suggested a photo-sensitized reaction. The lower photolysis rate of pentachlorophenol in estuarine water relative to distilled
water was due to inhibition of photolysis by chloride
ion.

Chlorophenols enter estuaries through their use in industry and
agriculture. For example, the effluents from the pulp and paper
industry contain chlorophenols and more chlorinated phenols form
downstream due to the reaction between chlorine in bleaching liquors
and phenols derived from wood extractives (1). A number of studies
have shown differences in the photolysis rates of xenobiotics between natural and distilled water, these differences result from particulate and dissolved substances in natural waters which influence
photolysis of xenobiotics through attenuation of sunlight, secondary
photoreactions, and chemical or physical interactions that change
the speciation or availability of the xenobiotics (2). Some examples
include the greatly accelerated photochemical degradation of parathion in river or swamp water relative to distilled water (3) and
the absence of photolysis of the herbicide molinate in distilled
water but rapid photolysis in natural waters (4). In contrast, the
photolysis rate of pentachlorophenol is slower in seawater than in
distilled water due to the photonucleophilic substitution of
chloride ions in seawater for chloride in pentachlorophenol (5).
Instead of being a sensitizer, the humic substances in natural
waters can also act as quenchers in the photolysis of some polyaromatic hydrocarbons (6). The photolysis of phenols is affected by pH
changes, since phenolic compounds dissociate to phenoxide ions in
basic waters, resulting in altered photoreactivities (7). Many photolysis studies have limited the light source to a particular intensity and a narrowly defined wavelength band. While this simplifies
interpretation of results, it can prevent extrapolation of laboratory data to natural environmental conditions. Zika (8) has pointed
out that limiting the wavelength of radiation often reduces the
number of possible reaction routes and that the light intensity
affects the steady-state concentrations of reactive transients in
the solution which can affect the secondary reaction rates. In
natural waters photochemical reactions are affected by changes in
sunlight intensity and wavelength associated with season and time of
day, amount of dissolved and particulate substances and presence of
photosensitizers.
    The objectives of this study were to determine the photolysis
rates of phenol and some chlorophenols in estuarine and distilled
water under natural sunlight conditions. Effects of sunlight irradiance, pH, and chloride ions concentration on photolysis rates were
determined. Spectral data and sunlight photolysis rate constants of
both the actinometer and the chlorophenols were used to calculate
the apparent quantum yields of the various chlorophenols.

Materials and Methods

Sample Collection. Surface water samples were collected from Skidaway River, an estuarine river near Savannah, Georgia. Water samples (4 liters) were taken in acid-washed, 2.5 gal. polyethylene containers. Assays were initiated within one hour of collection. Temperature, pH, and salinity were measured at the time samples were collected.

Reagents. Ring-UL-^{14}C-labeled p-chlorophenol (11.61 mci/mM), 2,4-dichlorophenol (10.7 mci/mM), and 2,4,5-trichlorophenol (0.80 mci/mM) were obtained from Pathfinder Laboratories Inc. Ring-UL-^{14}C-labeled phenol (58 mci/mM) and pentachlorophenol (8.8 mci/mM) were obtained from California Bionuclear Corp. Purity ranged from 95% to 99%. Unlabeled compounds and valerophenone (99% pure) were obtained from Aldrich Chemical Company. Malachite green leucocyanide actinometer (MGLC) was obtained as a gift from Dr. R.G. Zepp of the Environmental Protection Agency (Athens, Georgia).

Incubation and Degradation Measurements. Radiolabeled or unlabeled compounds were dissolved in acetone and added to 60 ml of estuarine or phosphate-buffered distilled water (pH 7.7 $\pm$ 0.2; 16 mM) in 150 ml quartz flasks (Quartz Scientific, Inc.). Acetone was at a final concentration of 1 x 10^{-6}M and there was no photosensitization of the compounds by acetone in distilled water. These flasks allow more than 85% transmission of light of wavelength longer than 260 nm. Approximately 0.1 μci of the selected compound was added to each flask. The final concentration of each compound in the flasks was adjusted to 25 μg L^{-1} by the addition of unlabeled compound. The flasks were suspended in an outdoor tank containing flowing estuarine water. Flasks were suspended 3 cm below the surface. Dark controls consisted of flasks covered with aluminum foil. All samples contained formaldehyde (0.4%) to prevent microbial degradation of the compounds. Ultraviolet absorption by the formaldehyde solution at this concentration was negligible. At various times the amount of parent compound degraded (photo-transformation) and production of $^{14}CO_2$ (photo-mineralization) were determined. Since phenol and p-chlorophenol photolyzed slowly, they were exposed to sunlight for up to 3 days, while the other chlorophenols were exposed to midday sunlight (between 10:00 and 14:00) for photo-transformation studies. Water samples for photo-mineralization studies were incubated for 24, 48, or 72 hr to allow for the accumulation of enough $^{14}CO_2$ to measure. The $^{14}CO_2$ produced was determined as described in earlier work (9, 10). To determine loss of parent compound (photo-transformation), each sample was acidified with 4N H_2SO_4 to pH 2 and the parent compound and its degradation products were extracted with ethyl acetate. Extraction efficiency for the parent compounds averaged greater than 95%. The extracts were concentrated and applied to silica gel thin-layer chromatography plates (E. Merck) using a solvent system of hexane:acetone (1:1, vol:vol). Parent compounds and their degradation products were scraped from thin-layer plates and their radioactivity determined with a scintillation counter (Packard TRI-carb-300C). The analysis of the malachite green leucocyanide actinometer was carried out

using the procedures described by Miller and Zepp (11). The screening factor was determined by exposing valerophenone solutions
(10 μM) to midday sunlight (12) for various periods up to 1 hr.
Analyses for valerophenone were conducted with high pressure liquid
chromatography using a Micromeritics Model 7000B equipped with a
4.6x250 mm reverse-phase column of 10 μm ODS/Spherisorb (mobil phase
70:30 methanol/water, flow rate 2.0 ml min^{-1}, detector wavelength
260 nm).

Procedures for Kinetic Studies. Triplicates of each radiolabeled
compound and duplicates of valerophenone solution were exposed to
sunlight. Photo-transformation and photo-mineralization rate constants were calculated assuming that the reactions were first-order.
The rate constants were corrected for abiotic dark degradation
(always less than 5% of total) and attenuation of sunlight by dissolved organic material in the estuarine water samples. Unless specified, photolysis rate constants and half-lives of the compounds
were determined during sunny days. Solar radiation was determined
with a radiometer (LI-COR Inc., Model LI-550B; active range, 400-700
nm). The light screening factor (S) was assumed to be equal to the
ratio of the valerophenone photolysis rate constant in particulate-
free estuarine water to the photolysis rate constant in distilled
water (13).

Properties of Estuarine Water. The concentration of suspended particulates in estuarine water was determined by filtering 1 liter of
water through pre-dried and pre-weighed glass fiber filters (GF/C,
Whatman). The filters containing particulates were dried and
weighed. An estuarine water sample was ultracentrifuged at 100,000
xg for 1 hr to obtain particulate-free water (Beckman Ultracentri-
fuge Model L5-40). The particulate-free estuarine water was used in
determining the screening factor. Ultraviolet absorption spectra of
the particulate-free estuarine water were obtained with a spectrophotometer (Beckman Model DU-6). The diffuse attenuation coefficients (K) at 330 nm (the coefficients derived from direct measurements of solar irradiance at various depths in a water body) of the
estuarine water were determined using malachite green leucocyanide,
by the methods described by Miller and Zepp (11). The component of
K from the dissolved substances was calculated by multiplying absorbance of particulate-free estuarine water by 2.303 and the distribution function (D) (14). D refers to the mean pathlength of light in
an horizontal layer of the water sample divided by thickness of the
layer (11), and in our experments it was 1.1. For analysis of particulate organic carbon and particulate nitrogen, 500 ml of water
was passed sequentially through two Gelman type A glass fiber
filters which has been precombusted at 500°C. The filters were
rinsed with 0.01 N HCl to remove inorganic carbon and dried and
stored in a 60°C oven. Particulate organic carbon on the filters was
determined by the methods of Menzel and Vaccaro (15). Particulate
organic nitrogen was determined by the classical micro-Dumas method
as described by Strickland and Parsons (16). The analysis of dissolved organic carbon consisted of the wet oxidation of filtered
estuarine water by potassium persulfate in a sealed glass ampoule.
Samples were subsequently analyzed by the methods of Menzel and

Vaccaro (15). Nitrate and phosphate were analyzed by methods described by Strickland and Parsons (16).

Apparent Quantum Yield ($\emptyset_r$) of the Direct Photolysis of Chlorophenols. The spectral data and sunlight photolysis rate constants of both actinometer valerophenone and the compound, and reaction quantum yield of valerophenone were used to calculate $\emptyset_r$ of chlorophenols using GCSOLAR program (13).

Results

Photolysis of various chlorophenols as a function of time are shown in Fig. 1. The photo-transformation and photo-mineralization of the compounds followed a first-order equation ln (C_0 /C) = k_pt, where C_0 and C are the concentrations of the compound at time zero and time t, while k_p is the first-order photolysis rate constant. The photolysis half-lives of the compounds were calculated using the equation $t_{1/2}$ = 0.693/k_p. The relative rates of photolysis in estuarine water decreased in the order 2,4,5-trichlorophenol, 2,4-dichlorophenol, pentachlorophenol, p-chlorophenol, phenol (Table I).

The photo-transformation rate constants for 2,4-dichlorophenol, 2,4,5-trichlorophenol, and pentachlorophenol ranged from 0.3 to 1.2 hr^{-1} with half-lives ranging from 0.6 to 3 hr (light hours). Phenol and p-chlorophenol were more resistant to photolysis and their half-lives ranged from 43 to 118 hr. Similar differences were observed for photo-mineralization with half-lives ranging from 6 to 14 days for dichlorophenol, trichlorophenol, and pentachlorophenol and 16 to 334 days for phenol and p-chlorophenol. These relative photolysis rates would be predicted by the absorbance and reaction quantum yields for the compounds as given in Table II. Dichlorophenol, trichlorophenol, and pentachlorophenol had high molar absorptivities in the ultraviolet-blue region with absorbance maxima at 304, 310, and 320 nm, respectively. In contrast both phenol and chlorophenol had maxima in the ultraviolet at 269 and 280 nm, respectively. Listed in order of decreasing quantum yield are trichlorophenol, dichlorophenol, p-chlorophenol, and pentachlorophenol.

With the exception of dichlorophenol and pentachlorophenol, the compounds photolyzed at about the same rate in distilled and estuarine water when the attenuation of light, i.e., screening factor, by estuarine water was taken into account. Dichlorophenol photolyzed at a significantly higher rate in estuarine water than in distilled water. The higher photolysis rate of 2,4-dichlorophenol in estuarine water relative to distilled water suggested that the photolysis of dichlorophenol in estuary involved a photo-sensitized reaction. The photo-transformation rate of pentachlorophenol was significantly lower in estuarine relative to distilled water (Table I). This may have been due to chloride ion since sodium chloride added to distilled water with a final concentration of 0.5 M (salinity 30 ^{o}/oo) inhibited photolysis of pentachlorophenol. Photolysis of dichlorophenol and trichlorophenol were not affected by chloride ion addition.

There was little change in the pH of the estuary during the year. When the pH of estuarine or buffered distilled water was changed, there were changes in the photolysis rate constants of the

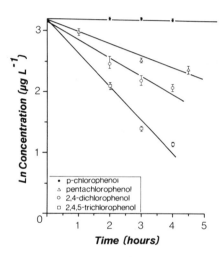

Figure 1. Photolysis of chlorophenols in estuarine water.
Chlorophenols were added to the water sample at a concentration
of 25 μg L^{-1} in December. Temperature was 14°C and pH was 7.6.
Transformation equations were ln c = 3.22-0.01 t (p-chlorophenol), ln c = 3.22-0.44 t (2,4-dichlorophenol), ln c = 3.22-
0.65 t (2,4,5-trichlorophenol), and ln c = 3.22-0.27 t (pentachlorophenol), where c is the concentration of the chlorophenol
at time t. Vertical bars represent 1 standard deviation with
n = 3.

Table I. Photolysis of Phenol and Chlorophenols[a]

Compound and Water Season (Temp. °C)	Midday Surface Irradiance (Einsteins/m²/hr)	Photo-transformation Rate Constant (hr⁻¹)	Photo-transformation Half-life (hr)	Photo-mineralization Rate Constant (day⁻¹)	Photo-mineralization Half-life (day)
Phenol					
distilled[b]					
summer (24)	4.9 ± 1.3	0.015 ± 0.006	46	0.04 ± 0.02	16
winter (10)	2.9 ± 1.1	0.0040 ± 0.0002	173	0.0041 ± 0.0005	169
estuary					
summer (24)	4.9 ± 1.3	0.016 ± 0.006	43	0.04 ± 0.02	16
winter (10)	2.9 ± 1.1	0.006 ± 0.001	118	0.0063 ± 0.0008	110
p-Chlorophenol					
distilled					
summer (25)	5.9 ± 0.6	0.011 ± 0.006	63	0.012 ± 0.003	58
winter (14)	2.7 ± 1.3	0.007 ± 0.002	99	0.003 ± 0.002	224
estuary					
summer (25)	5.9 ± 0.6	0.015 ± 0.007	46	0.013 ± 0.004	53
winter (14)	2.7 ± 1.3	0.011 ± 0.004	63	0.0021 ± 0.0005	334
2,4-Dichlorophenol					
distilled					
summer (25)	5.7 ± 0.2	0.82 ± 0.06	0.8	0.09 ± 0.03	8
winter (11)	1.8 ± 1.0	0.21 ± 0.05	3	0.049 ± 0.005	14
winter (20)	2.8 ± 0.5	0.19 ± 0.02	4		
estuary					
summer (25)	5.7 ± 0.2	1.00 ± 0.06	0.7	0.12 ± 0.05	6
winter (11)	2.5 ± 0.4	0.38 ± 0.02	2	0.05 ± 0.01	14
winter (20)	2.8 ± 0.5	0.37 ± 0.02	2		
2,4,5-Trichlorophenol					
distilled					
summer (25)	5.3 ± 0.5	1.3 ± 0.2	0.5	0.10 ± 0.03	7
winter (18)	2.3 ± 1.2	0.61 ± 0.08	1	0.050 ± 0.009	14
estuary					
summer (25)	5.3 ± 0.5	1.2 ± 0.3	0.6	0.12 ± 0.04	6
winter (18)	2.3 ± 1.2	0.65 ± 0.06	1	0.05 ± 0.01	14
Pentachlorophenol					
distilled					
summer (25)	5.2 ± 1.5	0.6 ± 0.1	1	0.11 ± 0.04	6
winter (11)	1.9 ± 0.8	0.37 ± 0.06	2	0.049 ± 0.008	14
estuary					
summer (25)	5.2 ± 1.5	0.37 ± 0.08	2	0.12 ± 0.05	6
winter (11)	1.9 ± 0.8	0.27 ± 0.04	3	0.07 ± 0.01	10

a. ^{14}C-labeled compounds were incubated in quartz flasks at a concentration of 25 μg L⁻¹. The flasks with distilled or estuarine water were exposed during days when there was full sunlight, i.e., no clouds. All samples were treated with formaldehyde (0.4%). Values are expressed as the mean ± standard deviation (n = 3). 2,4-dichlorophenol, 2,4,5-trichlorophenol, and pentachlorophenol were exposed to midday sunlight for 4 hr, and half-lives were reported as "light hours". Because of slower photolysis rates phenol and p-chlorophenol were exposed to sunlight and darkness for up to 3 days. Degradations of the compounds in darkness were negligible.

b. Distilled water was buffered at pH 7.7 ± 0.2 (0.016 M phosphate).

Table II. Molar Absorptivities and Reaction Quantum Yields ($\emptyset$r) for Direct
Photolysis of Phenol and Chlorophenols [a]

Wavelength,	Molar Absorptivity (M^{-1} cm^{-1})				
nm	Phenol	p-CP	DCP	TCP	PCP
295	9	270	1813	2824	1902
297.5	7	161	1715	3219	1948
300	5	116	1683	3554	2134
302.5	3	97	1707	3851	2319
305	2	84	1707	4087	2644
307.5	1	64	1675	4285	2922
310		51	1585	4364	3154
312.5		32	1423	4305	3432
315		26	1171	4087	3757
317.5		19	986	3614	3943
320			618	2962	4035
323.1			350	2113	3803
330			65	553	2319
340				59	742
Reaction Quantum Yield $\emptyset$r[b]	–	0.066	0.075	0.080	0.013

[a]. The measurements were conducted in distilled water buffered at pH 7.6.
Abbreviations: p-CP: p-chlorophenol, DCP: 2,4-dichlorophenol, TCP:
2,4,5-trichlorophenol, PCP: pentachlorophenol.

[b]. Spectral data and sunlight photolysis rate constants of both actinometer valerophenone and chlorophenols in phosphate-buffered solutions (pH 7.6), and reaction quantum yield of valerophenone were used to calculate $\emptyset$r of chlorophenols using GCSOLAR program (Skurlatov et al., 1983).

chlorophenols (Table III). Highest photolysis rates were obtained at
high pH (pH 10) where the chlorophenols exist as the phenoxide ion.
At pH below the pK_a the photolysis rates were relatively low, thus
the photolysis rate constant for dichlorophenol was 0.13, 1.0, and
1.8 hr^{-1} at pH 5.5, pH 7.6, and pH 10, respectively.

Borosilicate glass is often used in photolysis studies. However,
sections of borosilicate glass were found to only transmit 50% of
the light at 310 nm while quartz section transmitted 100% of this
light. Therefore, for compounds which absorb ultraviolet-blue light
(280-320 nm), quartz glassware is necessary for photolysis studies.
Figure 3 shows the photolysis of 2,4,5-trichlorophenol in borosilicate and quartz flasks. The photolysis rate constants were 0.74
hr^{-1} and 1.07 hr^{-1} in borosilicate and quartz, respectively, which
were shown to be significantly different by a t-test (p $\leq$ 0.05).
All other photolysis studies used quartz flasks.

The physical and chemical properties of the Skidaway River
measured during different times of the year are listed in Table IV.
There were few changes during the year in pH, a_{330} (absorbance of
the particulate-free estuarine water at 330 nm) and the screening
factor. Other properties including concentration of suspended particulates, K_{330} (diffuse attenuation coefficient at 330 nm) and K_s
(specific attenuation coefficient due to suspended particulates)
varied significantly during the year. For example, K_{330} of the
estuarine water increased from 0.05 to 0.22 cm^{-1} from winter to
summer, showing that ultraviolet-blue light was attenuated by a
factor of four in the summer. Thus, while surface irradiance increased going from winter to summer (Table I) the attenuation of
light by estuarine water was greater in the summer, due to high concentrations of suspended particulates (Table IV).

As noted above photolysis rates in estuarine water decreased in
the order trichlorophenol, dichlorophenol, pentachlorophenol, chlorophenol, and phenol. With the exception of the transformation rates
for p-chlorophenol and the photolysis rates for pentachlorophenol,
for all compounds the photolysis rates including both photo-transformation and photo-mineralization were higher in the summer than in
the winter (t-test, p $\leq$ 0.05; Table I, Fig. 2). For example, the
photo-transformation rate constant of dichlorophenol increased from
0.38 to 1.00 hr^{-1} going from winter to summer, and the photo-mineralization rate constant of phenol increased from 0.006 to 0.04 day^{-1}
going from winter to summer.

In addition to changes in sunlight irradiance during different
seasons, there are also changes in the irradiance during the same
season, e.g., cloud cover. Fig. 3 compares the photolysis rate of
trichlorophenol on a sunny and overcast day in May. A decrease in
the midday surface irradiance from 5.4 to 2.6 Einsteins/ m^2/hr due
to cloud cover resulted in the transformation rate constant going
from 1.07 to 0.30 hr^{-1}. The decrease in trichlorophenol photolysis
was proportionally greater than the decrease in measured irradiance,
this may have been due to clouds attenuating ultraviolet-blue light
more than visible light since the radiometer only measured radiation
in the visible region (400-700 nm). Maximum absorbance of trichlorophenol was at 310 nm (Table II).

Table III. Effect of pH on Photolysis of Chlorophenols in Water [a]

First Order Rate Constant (hr^{-1})

	2,4-Dichlorophenol		2,4,5-Trichlorophenol		Pentachlorophenol
	Distilled Water	Estuarine Water	Distilled Water	Estuarine Water	Distilled Water
pH 5.5[b]	0.07 ± 0.06*	0.13 ± 0.06*	0.13 ± 0.04*	0.40 ± 0.05*	0.4 ± 0.1
pH 7.6	0.82 ± 0.06	1.00 ± 0.06	1.3 ± 0.2	1.2 ± 0.3	0.6 ± 0.1
pH 10	1.4 ± 0.2*	1.8 ± 0.3*	1.46 ± 0.09	1.57 ± 0.06	0.7 ± 0.1

a. pK_a values of dichlorophenol, trichlorophenol, and pentachlorophenol are 7.6, 7.0, and 4.8, respectively (Boule et al., Ernst and Wever, 1978). Asterisks (*) denote significant differences from the rate constants obtained at pH 7.6 (t-test; p ≤ 0.05).

b. pH of phosphate-buffered distilled water (0.017 M) or estuarine water was adjusted using either 2N NaOH or 2N H_2SO_4.

Table IV. Physical and Chemical Properties of Skidaway River Water[a], 1983-1985

Physical Properties		Chemical Properties	
Temp (°C)	21.7 ± 6.3 (7-29)	pH	7.7 ± 0.2 (7.4-8.0)
Suspended Particulates (mg L^{-1})	31.3 ± 17.1 (12.9-68.3)	Dissolved organic carbon (mg L^{-1})	4.8 ± 0.3
$K(cm^{-1})$[b]	0.22 (Oct. 1983) 0.05 (Feb. 1984)	Particulate organic carbon (mg L^{-1})	0.9 ± 0.1
$Z_{99}(cm)$[c]	21 (Oct. 1983) 100 (Feb. 1984)	Particulate organic nitrogen (mg L^{-1})	0.20 ± 0.05
$(K-Da_{330})$[d] (cm^{-1})	0.15 (Oct. 1983) 0.01 (Feb. 1984)	C/N	4.6 ± 1.3
		Phosphate (μg-atom/L)	0.7 ± 0.3
a_{330}	0.05 ± 0.02 (0.030-0.096)	Nitrate (μg-atom/L)	1.4 ± 0.3
$K_s(1 \ mg^{-1} \ cm^{-1})$[e]	6.5×10^{-3} (Oct. 1983) 0.6×10^{-3} (Feb. 1984)	Salinity (°/oo)	22.8 ± 2.4 (18-25)
S[f]	0.85 ± 0.04 (0.82-0.88)		

a. Expressed as the annual mean $\pm$ standard deviation (range).

b. Diffuse attenuation coefficient.

c. $Z_{99} = 4.6/K$, photic zone depth.

d. Component of K due to light attenuation by suspended particulates. a_{330} is the absorbance (1-cm pathlength) of the particulate-free estuarine water. D: distribution coefficient in estuarine water.

e. Specific attenuation coefficient due to suspended particulates.

f. Screening factor is the ratio of valerophenone photolysis rate in estuarine water to that in distilled water.

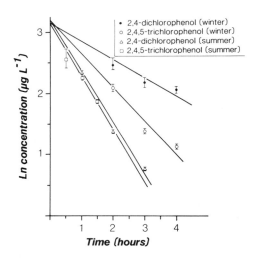

Figure 2. Photolysis of 2,4-dichlorophenol and 2,4,5-trichloro-
phenol in estuarine water.
Concentration of compounds was 25 μg L^{-1}. Temperatures were 14°C
in the winter and 25°C in the summer and pH 7.6. Transformation
equations were ln c = 3.22-0.38 t (dichlorophenol in winter),
ln c = 3.22-1.00 t (dichlorophenol in summer), ln c = 3.22-0.65 t
(trichlorophenol in winter), and ln c = 3.22-1.19 t (trichlorophenol in summer), where c is the concentration of the compound
at time t. Midday surface irradiance were 1.8 $\pm$ 1.0 (dichlorophenol in winter), 5.7 $\pm$ 0.2 (dichlorophenol in summer), 2.3 $\pm$
1.2 (trichlorophenol in winter), and 5.3 $\pm$ 0.5 (trichlorophenol
in summer). Irradiance units were Einsteins/m^2/hr.

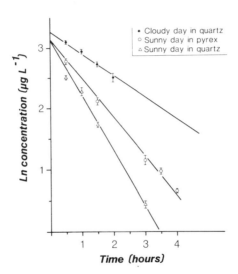

Figure 3. Photolysis of 2,4,5-trichlorophenol in estuarine water. Concentration of trichlorophenol was 25 µg L^{-1}. Experiments were done in May when temperature was 25°C and pH 7.6. The equations for trichlorophenol transformation were: ln c = 3.22-0.30 t (quartz flasks on cloudy day), ln c = 3.22-1.07 t (quartz flasks on sunny day), and ln c = 3.22-0.74 t (pyrex flasks on sunny day), where c is the concentration of trichlorophenol at time t. The midday surface irradiance were 2.6 ± 1.2 on cloudy day and 5.4 ± 0.4 on sunny day. Irradiance units were Einsteins/m^2/hr.

Discussion

Our studies indicated rapid photolysis of trichlorophenol, dichlorophenol, and pentachlorophenol in both distilled and estuarine water. We can compare our results of pentachlorophenol with those of other investigators who have studied the photolysis of this compound in both fresh and marine waters (5, 17-20). The photolysis rate constant k_p for pentachlorophenol in a freshwater stream was 0.29 hr^{-1} ($t_{1/2}$ = 2.4 hr) at 3.8 cm in the summer (19), while we found a k_p of 0.37 hr^{-1} ($t_{1/2}$ = 2 hr, light hours) at a depth of 3.0 cm in the summer (Table I). The half-life of pentachlorophenol in a 1 m deep freshwater pond was 1.5 to 3 days (17) while in 5.5 m deep marine mesocosm the half-life was 22 days (18). Using lamps to simulate sunlight the pentachlorophenol in surface seawater was found to have a half-life of 2.4 hr. (5). Thus our rate constant and half-life for pentachlorophenol photolysis was similar to one determined by others in surface waters. Due to attenuation of light by substances in the water longer half-lives, i.e., days rather than hours, are found for pentachlorophenol when distributed throughout the water column.

Work by Boule et al. (21, 22) and Wong and Crosby (23) have provided information on the photodecomposition products of chlorophenols. In the case of pentachlorophenol degradation products included tetrachlorophenols, trichlorophenols, chlorinated dihydroxy benzenes, and nonaromatic fragments such as dichloromaleic acid (23). Other than CO_2 which came from photo-mineralization, we did not attempt to identify the products of pentachlorophenol decomposition in our experiments. Boule et al. (22) found that 2,4-dichlorophenol in distilled water exposed to 296 nm light decomposed to three chlorocyclopentadienic carboxylic acids. Experiments with 2,4-dichlorophenol in estuarine water exposed to sunlight showed formation of a similar compound (Lee and Hwang, unpublished data).

Formaldehyde has been shown to influence photolysis rates for some compounds. In our experiments formaldehyde at a concentration of 0.4% did not show absorption above 295 nm and did not affect the photolysis rates of chlorophenols in distilled water (data not presented).

An important aspect of our studies were the effect of cloud cover, pH, chloride ion, and season on the photolysis of phenol and various chlorophenols. The effect of pH on the photolysis of chlorophenols is due to the higher rate of photolysis of the phenoxide ion relative to the nonionized compound, due to stronger absorbance by the phenoxide ion (21). The pK_a of dichlorophenol, trichlorophenol, and pentachlorophenol are 7.6, 7.0 and 4.8, respectively (22, 24). Low photolysis rates of chlorophenols in both estuarine and distilled water were obtained at pH below the pK_a (Table III). At pH 7.6 found in estuarine water 50%, 80%, and 99.8% of the dichlorophenol, trichlorophenol, and pentachlorophenol, respectively, is in the form of the phenoxide ion. The photolysis rate of pentachlorophenol in estuarine water was lower than in distilled water (Table I). Addition of chloride ion to distilled water containing pentachlorophenol resulted in a decrease in the photolysis rate. Miille and Crosby (5) found that pentachlorophenol had a lower photolysis rate in seawater compared to distilled water due to the photonucleophilic interaction of pentachlorophenol with chloride ion. We found no chloride effect on the photolysis of dichlorophenol and trichloro-phenol. The number of chlorines and their position on the ring affect the interaction of chloride ion with the different chlorophe-nols (D.G. Crosby, personal communication).

Highest rates of photolysis were found in the summer, presumably due to high surface irradiance in that season. Temperatures are also highest in the summer and some photochemical reactions require a temperature dependent activation step resulting in photodegrada-tion rates increasing exponentially with temperature (25, 26). How-ever, for the chlorophenols we found no change in photolysis rates when the temperature was changed under the same sunlight conditions (Table I; note dichlorophenol photolysis at 11° and 20°C in winter).

For phenol the photo-transformation rate constant increased from 0.006 to 0.016 hr^{-1} in going from winter to summer, whereas surface irradiance increased from 2.9 to 4.9 Einsteins/m^2/hr. Thus, a 1.7 fold irradiance increase resulted in a 2.7 fold photolysis rate in-crease. Our irradiance measurements covered wavelengths between 400-700 nm. For latitude 30°N (our latitude is 32°N) the irradi-ance at 304 nm increased 3.5 fold whereas the irradiance at 460 nm increased 1.9 fold in going from winter to summer (27). Thus, since phenol absorbs in the ultraviolet region its photolysis rate relates more closely to changes in irradiance in the ultraviolet region. For the other compounds studied the photolysis increase between winter and summer were less than the irradiance increase. This may be par-tially explained by the increase in level of suspended particulates in the estuary in the summer. This increase in particulates resulted in 4-fold higher diffuse attenation coefficient at 330 nm in the summer relative to winter. In the summer we have an increase both in surface irradiance and in attenuation due to higher level of par-ticulates. For surface waters the irradiance increase from winter to summer appears to be a more important factor than the increase in attenuation. However, for deeper waters the increased attenuation by particulates in the summer may be a major factor affecting photo-lysis rates.

In summary, photolysis appears to be the major degradation pro-cess in the removal of dichlorophenols, trichlorophenols, and penta-chlorophenol from estuarine waters but is less important in the deg-radation of phenol and chlorophenol.

Acknowledgments

We are greatly indebted to Dr. R.G. Zepp of the EPA in Athens for his advice and assistance in this work. We thank Dannah McCauley and Ching-Lee Hwang for their excellent typing work. This work is a result of research sponsored by NOAA office of Sea Grant, U.S.A. Department of Commerce, under grant NA84AA-D-00072.

Literature Cited

1. Keith, L. H. "Identification and Analysis of Organic Pollutants in Water"; Ann Arbor Science Publishers, Inc.: Ann Arbor, 1976; pp. 671-707.

2. Zepp, R. G.; Schlotzhauer, P. G.; Simmons, M. S.; Miller, G. C.; Baughman, G. L.; Wolfe, N. L. Fresenius Z Anal. Chem. 1984, 319, 119.
3. Zepp, R. G.; Baughman, G. L. In "Aquatic Pollutants: Transformation and Biological Effects"; Hutzinger, O.; Van Lelyveld, L. H.; Zoeteman, B. C. J., Eds.; Pergamon Press: New York, 1977; pp. 237-263.
4. Soderquist, C. J.; Bowers, J. B.; Crosby, D. G. J. Agric. Food Chem. 1977, 25, 940.
5. Miille, M. J.; Crosby, D. G. Mar. Chem. 1983, 14, 111.
6. Choudhry, G. G. "Humic Substances: Structural, Photophysical, Photochemical and Free Radical Aspects and Interactions with Environmental Chemicals"; Gordon and Breach Science Publishers: New York, 1984; pp. 143-169.
7. Aly, O. M.; El-Dib, M. A. In "Organic Compounds in Aquatic Environments"; Faust, S. J.; Hunter, J. V., Eds.; Marcel Dekker: New York, 1971; pp. 469-493.
8. Zika, R. G. In "Marine Organic Chemistry: Evolution, Composition, Interactions and Chemistry of Organic Matter in Seawater"; Duursma, E. K.; Dawson, R., Eds.; Elsevier Scientific Publishing Company: New York, 1981; pp. 299-325.
9. Hodson, R. E.; Azam, F.; Lee, R. F. Bull. Mar. Sci. 1977, 27, 119.
10. Lee, R. F.; Ryan, C. In "Microbial Degradation of Pollutants in Marine Environments"; Bourquin, A. W.; Pritchard, P. H., Eds.; EPA-600/9-79-012, U.S. EPA: Gulf Breeze, Fla., 1979; pp. 443-450.
11. Miller, G. C.; Zepp, R. G. Water Res. 1979, 13, 453.
12. Zepp, R. G.; Schlotzhauer, P. G.; Sink, R. M. Environ. Sci. Technol. 1985, 19, 74.
13. Skurlatov, Y. I.; Zepp, R. G.; Baughman, G. L. J. Agric. Food Chem. 1983, 31, 1065.
14. Miller, G. C.; Zisook, R.; Zepp, R. J. Agric. Food Chem. 1980, 28, 1053.
15. Menzel, D. W.; Vaccaro, R. F. Limnol. Oceanogr. 1964, 9, 138.
16. Strickland, J. D. H.; Parsons, T. R. "A Practical Handbook of Seawater Analysis"; Fisheries Research Board of Canada: Ottawa, Canada, 1972.
17. Crossland, N. O.; Wolff, C. J. M. Environ. Toxicol. Chem. 1985, 4, 73.
18. Lee, R. F.; Hinga, K.; Almquist, G. In "Marine Mesocosms: Biological and Chemical Research in Experimental Ecosystems"; Grice, G. D.; Reeve, M. R., Eds.; Springer-Verlag: New York, 1982; pp. 123-135.
19. Pignatello, J. J.; Martinson, M. M.; Steiert, J. G.; Carlson, R. E.; Crawford, R. L. Appl. Environ. Microbiol. 1983, 46, 1024.
20. Sugiura, K.; Aoki, M.; Kaneko, S.; Daisaku, I.; Komatsu, Y.; Shibuya, H.; Suzuki, H.; Goto, M. Arch. Environ. Contam. Toxicol. 1984, 13, 745.
21. Boule, P.; Guyon, C.; Lemaire, J. Chemosphere 1982, 11, 1179.
22. Boule, P.; Guyon, C.; Lemaire, J. Chemosphere 1984, 13, 603.
23. Wong, A. S.; Crosby, D. G. J. Agric. Food Chem. 1981, 29, 125.
24. Ernst, W.; Weber, K. Chemosphere 1978, 11, 867.

25. Barltrop, J. A.; Coyle, J. D. "Excited States in Organic Chemistry"; John Wiley & Sons, Inc.: New York, 1975.
26. Suess, M. J. Zblt. Bakt. Hyg. 1972, 155, 541.
27. Mill, T.; Mabey, W. R.; Bomberger, D. C.; Chou, T.-W.; Hendry, D. G.; Smith, J. H. "Laboratory Protocols for Evaluating the Fate of Organic Chemicals in Air and Water"; EPA-600/3-82-022, U.S. E.P.A.: Washington, D.C., 1982.

RECEIVED May 27, 1986

Chapter 4

Sunlight Photolysis of Selected Indoles and Carbazole in Aqueous Coal-Oil Systems

Kurt C. Picel[1], Milagros S. Simmons[2], and Vassilis C. Stamoudis[1]

[1]Geochemistry Section, Energy and Environmental Systems Division, Argonne National Laboratory, Argonne, IL 60439
[2]Department of Environmental and Industrial Health, School of Public Health, The University of Michigan, Ann Arbor, MI 48109

Photolysis rates of indole, 2-methylindole (2-MI), 3-MI, 5-MI, and 7-MI, which ranged from 0.038 hr^{-1} to 0.18 hr^{-1} in distilled water, were enhanced 1.3- to 5.0-fold in aqueous CRM-1 (coal-oil research material). Conversely, the rate for carbazole was 2.2-fold lower in aqueous CRM-1 than in distilled water (0.51 hr^{-1}). Sunlight quantum yields of indoles were high (0.02-1.2), evidence that auto-catalysis occurred in distilled water. In aqueous CRM-1, indoles underwent sensitized photolysis, possibly through a superoxide or singlet-oxygen intermediate. The same photoproduct of 3-MI, o-(N-formyl)aminoacetophenone, was found in both distilled water and in aqueous CRM-1. Carbazole underwent direct photolysis in both distilled water and aqueous CRM-1, indicating that it has a different photolysis mechanism from that of indoles in the two systems studied.

Photolysis by sunlight is an important environmental degradation process for many pollutants in aquatic systems. Photolytic reactions in complex organic mixtures such as those found in natural waters, wastewaters, and other surface waters are likely to be enhanced by "sensitizers" or retarded by "quenchers" that may be present in complex organic matrices.

Dissolved components in aqueous environments may undergo photolytic degradation by several means. They may photolyze directly through absorption of radiation, or they may be subjected to indirect photolysis through interaction with a second species that has directly absorbed light or has been excited by a light-absorbing species (1). Dissolved compounds may also be attacked by photochemically produced oxidants such as hydroperoxides or free radicals in conventional thermal reactions (2). In a complex matrix such as aqueous coal oil, all of these processes may occur simultaneously.

Direct photolysis, which follows first-order kinetics, can be accurately estimated from measurements of the absorbance spectrum

0097-6156/87/0327-0044$06.00/0

and quantum yield of a given chemical using known solar irradiance values. A laboratory procedure for calculating rates for direct photolysis in aquatic systems from laboratory data is given in Refs. 3-5. This procedure has been used to accurately predict rates of direct photolysis of polycyclic aromatic hydrocarbons (PAH) in the environment. Indirect photolysis has been treated mathematically in Ref. 5. These models are more complex than those for direct photolysis and are not as accurate because of the greater number of variables and the uncertainty in the identity, concentration, and quantum efficiencies of naturally occurring photosensitizers.

We are interested in the fate of components of coal-derived fuels and fuel by-products in the aquatic environment. Among the many chemical classes present in coal-derived liquids (6), PAH and neutral azaarenes (indoles and carbazoles) are known to be photosensitive. For several PAH, direct photolysis by sunlight is the primary route of environmental transformation (7). Reduced rates were observed for the photolysis of selected PAH in aqueous coal oil (8), in lake water and lake microlayers (9), and in the presence of humic substances (10). Zepp and Schlotzhauer (11), however, found little difference in PAH photolysis rates in distilled water and several natural waters. Therefore, the role of the organic matrix in the photodegradation of components of complex mixtures is unpredictable and must be studied on an individual basis for a given compound in a given organic matrix.

In a screening study, neutral azaarenes exhibited high photodecomposition rates in aqueous coal oil exposed to sunlight (8). In this work, we chose the following six test compounds from the neutral azaarene fraction of aqueous coal oil for further study: indole, 2-methylindole (2-MI), 3-MI, 5-MI, 7-MI, and carbazole. Our purpose was to examine the photolytic behavior of these compounds in aqueous solutions exposed to sunlight in the presence and absence of the coal-oil matrix, that is, to measure the effect of the coal-oil matrix on their photodegradation rates.

Experimental

The test material used in these experiments was CRM-1, a coal-oil comparative research material obtained from Oak Ridge National Laboratory. CRM-1 is a liquid product from the SRC-II (solvent-refined-coal-II) process and is a mixture of middle and heavy distillates in a ratio of 2.9 to 1. Aqueous solutions of the test material were prepared by stirring crude CRM-1 with distilled water in 1-gal solvent bottles at a level of 2 g/L for five days. After equilibration, undissolved oil was removed by passing the sample through a coarse glass frit, followed by filtration through a 0.45-μ membrane filter three times to ensure a true aqueous solution with no visible droplets of undissolved oil.

Aliquots (900 mL) of the prepared solution were transferred to 1-L Erlenmeyer flasks (Pyrex, glass-stoppered) covered with aluminum foil. Aqueous solutions (5 μM) of p-nitroanisole (p-NA) in 250-mL Erlenmeyer flasks were used as an actinometer for the experiments to monitor sunlight intensity during exposure. Triplicate control samples of both the test and actinometer solutions were kept in the dark. The test solutions were exposed to sunlight in an unobstructed area on the rooftop of the laboratory. The samples (nine test and three actinometer) were clamped to horizontal rods and suspended at a 45° angle to the western horizon. The exposures were conducted near midday in late September at 42° north latitude under clear skies. Sample flasks were then taken off in sets of three after exposure periods of 30, 90, and 180 min. The three actinometer flasks were exposed for the full 180 min.

After exposure the samples and controls were extracted within 48 hr with methylene chloride (CH_2Cl_2) and fractionated into acidic, basic, and neutral components by liquid/liquid partitioning with aqueous NaOH or HCl (8). The neutral components from this step were further fractionated into major chemical classes on silica gel. A 1-cm-diameter glass column containing 10 g of silica gel (activation at 150°C) was used, and elutions were carried out with four solvents, namely: (S1) 20% (V/V) CH_2Cl_2 in pentane; (S2) 40% (V/V) CH_2Cl_2 in pentane; (S3) ethyl ether; and (S4) methanol. Fraction S1 contained the aliphatic and aromatic hydrocarbons, S2 contained the neutral azaarenes, and S3 and S4 contained moderately polar and highly polar constituents of the neutral fraction. The presence of the test compounds in the neutral azaarene fraction was verified by electron-impact gas chromatography/mass-spectrometry (GC/MS) (Hewlett Packard Model 5984A).

The exposed samples were analyzed with a Hewlett Packard 5880A GC. The instrument was equipped with a split/splitless injector, a flame ionization detector, and a Level Four BASIC data system. Analyses were performed on a 20-m × 0.25-mm ID SE-54 fused-silica capillary column with a 0.25-μm film thickness. Helium was used as the carrier gas at a flow rate of 45 cm/s. The GC oven was temperature programmed from 50°C to 250°C at a rate of 6C°/min during the analyses. Sample components were quantified using an external standard.

Results and Discussion

Photolysis in Aqueous Coal Oil.

The neutral azaarene fraction of aqueous CRM-1, which is composed primarily of (C_0-C_4)-indoles and (C_0-C_1)-carbazoles was photosensitive. All of the components monitored in this fraction in a screening procedure (8) degraded detectably over the 180-min exposure period. Table I gives the concentrations, rate constants, correlation coefficients, and half-lives for the six test compounds in this fraction.

First-order photolysis was assumed in the initial examination of the kinetic data. Photolysis rate constants, k_ps, were determined from the slope of the linear regression analysis of concentration versus time data fitted to the following first-order relationship:

$$\ln(C_0/C) = k_p t \qquad (1)$$

where C_0 is the concentration of a component at time zero, and C is the concentration at time t. Concentration data from the 0-, 30-, and 90-min exposure periods over which a good degree of first-order linearity was obtained were used. Data from the 180-min exposure

Table I. Aqueous Concentrations and Photolysis Data
for Indoles and Carbazole in Aqueous CRM-1

Compound	Concentration (mg/L)	$k_p{}^a$ (hr^{-1})	$t_{1/2}{}^b$ (hr)	r^{2c}
Indole	3.14 ± 0.01	0.037	19	0.986
2-MI + 3-MI	1.67 ± 0.05	0.20	3.4	0.990
5-MI	1.48 ± 0.05	0.070	9.9	0.999
7-MI	0.65 ± 0.02	0.055	13	0.997
Carbazole	0.42 ± 0.02	0.17	4.0	0.990

[a]Photolysis rate constants were determined from the
first 90 min of exposure.

[b]Half-lives were projected from the k_p values.

[c]Correlation coefficients were calculated from
photolysis data at times t_0, t_{30}, and t_{90} min.

period were excluded because of markedly reduced photolysis rates
(Figure 1). Reduced rates were probably caused by chemical and
spectral changes in the solutions, as indicated by the development
of color during photolysis and by decreased sunlight intensity late
in the exposure period. The values reported in Table I, then,
represent initial rate constants through 90 min of exposure. The
rates were normalized to the photolysis rate for the p-NA
actinometer (0.15 hr^{-1}) for comparison with other experiments.

Carbazole exhibited a photolysis rate comparable to that of
the faster indoles. All test compounds exhibited high correlation
coefficients in the first-order regression analyses. The indoles
had a broader range of rates and generally behaved less linearly
than carbazole beyond 90 min of exposure. While the photolysis of
carbazole was nearly linear through 180 min, that of the indoles
generally decreased. This difference in behavior indicates that
photolysis of the two classes of chemicals in this matrix occurs by
different mechanisms.

Using the initial rate constants resulted in projected half-
lives for the test compounds that ranged from 3.4 hr to 19 hr.
Actual half-lives will be longer because of product buildup and
changes in the spectral qualities of the solution, which will
reduce the photolysis rates. In natural systems, other processes
(e.g., sorption) will intercede and extend the lifetimes significantly. In summary, the rates indicate that these compounds have
relatively short lifetimes in aqueous solutions exposed to sunlight
and that photodegradation should be a major transformation process
for these chemicals in aquatic systems because of their relatively
high water solubility and their low tendency to adsorb to

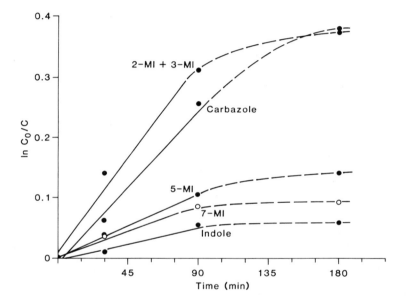

Figure 1. First-order plot of photolysis of selected indoles and carbazole in aqueous CRM-1. 2-MI and 3-MI coelute; C_0 and C refer to concentrations at time zero and time t, respectively.

particulate matter compared with highly hydrophobic substances such as PAH.

Photolysis in Distilled Water. The six test compounds were exposed to sunlight individually in distilled water to study their photolytic behavior in the absence of an organic matrix. These results were then compared with those obtained in aqueous CRM-1 to evaluate the effect of the presence of the matrix.

Aqueous solutions of the compounds were prepared and exposed in duplicate in 1 cm   10 cm Pyrex test tubes at concentrations comparable with those in aqueous CRM-1. After exposure, the samples were extracted and analyzed by GC using an internal standard. Figure 2 shows the first-order plots for the photolysis of these compounds for exposure periods of either 60 min or 180 min, depending on the individual rates. Autocatalysis is apparent in the case of 2-MI, 3-MI, and 5-MI. For 2-MI and 3-MI, the catalyzed rates appear to be first order. Photolysis of indole and 7-MI proceeded at slower rates; whether autocatalysis occurred cannot be ascertained from the data. The results for carbazole show no indication of autocatalysis. The photolysis rate observed is linear up to two half-lives, after which it begins to level off, possibly due to diminishing sunlight intensity.

Autocatalysis of substituted indoles through formation of intermediate hydroperoxides was reported in the early 1950s (12–15). Draper and Crosby (16-17) report the formation of hydrogen peroxide in the photooxidation of indole and tryptophan. Attack by autogenerated oxidants, possibly hydroperoxides or hydrogen peroxide, for 2-MI and 3-MI is supported by their kinetic behavior as shown in Figure 2. After an initial buildup during which the intermediate oxidants are generated by direct photolysis, decomposition proceeds at a much greater rate as the oxidants generated initiate reactions that consume the original substituted indoles.

Rate Comparisons and Matrix Effects. Indole photolysis experiments in distilled water and aqueous CRM-1 were run in borosilicate glass vessels of roughly 1 mm thickness (10-mL test tubes, and 1-L Erlenmeyer flasks, respectively). The glass vessels filtered some radiation below 320 nm important to indoles (transmittance dropped to 61% at 310 nm and 41% at 300 nm), which generally had absorbance maxima around 270 nm, with only weak tails extending above 300 nm. This degree of filtering may have reduced the direct photolysis of indoles somewhat, but should not affect comparisons of the two experiments, because both were run in borosilicate glass.

The actinometer-normalized rate constants for the selected indoles and carbazole in distilled water and aqueous CRM-1 are compared in Table II.

The rates in distilled water were taken from the points in Figure 2 before significant autocatalysis was apparent. For aqueous CRM-1 (Figure 1), initial rates through 90 min of exposure were used. The rate constants for the p-NA actinometer in experiments with the individual test compounds ranged from 0.16 hr^{-1} to 0.21 hr^{-1} on three separate days; a value of 0.15 hr^{-1} was obtained in the aqueous CRM-1 experiment. The pH of all test solutions was near neutral.

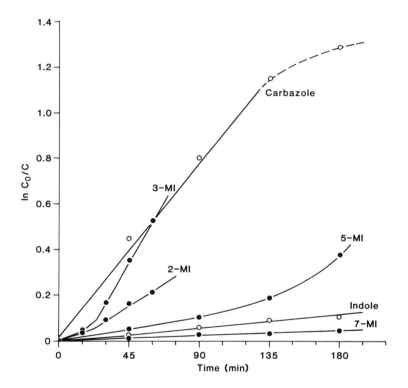

Figure 2. First-order plot of photolysis of selected indoles and carbazole in distilled water. C_0 and C refer to concentrations at time zero and time t, respectively.

Table II. Photolysis Rates of Selected Indoles and Carbazole
in Distilled Water and Aqueous CRM-1

| Compound | $k_p{}^a$ (hr^{-1}) | | $k_{rel}{}^b$ | | |
	Distilled Water	Aqueous CRM-1	Distilled Water	Aqueous CRM-1	Ratio^c
Indole	0.038	0.037	0.18	0.25	1.4
2-MI	0.15	0.20^d	0.94	1.3^d	1.3^d
3-MI	0.18		1.1		
5-MI	0.065	0.070	0.34	0.47	1.4
7-MI	0.014	0.055	0.074	0.37	5.0
Carbazole	0.51	0.17	2.4	1.1	0.46

$^a k_p$ = initial photolysis rate.

$^b k_{rel}$ = actinometer-normalized rate ($k_{rel} = k_p/k_a$).

^{c}Ratio = k_{rel}(aqueous CRM-1)/k_{rel}(distilled water).

^{d}2-MI and 3-MI coelute; the rates in aqueous CRM-1 are for
the combination of the two. The average of the rates in
distilled water was used in calculating the k_{rel} ratio.

In all cases, the initial rates for the indoles in aqueous
CRM-1 were elevated compared with those in distilled water. The
increases ranged from 1.3-fold for the 2-MI/3-MI pair up to 5.0-
fold for 7-MI. Carbazole, by contrast, had a 2.2-fold reduced rate
in aqueous CRM-1, which is indicative of differing photolysis
mechanisms for carbazole and indoles.

A comparison of the spectral qualities of the test compounds
and those of aqueous CRM-1 indicates that the indoles underwent
sensitized photolysis in the aqueous CRM-1 matrix. The matrix
absorbed significantly at wavelengths below 320 nm, which is the
important region for direct photolysis of the indoles studied.
Since direct light absorption was significantly diminished by the
matrix while observed photolysis rates were enhanced, the indoles
probably underwent sensitized photolysis initiated by other
components in the matrix. Such a process could account for the
increased photolysis rates for indoles in the matrix.

These observations indicate that components other than indoles
are capable of producing photooxidants in aqueous CRM-1. Draper
and Crosby (17) report that photolytic dechlorination of chloro-
acetic acid was sensitized by p-cresol and aniline. These compounds are representative of two of the most abundant chemical
classes present in aqueous CRM-1. Photolysis of these components
may produce oxidants that are attacking the indoles. Indoles may

also undergo sensitized photolysis of an energy-transfer type from strong light absorbers in the CRM-1 matrix, either directly (18) or through a singlet oxygen intermediate (as related to tryptophan [19]).

Carbazole apparently underwent direct photolysis in both distilled water and aqueous CRM-1 as indicated by its first-order behavior in both matrices. Its 2.2-fold reduced rate in aqueous CRM-1 is similar to the sixfold to ninefold reduced rates observed for selected PAH in aqueous CRM-1 (8).

Light attenuation by the matrix was probably not responsible for the reduction in rate for carbazole because a significant portion of its absorption spectrum lies above 320 nm, where the matrix did not absorb appreciably and the solar flux is the greatest. The inhibition could conceivably be due to quenching of the long-lived triplet excited state of carbazole by triplet-triplet energy transfer to other matrix components. The PAH present in the matrix are possible quenchers because of their relatively low triplet energies; naphthalene, for instance, is known to be a good triplet quencher for carbazole (20).

Quantum Yields. Sunlight quantum yields were calculated for the six test compounds from measurements of their photolysis rates in distilled water and from their UV-absorbance spectra using solar irradiance data from the literature. The method used is described in Refs. 5 and 21. Yields were determined from the known quantum yield of the p-NA actinometer using the following formula:

$$\phi_{cE} = \phi_a \frac{\Sigma L_\lambda \epsilon_\lambda^a}{S \Sigma L_\lambda \epsilon_\lambda^c} \tag{2}$$

where:

ϕ_{cE} = environmental (sunlight) quantum yield of the test chemical,

ϕ_a = quantum yield for the actinometer ($\phi_a = \phi_{p-NA} = 2.9 \times 10^{-4}$ at 366 nm [Ref. 21]),

S = photolysis rate constant for the actinometer divided by that for the test chemical ($S = k_a/k_p$),

L_λ = solar photon flux at wavelength λ (photons $cm^{-2}s^{-1}$), and

ϵ_λ = molar extinction coefficient for the actinometer (a) or the test chemical (c) at wavelength λ (L/mole-cm).

For the indoles, the rate constants used were determined from the early portions of the curves in Figure 2, which represent a time prior to discernible autocatalysis. The solar flux values were taken from Ref. 3, which lists midseason fluxes for specific wavelength intervals at 40° north latitude. The data were interpolated to the dates of the individual experiments, which were performed at 42° north latitude.

Table III lists the sunlight quantum yields determined in this manner for the six test compounds. Quantum yields approach or exceed unity for several indoles, indicating that the photolysis rates used for the indoles include an element of autocatalysis that is difficult to separate from the overall process. The results show that indoles are much more efficiently photolyzed than carbazole as evidenced by their higher quantum yields. In spite of their high quantum yields, the sunlight photolysis rates of indoles are slower than those of carbazole. This result is explained by the very weak absorbance of indoles in the solar wavelength region as opposed to the strong absorbance of carbazole in this region.

No differences related to structure were apparent from the ϕ_{cE} values for indole and the methyl derivatives tested, with the exception of 2-MI, which had a ϕ_{cE} that was an order of magnitude lower than those for the other indoles. 2-MI was a much stronger sunlight absorber than the other indoles because of a low-level absorbance band extending well into the solar wavelength region. Since its greater absorbance was not balanced by a greater photolysis rate, the resulting ϕ_{cE} was much lower than those for the other indoles.

Photolysis Mechanism. The photophysics and photochemistry of the indole ring have been comprehensively reviewed in Refs. 21-23. The unique properties of the indole-ring excited states, either the singlet or the triplet, include effects by solvents, temperature, and polarity.

Table III. Sunlight Quantum Yields for
Selected Indoles and Carbazole

Compound	k_{rel}[a]	ϕ_{cE}[b]	$\phi(313_{nm})$[c]
Indole	0.18	1.2	
2-MI	0.94	0.020	
3-MI	1.1	0.48	
5-MI	0.34	0.95	
7-MI	0.074	0.22	
Carbazole	2.4	0.0036	0.0076

[a]Actinometer-normalized rate (k_{rel} = k_p/k_a).

[b]Sunlight quantum yield from Eq. 2.

[c]Quantum yield for carbazole from Ref. 10.

In aqueous solutions and at room temperature, the hydrated electron e_{aq}^- is formed along with the indole cation radical $IH^{+\cdot}$.

$$IH \xrightarrow{\quad h\nu \quad} IH^* \xrightarrow{\quad\quad} IH^{+\cdot} + e_{aq}^-$$

The photoionization process was exhibited both by steady state ultraviolet irradiations and flash photolysis studies (24-31). Feitelson (24) studied the electron ejection process by steady state ultraviolet irradiations at 254 nm in aqueous solutions as a function of pH and temperature. His work indicated that the hydrated electrons originated from the fluorescent state. Mialocq et al. (31) monitored the formation of both e_{aq}^- at 660 nm and the indole cation radical $IH^{+\cdot}$ at 600 nm in picosecond laser photolysis of indole and tryptophan. They report a quantum yield of 0.21 for the formation of e_{aq}^- and conclude that it arises primarily from a monophotonic process involving an excited singlet state.

Zechner et al. (30) also report that photoionization is the major primary photoprocess for indole in aqueous solutions. However, they conclude that electrons are ejected from a relaxed singlet state. In earlier work, Bent and Hayon (26) also observed spectrophotometrically the production of e_{aq}^- and $IH^{+\cdot}$ in nanosecond laser pulses. They conclude that the photoionization of indole occurs primarily by way of a monophotonic process involving either a higher excited single state or a vibrationally excited lowest singlet state, or both. They report a photoionization quantum yield of 0.26 for indole at 25°C.

The indoles have also been shown to form exciplexes (solute-solvent excited-state complexes) with a wide range of electrophilic and nucleophilic compounds (32). Exciplex formation is especially evident in polar solvents. A fluorescence red shift from nonpolar to polar solvents and the concomitant loss of the vibrational structure of the fluorescent spectrum with no corresponding shift in the indole absorption spectra accounts for this postulated exciplex formation. Hershberger and Lumry (33) suggest that some charge-transfer mechanism stabilizes the excited complex and is a likely precursor to electron ejection.

Summarizing these studies, we deduced that electron production occurred by two possible mechanism: (1) from the lowest excited singlet state (fluorescent state), S_1 (24, 30), or an exciplex (25, 33), or (2) from a vibrationally nonrelaxed precursor of S_1 (26, 28, 31).

The concept of formation of a hydrated electron in aqueous solutions can be extended to environmental studies using sunlight irradiations. The hydrated electrons are easily quenched by molecular oxygen, leading to formation of superoxide, and subsequently, of hydroxyl radicals. Evidence exists that autosensitized photooxidation of indoles occurs through a superoxide radical ion $O_2^{-\cdot}$. Draper and Crosby (17) report the formation of $O_2^{-\cdot}$ from photolysis of indole (as well as p-cresol and aniline) via photoionization. Superoxide may attack indoles directly to form hydroperoxides, or it may first react in water to form hydrogen peroxide, which may be the primary oxidant. Hydrogen peroxide oxidation probably involves formation of hydroxyl radicals from the photolytic homolysis of H_2O_2, which are involved in free-radical oxidations (34).

As discussed in the section on matrix effects, indoles showed 1.3- to 5.0-fold enhancement (sensitization) of their photo-decomposition rates in the aqueous CRM-1 matrix. One route of sensitized photooxidation of indoles may be through a singlet oxygen (excited molecular oxygen) intermediate. The electron-rich 2,3-double bond of indole and its amino acid derivative tryptophan are susceptible to attack by singlet oxygen (19, 35-37). PAH are known sensitizers for singlet oxygen production (36) and are present at low levels in aqueous CRM-1. Heterocyclic PAH in solution possibly produce singlet oxygen as well.

With regard to direct energy transfer to indoles, the yields of indole triplets in triplet acetone quenching were measured by Kasama et al. (18). The yields obtained for the test indoles were 0.2-0.43. The presence of chromophores in the aqueous CRM-1 solution, therefore, could sensitize the photolysis of indoles directly by energy transfer to the triplet state.

Because of the complex chemical nature of aqueous CRM-1, and the multiple pathways of photolysis of indoles in solutions, we can only speculate as to the exact mechanism or mechanisms of the sensitization process in this matrix. We found, however, that the photoproduct obtained from 3-MI in distilled water was the same photoproduct isolated in aqueous CRM-1 solution. This observation is discussed in the next section.

The photolysis of carbazole in distilled water and in aqueous CRM-1 produced kinetic data similar to those obtained for PAH. Obviously, the photolytic behavior of carbazole is closer to that of PAH than to that of the indoles selected for this study.

Photoproducts. Products produced during the exposure of aqueous CRM-1 to sunlight were studied by analyzing colored fractions of the extracts by GC/MS and spectrophotometry. A reddish-orange color appeared primarily in the acid and base fractions, and in the ether subfraction (S3) of the neutral fraction. The acid and base fractions, which had low color-to-mass ratios, were examined only spectrophotometrically. The neutral S3 subfraction was studied in detail because of its intense color and relatively small mass.

Isolation of the products residing in the neutral S3 sub-fraction required further subfractionation on silica gel to obtain enriched colored subfractions (f1-f5) from the bulk of the material, which consisted of alkylated phenols. The neutral S3 subfraction was placed on a 10-g, 1-cm-diameter silica gel column, and the following subfractions were collected: f1, 30 mL of CH_2Cl_2; f2, 20 mL of 10% ethyl ether in CH_2Cl_2; f3, 20 mL of 20% ethyl ether in CH_2Cl_2; f4, 20 mL of 50% ethyl ether in CH_2Cl_2; and f5, 30 mL of 100% ethyl ether. The chromatograms of the highly colored f4 subfraction from both the 180-min exposure sample and the dark control are compared in Figure 3. A major new peak (labeled "a," R_t = 15.7 min) and several minor new peaks appear in the exposed sample between 13 min and 19 min.

Mass spectra were taken of these product peaks and of product peaks from the individual exposures of the test compounds. The mass spectrum and retention time of the major photoproduct of 3-MI matched those of peak "a" in Figure 3. It is reasonable that the most abundant products found in aqueous CRM-1 arise from breakdown

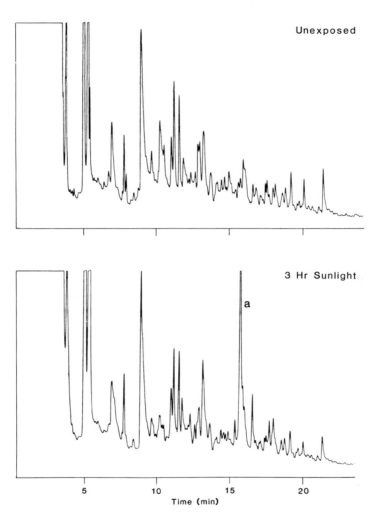

Figure 3. Chromatograms of the neutral f4 subfractions of the sunlight-exposed (3 hr) and unexposed samples. Peak "a" was identified as a photoproduct of 3-MI (structure V).

of 2-MI or 3-MI because the combined 2-MI and 3-MI peak underwent by far the greatest degree of degradation of any of the component peaks monitored in aqueous CRM-1. The major product found in the photolysis of 2-MI (molecular weight = 161) in distilled water did not appear in the S3 subfraction of the exposed aqueous CRM-1.

Beer et al. (15) report that the autoxidation of substituted indoles (I) produces hydroperoxide intermediates (II), which decom-

pose with ring cleavage to form o-acylamino-ketones (III). The hydroperoxide (II) in this process catalyzes its own production. It must be noted that product III can probably also be produced by singlet oxygen attack on the 2,3-double bond of substituted indoles (see Ref. 36).

For 3-MI (IV), structure V is proposed as the major product of photooxidation in water. This structure, o-(N-formyl)amino-acetophenone (molecular weight = 163), is supported by the mass spectrum of the 3-MI product found in aqueous CRM-1 (120 [100%], 92 [51%], 135 [45%], and 163 [16%]). Spectra of the other product peaks suggest that they are analogous products (acylamino derivatives) from the photooxidation of other alkylated indoles.

Spectrophotometric analysis detected product formation in all three colored fractions, that is, the acid and base fractions, and the neutral S3 subfraction. All colored fractions exhibited a bathochromic shift with time to stronger absorbance in the wavelength range of 300–500 nm. This absorbance in the blue/green region of the spectrum explains the complimentary appearance of color in the yellow/red region. The shift was possibly caused by formation of oxidation products containing carbonyl or hydroxyl groups.

The acid fraction exhibited a continuous increase in absorbance with increasing exposure time. The products in this fraction likely contain hydroxyl groups as their acidic functionality. Product absorbance in the base fraction appeared primarily after 90 min of exposure. The basic products may be the result of a product-catalyzed reaction, or they may be secondary photolysis products from the photolytic breakdown of initial products. The absorbance in the neutral S3 fraction was probably due primarily to formation of the o-acylamino-ketones from the photolysis of indoles, as discussed above.

Summary

Indoles and carbazoles are photosensitive components of aqueous coal oil. In sunlight exposures in distilled water, indoles underwent autocatalyzed photooxidation, which likely contributed to their very high quantum yields. In aqueous CRM-1, indoles apparently underwent sensitized photolysis because photolysis rates were enhanced, while available radiation was reduced markedly by absorption by the matrix. Carbazole, on the other hand, underwent direct photolysis in both the aqueous CRM-1 matrix and in distilled water. It exhibited a reduced photolysis rate in the matrix, similar to the behavior previously observed for PAH.

Photoproducts were isolated from the neutral fraction in a highly colored polar subfraction. The major product peak found in aqueous CRM-1 matched that found in the individual photolysis of 3-MI in distilled water. This product is thought to be o-(N-formyl)aminoacetophenone. Photoproducts were also detected in the acid and base fractions of aqueous CRM-1 by spectrophotometry.

Acknowledgments

Work supported by the U.S. Department of Energy, Assistant Secretary for Fossil Energy, under Contract W-31-109-Eng-38.

Literature Cited

1. Zepp, R. G.; Schlotzhauer, P. F.; Sink, R. M. Environ. Sci. Technol. 1985, 19, 74-81.
2. Zepp, R. G.; Baughman, G. L. In "Aquatic Pollutants: Transformation and Biological Effects," O. Hutzinger, I. H. Van Lelyveld, and B. C. J. Zoeteman, Eds., Pergamon Press: Oxford and New York, 1978, pp. 237-263.
3. Zepp, R. G.; Cline, D. M. Environ. Sci. Technol. 1977, 11, 359-366.
4. Zepp, R. G. In "The Handbook of Environmental Chemistry," Vol. 2, Part B, O. Hutzinger, Ed.; Springer-Verlag: Berlin, Heidelberg, and New York, 1982, pp. 19-42.
5. Miller, G. C.; Zepp, R. G. Residue Rev. 1983, 85, 89-110.
6. Stamoudis, V. C.; Bourne, S.; Haugen, D. A.; Peak, M. J.; Reilly, C. A. Jr.; Stetter, J.R.; Wilzbach, K. In "Coal Conversion and the Environment: Chemical, Biomedical, and Ecological Considerations," Proc. 20th Hanford Life Sciences Symposium, D. D. Mahlum, R. H. Gray, and W. D. Felix, Eds., U.S. Dept. of Energy Report CONF-80-1039, pp. 67-95, 1981.
7. Smith, J. H.; Mabey, W. R.; Bohonos, N.; Holt, B. R.; Lee, S. S.; Chou, T. W.; Bomberger, D. C.; Mill, T. "Environmental Pathways of Selected Chemicals in Freshwater Systems, Part II: Laboratory Studies," U.S. Environmental Protection Agency Report EPA-600/7-78-074, 1978.

8. Picel, K. C.; Stamoudis, V. C.; Simmons, M. S. "Photolytic and Partitioning Behavior of Polynuclear Aromatic Compounds, Aromatic Amines, and Phenols in Aqueous Coal Oil," U.S. Dept. of Energy Report DOE/MC/49533-1837 (ANL/SER-4), 1985.
9. Zadelis, D.; Simmons, M S. In "Polynuclear Aromatic Hydrocarbons: Formation, Metabolism, and Measurement," W. M. Cooke and A. J. Dennis, Eds., Battelle Press, Columbus, Ohio, 1983, pp. 1279-1290.
10. Mill, T.; Mabey, W. R.; Lan, B. Y.; Bareze, A. Chemosphere 1981, 10, 1281-1290.
11. Zepp, R. G.; Schlotzhauer, P. F. In "Polynuclear Aromatic Hydrocarbons: Third International Symposium on Chemistry and Biology -- Carcinogenesis and Mutagenesis," P. W. Jones and P. Leber, Eds., Ann Arbor Science: Ann Arbor, Mich, 1979, pp. 141-158.
12. Witcop, B.; Patrick, J. B. J. Am. Chem. Soc. 1951, 73, 713-718.
13. Witcop, B.; Patrick, J. B. J. Am. Chem. Soc. 1951, 73, 2196-2200.
14. Witcop, B.; Patrick, J. B. J. Am. Chem. Soc. 1952, 74, 3855-3860.
15. Beer, R. J. S.; Donavanik, T.; Robertson, A. J. Chem. Soc. 1954, 4139-4142.
16. Draper, W. M.; Crosby, D. G. Arch. Environ. Contam. Toxicol. 1983, 12, 121-126.
17. Draper, W. M.; Crosby, D. G. J. Agric. Food Chem. 1983, 31, 734-737.
18. Kasama, K.; Takematsu, A.; Aral, S. J. Phys. Chem. 1982, 86, 2420-2428.
19. Nilsson, R.; Merkel, P.B.; Kearns, D. R. Photochem. Photobiol. 1972, 16, 117-124.
20. Turro, N. J. "Molecular Photochemistry"; W. A. Benjamin: New York, 1965.
21. Dulin, D.; Mill, T. Environ. Sci. Technol. 1982, 16, 815-820.
22. Grossweiner, L. I. Curr. Top. in Radiat. Res. Quart. 1976, 11, 141-199.
23. Santus, R.; Bazin, M.; Aubailly, M. Rev. Chem. Intermed. 1980, 3, 231-283.
23. Creed, D. Photochem. Photobiol. 1984, 39, 537-562.
24. Feitelson, J. Photochem. Photobiol. 1971, 13, 87-96.
25. Hopkins, T. R.; Lumry, R. W. Photochem. Photobiol. 1972, 15, 555-556.
26. Bent, D. V.; Hayon, E. J. Am. Chem. Soc. 1975, 91, 2612-2619.
27. Bryant, F. D.; Santus, R.; Grossweiner, L. I. J. Phys. Chem. 1975, 79, 2711-2716.
28. Grossweiner, L. I.; Brendzel, A. M.; Blum, A. Chem. Phys. 1981, 57, 147-156.
29. Klein, R.; Tatischeff, I.; Bazin, M.; Santus, R. J. Phys. Chem. 1981, 85, 670-677.
30. Zechner, J.; Köhler, G.; Getoff, N.; Tatischeff, I.; Klein, R. Photochem. Photobiol. 1981, 34, 163-168.

31. Mialocq, J. C.; Amouyal, E.; Bernas, A.; Grand, D. J. Phys.
     Chem. 1982, 86, 3173-3177.
32. Hershberger, M. V.; Lumry, R. W.; Verrall, R. Photochem.
     Photobiol. 1981, 34, 609-617.
33. Hershberger, M. V.; Lumry, R. W. Photochem. Photobiol. 1976,
     23, 391-397.
34. Draper, W. M.; Crosby, D. G. J. Agric. Food Chem. 1981, 29,
     699-702.
35. Foote, C. S. Acc. Chem. Res. 1968, 1, 104-110.
36. Kearns, D. R. Chem. Rev. 1971, 71, 395-427.
37. Matheson, I. B. C.; Lee, J. Photochem. Photobiol. 1979, 29,
     879-881.

RECEIVED May 27, 1986

Chapter 5

Quantum Yields of Polychlorodibenzo-*p*-dioxins
In Water–Acetonitrile Mixtures and Their Environmental Phototransformation Rates

Ghulam Ghaus Choudhry and G. R. Barrie Webster

Pesticide Research Laboratory, Department of Soil Science, The University of Manitoba, Winnipeg, Manitoba, Canada R3T 2N2

Photochemistry of four individual isomers of polychlorodibenzo-p-dioxins (PCDDs), namely 1,2,3,4,7-pentachlorodibenzo-p-dioxin (1,2,3,4,7-P_5CDD) (1), 1,2,3,4,7,8-H_6CDD (2), 1,2,3,4,6,7,8-H_7CDD (3) and O_8CDD (4) in water-acetonitrile (2:3 v/v) was investigated using laboratory radiations of wavelength 313 nm. The quantum yields for the phototransformation of the dioxins 1-4 in these solvent systems were (9.8 ± 2.4) x 10^{-5}, (1.10 ± 0.02) x 10^{-4}, (1.53 ± 0.17) x 10^{-5} and (2.26 ±0.33) x 10^{-5}, respectively. These quantum yields and the measured absorption spectra together with solar intensity data available in the literature were utilized to estimate the sunlight (environmental) phototransformation first-order rate constants of the PCDD congeners 1-4 in water under conditions of variable sunlight intensity during various seasons; the corresponding half-lives were also determined. In summer, typical half-lives for the phototransformation of the pollutants 1-4 near the surface of water bodies at 40° north latitude would be 15 ± 4, 6.3 ± 0.1, 47 ±5, and 18 ±3 days, respectively.

Concern has grown regarding environmental contamination by polychlorinated dibenzo-p-dioxins (PCDDs). PCDDs include 75 congeners. Some of these tricyclic aromatics possess remarkable toxic, teratogenic, mutagenic, and acnegenic characterisitics (1,2). For instance, the LD_{50} for 2,3,7,8-tetrachlorodibenzo-p-dioxin (2,3,7,8-T_4CDD) in female rats is 45 µg/kg. Although the extent of toxicity is related to the degree of chlorination, the role of positional isomerisation is also critical and perhaps the dominant one; 2,3,7,8-T_4CDD is at least 800 times more toxic than 1,2,3,4-T_4CDD (2).
Recently, in addition to several other organic compounds, PCDDs have been detected in the flue gas and fly ash emitted by some municipal and industrial incinerators located in Canada, Japan, Switzerland, and the Netherlands (references cited in Choudhry and

Hutzinger ($\underline{3}$,$\underline{4}$) and Choudhry et al. ($\underline{5}$)). For instance, incinerator fly ash is known to contain relatively large amounts of octa-, hepta-, and hexa-chloro isomers (O_8CDD, H_7CDDs, and H_6CDDs) of dioxin but only low levels of $2,3,7,8-T_4CDD$ ($\underline{6}$). Moreover, Jones ($\underline{7}$) reported that the PCDDs released near the Dow Chemical Co., Midland, Michigan were > 99.5% H_6CDDs, H_7CDDs, and O_8CDD, respectively and tetrachloro isomers other than $2,3,7,8-T_4CDD$. In addition, commercial 2,3,5-tri-, 2,4,6-tri- and pentachlorophenol have been shown to contain 2,7-dichlorodibenzo-$\underline{p}$-dioxin ($2,7-D_2CDD$) and $1,3,6,8-T_4CDD$ together with H_6CDDs, H_7CDDs, and O_8CDD in ppm levels in spite of improved manufacturing techniques ($\underline{7}$). Chlorinated phenols have widespread use as fungicides, bactericides, slimicides, herbicides, etc., and they are also used in the production of phenoxy acids such as 2,4-di- and 2,4,5-trichlorophenoxyacetic acid (2,4-D and 2,4,5-T, respectively ($\underline{8}$). For almost four decades, 2,4-D and 2,4,5-T and their derivatives have received wide use as herbicides, especially for the control of brush, jungle vegetation, and aquatic weeds. Technical 2,4-D herbicide products have been reported to contain $2,7-D_2CDD$ and $1,3,6,8-T_4CDD$ amounting to 1.8-8.7 ppm ($\underline{9}$). Likewise, a mean of more than 1.9 and a maximum of 47 ppm of $2,3,7,8-T_4CDD$ has been identified in the military defoliant Agent Orange (butyl esters of 2,4-D and 2,4,5-T in equal amounts ($\underline{8}$). Throughout the world on several occasions, public anxiety because of the release of PCDDs into our environment has been seen. For example, in the autumn of 1957, millions of chickens in the Eastern and Midwestern United States died of a disease caused by a whole series of PCDDs present in their feed. On July 10, 1976, a wide area near Seveso, Italy was contaminated by an extremely toxic fallout consisiting of $2,3,7,8-T_4CDD$ in a chemical mixture of other organochlorine compounds. Similarly, a large quantity of Agent Orange heavily contaminated with $2,3,7,8-T_4CDD$ was applied from the air over jungles in South East Asia ($\underline{8}$). Finally, in 1982, due to an electrical transformer (fluid: 65% polychlorobiphenyls (Aroclor 1254) and 35% tri- and tetrachlorobenzenes) fire, an office building in Binghamton, New York, U.S.A. was contaminated by numerous dioxin congeners containing 4-8 chlorine constituents ($\underline{10}$).

The photochemical degradation is an important process with atmospheric contaminants and some chemicals that reside on surfaces such as pesticides on leaves and vegetation or in water bodies. Although a good deal of research work on the photochemical fate of PCDDs, both in solution and in the solid phase has appeared ($\underline{8}$,$\underline{11}$), to the best of our knowledge no investigator has reported the quantum yield (ϕ) for the photolysis of these environmental pollutants. We have determined the quantum yields (ϕ_r) for the photochemical transformation reactions of four individual dioxin isomers, namely 1,2,3,4,7-pentachlorodibenzo-$\underline{p}$-dioxin ($1,2,3,4,7-P_5CDD$) (1), $1,2,3,4,7,8-H_6CDD$ (2), $1,2,3,4,6,7,8-H_7CDD$ (3) and $1,2,3,4,6,7,8,9-O_8CDD$ (4) in water-acetonitrile (2:3 v/v) solution using UV light of mainly 313 nm. The present chapter reports the values of laboratory ϕ_r and the estimated sunlight photolysis half-lives ($(t_{1/2})_{sp}$) of PCDDs 1-4.

Experimental

Substrates and Solvents. Sources of the substrates, viz., PCDDs 1-4

1

2

3

4

(Table I), o-nitrobenzaldehyde, o-nitrosobenzoic acid, p-nitrotoluene and 1,2,3,4-tetrachlorobenzene and solvents were the same as previously reported (12).

Preparation of Solutions of PCDDs 1-4 in Water-Acetonitrile (2:3 v/v). The procedures for the prepration of the solutions of 1,2,3,4,7-P_5CDD (1) and 1,2,3,4,7,8-H_6CDD (2) in H_2O-CH_3CN (2:3 v/v) have been described elsewhere (12). Techniques for the preparation of the solution of H_6CDD 2 in water-acetonitrile (2:3 v/v) reported by Choudhry and Webster (12) were followed to prepare similar solutions of dioxins 3 and 4. For these investigations, the concentration of PCDDs 1-4 were 2.805, 3.328, 2.780 and 0.310 μM, respectively (Table II).

UV Absorption Spectroscopy. UV absorption spectral data for dioxins 1-4 documented in Table I were obtained using a single beam Bausch and Lomb Spectronic 710 Spectrophotometer.

Irradiation Equipment and Experiments. The previously described (13,14) Rayonet Photochemical Reactor (having an energy output of 90% between 290 and 310 nm) equipped with a merry-go-round apparatus was used. The Pyrex photoreaction cells (pathlength (ℓ), 1 cm) and chemical filter solution (consisting of K_2CrO_4 (0.270 g/L) and Na_2CO_3 (1.000 g/L) in water) used for the isolation of 313 nm line from the Rayonett RPR 3000 Å lamps have been described (12). Optically thick solutions of o-nitrobenzaldehyde (10 mM) in acetonitrile were utilized as a chemical actinometer for the determination of the intensity (I_λ) of the filtered incident light (12-15). For this purpose, the concentration of the photoproduct o-nitrosobenzoic acid arising from the actinometer was monitored (12).

Analyses. All analyses were carried out by HPLC on a Waters Scientific liquid chromatograph (Model 6000A pump, U6K injector, and an M440 UV absorbance detector). Separations were made with a 30 cm x 3.9 mm μBondapak C_{18} column (reverse phase, RP) (12). The analyses of the sample solution of the H_7CDD 3 and O_8CDD 4 were performed by this RP-HPLC using CH_3OH-H_2O (19:1 v/v) and CH_3OH as eluants, respectively at a flow rate of 1.0 mL/min. In the case of 3 and 4, 20 μL of p-nitrotoluene (2.055 mM) and 90 μL of 1,2,3,4-tetrachlorobenzene (0.757 mM) both in CH_3CN, were added respectively to each 2.0 mL sample solution as internal standard prior to analyses. Analytical procedures for 1,2,3,4,7-P_5CDD (1), 1,2,3,4,7,8-H_6CDD (2) and actinometry have been described elsewhere (12).

Results

Table I records the molar extinction coefficient (ϵ_λ) at various wavelengths (λ), of solutions of PCDDs 1-4. Water-acetonitrile (2:3 v/v) was used as a solvent for compounds 1-3; whereas, in the case of O_8-CDD 4, the solvent was neat acetonitrile. These spectral data were used in the prediction of the direct sunlight photolysis rates, i.e., k_{sp} and corresponding half-life $(t_{1/2})_{sp}$ of the pollutants 1-4 in aquatic environments (see below).
    Typical first-order plots (Equation 1) of the photolysis date for

Table I. Light Absorption Spectra[a] of PCDDs[b]

Wavelength, λ (nm)	Molar extinction coefficients, ε_λ (L.Mol^{-1}.cm^{-1}) for			
	1,2,3,4,7-P$_5$CDD (1)	1,2,3,4,7,8-H$_6$CDD (2)	1,2,3,4,6,7,8-H$_7$CDD (3)	1,2,3,4,6,7,8,9-O$_8$CDD (4)
254.0	10434	25244	23020	44068
297.5	2660	9015	3597	5307
300.0	2660	8114	3597	4986
302.5	2660	6912	3957	4825
305.0	2660	6311	3957	4664
307.5	2455	5409	3957	4342
310.0	2455	5109	4316	4182
312.5	2455	4808	4316	4182
313.0	2250	4808	4316	4182
315.0	2250	4808	4316	4021
317.5	2250	3907	4316	4021
320.0	2046	3306	3237	3860
323.1	1227	2104	2158	3217
330.0	0	301	360	965
340.0		0	0	483
350.0				322
360.0				322
370.0				161
380.0				161
390.0				0

[a]Data for PCDDs 1-3 were recorded using the solutions of the pollutants in H$_2$O-CH$_3$CN (2:3 v/v); while in the case of 4, the solvent was neat CH$_3$CN.
[b]The concentrations of PCDDs 1-4 were 4.881, 3.328, 2.780 and 6.218 μM, respectively.

Table II. Photolysis of PCDDs in Water-Acetonitrile (2:3 v/v) at 313 nm

Substrate No.	Initial concentration of the starting dioxin, P_o (10^{-6} M)	Maximum irradiation time, t_{max} (h)	Average percentage disappearance of the starting dioxin after t_{max} (%)	Photolysis first-order rate constant k_p (10^{-6} sec^{-1})	Absolute half-life[a], $t_{1/2}$ (h)	Quantum yield[b] for the photodegradation, ϕ_r
1	2.805	72	71.2	4.31±0.70	45.9±7.4	(9.8±2.4) x 10^{-5}
2	3.328	72	87.2	7.86±0.03	24.5±0.1	(1.1±0.02) x 10^{-4}
3	2.780	72	39.1	1.02±0.11	191±20	(1.53±0.17) x 10^{-5}
4	0.310	112	52.9	1.06±0.14	184±24	(2.26±0.33) x 10^{-5}

[a] Calculated using the following relationship: $t_{1/2} = \dfrac{\ln 2}{k_p}$
[b] Equation 2 was utilized.

$$\ln (P_o/P_t) = k_p t \tag{1}$$

dilute solutions (absorbance being <0.02 at 313 nm) of four individual congeners of PCDDs, namely $1,2,3,4,7-P_5CDD$ (1) (2.805 μM), $1,2,3,4,7,8-H_6CDD$ (2) (3.328 μM), $1,2,3,4,6,7,8-H_7CDD$ (3) (2.780 μM), and O_8CDD (4) (0.310 μM) are shown in Figures 1-4. In Equation 1, P_o and P_t are the concentrations of a PCDD congener at times zero and t, while k_p is the photolysis first-order rate constant of the pollutant. The plots in Figures 1-4 were drawn using standard linear regression (Energraphics); the special case $P_t = P_o$ was not used in order to avoid forcing the plot through the origin (15). The slopes of these plots provided the values of k_p (expressed in hours). Similar treatments of the additional photolysis data for all the investigated PCDDs were carried out.

Table II includes k_p values expressed in sec^{-1} for dioxins 1-4 determined in the above mentioned fashion. The values of ϵ_{313} (Table I), k_p (Table II) and I_λ measured with the aid of simultaneous photolysis of the actinometer solution (12) enabled the quantum yields (ϕ_r) to be determined at 313 nm for the photodecomposition reactions using Equation 2 (16-19):

$$\phi_r = \frac{k_p}{2.303 \, I_\lambda \epsilon_\lambda \ell} \tag{2}$$

where ℓ (cell pathlength) was 1.00 cm. Table II indicates that the values of ϕ_r's for dioxins 1-4, determined in this manner are (9.8 $\pm$ 2.4) x 10^{-5}, (11.0 $\pm$0.2) x 10^{-5}, (1.53 $\pm$0.17) x 10^{-5} and (2.26 $\pm$0.33) x 10^{-5}, respectively. It should be cited that in order to eliminate the introduction of a possible systematic error due to the probability of ℓ being > 1 cm during the determination of these ϕ_r's, observed values of P_t (see Equation 1) and those of the concentrations of the photoproduct o-nitrosobenzoic acid of the actinometer (which were subsequently utilized for the determination of I_λ) were corrected with the aid of correction factors for each photochemical cell (for further details, reference (12) can be consulted).

In estimating the first-order sunlight (environmental) photoconversion rate constants (k_{sp}) of these environmental contaminants, the following relationship can be utilized (Equation 3) (16,17,20-22):

$$k_{sp} = \phi_r \, k_{a,\lambda} = \phi_r \, \frac{2.303}{j} \, \Sigma \epsilon_\lambda Z_\lambda \tag{3}$$

In Equation 3, $k_{a,\lambda}$ is the sunlight absorption rate summed over all the λ's of the sunlight that are absorbed by the pollutant; Z_λ is the sunlight intensity for a specified wavelength interval (N) centered at wavelength (λ) (units, photons cm^{-2} sec^{-1} N nm^{-1}); j = 6.023 x 10^{20} is a conversion constant that makes the units of Z and ϵ compatible; and ϕ_r and ϵ_λ have been defined above (Equation 2). The latter two data are measured in the laboratory (cf. Table I and II); while the solar intensity (Z_λ) data as functions of time of day, season, and latitude for the range $\lambda = 297.5$ to 800 nm are available

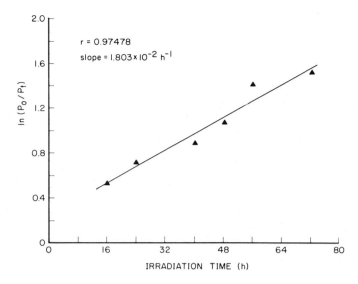

Figure 1. First-order treatment of the photolysis data for
1,2,3,4,7-P_5CDD (1) in water-acetonitrile (2:3 v/v).

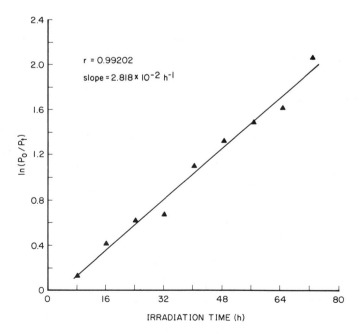

Figure 2. First-order treatment of the photolysis data for
1,2,3,4,7,8-H_6CDD (2) in water-acetonitrile (2:3 v/v).

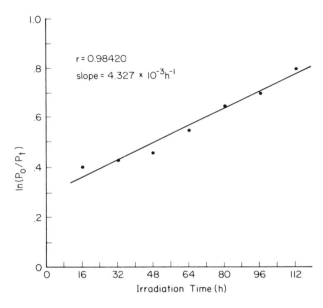

Figure 3.   First-order treatment of the photolysis data for 1,2,3,4,6,7,8-H_7CDD (3) in water-acetonitrile (2:3 v/v).

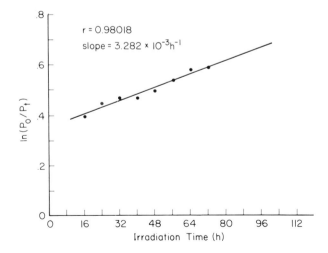

Figure 4.   First-order treatment of the photolysis data for 1,2,3,4,6,7,8,9-O_8CDD (4) in water-acetonitrile (2:3 v/v).

in the literature ($\underline{23}$-$\underline{24}$). For the calculation of k_{sp} by using
Equation 3, it is assumed that the quantum yield for a chemical
determined at a wavelength, $\underline{viz}$., 313 nm is wavelength independent
for the region of sunlight absorption of the substrate.

We have also calculated the rate constants (k_{sp}) for the
phototransformation of each dioxin, 1-4, present near the surface of
the water bodies anticipated to be caused by natural sunlight at 40°N
latitude during the various seasons (Table III). These estimations
of k_{sp} have been carried out by utilizing Equation 3 together with
the quantum yields (at 313 nm) and the UV absorption spectral data
(Table I, except ϵ_{254} and ϵ_{313}) of the pollutants, and the
corresponding solar radiation data from Roof ($\underline{25}$) in the case of
spring, summer, fall, and winter with the assumption that ϕ_r,s are
independent of wavelength of the incidental light. Likewise, Table
III also includes sunlight photolysis half-lives $(t_{1/2})_{sp}$) calculated
by using Equation 4 ($\underline{16}$):

$$(t_{1/2})_{sp} = \frac{\ln 2}{k_{sp}} \tag{4}$$

Discussion

It is well known that during the solution-phase photolysis of PCDDs,
substrates with chlorine atoms in the 2-, 3-, 7-, and 8-position(s)
($\underline{i.e.}$, with lateral chlorine atoms) photolyse more rapidly than those
with chlorine atoms in the 1-, 4-, 6-, and 9-position ($\underline{i.e.}$, with
peri chlorine atoms) (refs. cited in Choudhry and Hutzinger ($\underline{8}$).
Moreover, reductive dechlorination is the usual process involved in
the photodegradation of PCDDs containing 4 or more Cl contents ($\underline{8}$).
However, in the case of the irradiation of PCDDs with 3 or less
chlorine atoms, fission of the ether bond in the dioxin ring is the
most likely route ($\underline{8}$). In the case of our studies, the RP-HPLC
chromatograms of the photolyzates of dioxins 1-4 did not show any
photoproduct, for example, expected to be photoformed through the
reductive dechlorination of the starting dioxin as well as through
secondary photodecomposition; thus indicating that extensive
photodegradation of these pollutants may be occurring in the water-
acetonitrile system. The failure of the detection of the anticipated
reductively dechlorinated photoproducts can alternatively be
attributed to the fact that we have exposed rather dilute solution
($\underline{i.e.}$, 0.3-3.3 μM) of PCDDs to UV light; under such circumstances it
is likely that as soon as a photoreduced product is produced, it
undergoes further dechlorination. Such photoprocess probably
continue with the eventual formation of photoproducts which are not
observable with our RP-HPLC system (see Experimental). Another
reason can be that the photochemical quantum yields of the expected
primary photoproducts (from dioxin 1 only) and secondary
photoproducts (from all the investigated PCDDs), namely dibenzo-$\underline{p}$-
dioxin as well as mono- through tetrachlorodibenzo-$\underline{p}$-dioxins are
probably much greater than those of the starting dioxins.

Absolute half-life times $(t_{1/2})$ for 1,2,3,4,6,7,8-H_7CDD (3) and
1,2,3,4,6,7,8,9-O_8CDD (4) in $\underline{n}$-hexadecane reported by Nestrick and
his coworkers ($\underline{26}$) are 30 and 24 h, respectively; whereas, Dobbs and
Grant ($\underline{2}$) reported half-lives amounting to 11 and 16 h for dioxins 3
and 4 in $\underline{n}$-hexane, respectively. However, Table II shows that $t_{1/2}$

Table III. Calculated Sunlight Photolysis Rate Constants[a,b] (k_{sp}) and Half-Lives[c] ($(t_{1/2})_{sp}$) of PCDDs in Aquatic Bodies for Various Seasons

Seasons	1,2,3,4,7-P$_5$CDD (1)		1,2,3,4,7,8-H$_6$CDD (2)		1,2,3,4,6,7,8-H$_7$CDD (3)		O$_8$CDD (4)	
	k_{sp} x 10^2 (days^{-1})	$(t_{1/2})_{sp}$ (days)	k_{sp} x 10^2 (days^{-1})	$(t_{1/2})_{sp}$ (days)	k_{sp} x 10^2 (days^{-1})	$(t_{1/2})_{sp}$ (days)	k_{sp} x 10^2 (days^{-1})	$(t_{1/2})_{sp}$ (days)
Spring	4.03±0.98	18±4	9.16±0.16	7.6±0.1	1.24±0.14	57±6	3.45±0.51	21±3
Summer	4.86±1.18	15±4	11.06±0.20	6.3±0.1	1.48±0.16	47±5	3.97±0.58	18±3
Fall	2.58±0.62	29±7	5.84±0.10	11.9±0.2	0.80±0.09	88±10	2.27±0.33	31±5
Winter	1.41±0.35	52±13	3.21±0.06	21.6±0.4	0.45±0.05	156±17	1.40±0.21	51±7

[a] Equation 3 was utilized.
[b] Solar radiation data for latitude 40°N, near the surface of water bodies for the calculation of k_{sp} for four seasons was used from Roof (25).
[c] Equation 4 was used.

for the photolysis of compounds 3 and 4 in H_2O-CH_3CN (2:3 v/v) at 313 nm are respectively 191 and 184 h, thereby indicating that absolute half-life time for pollutant 3 is larger than that of 4. This trend agrees with the former investigators (26) and disagrees with the latter ones (2). It is notable that our $t_{1/2}$ data for 3 and 4 (Table II) are several-fold greater than those published by other researchers (2,26) which may be explained by taking into account the fact that water-acetonitrile systems are inferior hydrogen donors compared to neat organic solvents (27), viz., n-hexane, and n-hexadecane. It is apparent from Table II that the absolute first-order rate constants (k_p) for the photolysis of the investigated PCDDs at 313 nm decrease in the following order:

$$H_6CDD(2) > P_5CDD(1) > O_8CDD(4) > H_7CDD(3)$$

A similar trend is observable in the case of quantum yields (ϕ_r) (see Table II) and estimated sunlight photolysis rate constants (k_{sp}) (Table III). Likewise absolute half lives ($t_{1/2}$) at 313 nm (Table II) and calculated sunlight photolysis half-lives ($(t_{1/2})_{sp}$) (Table III) of these pollutants in a season increase in the following sequence:

$$2 < 1 < 4 < 3.$$

For instance, the trend $2 > 1 > 4 > 3$ for the k_p and k_{sp} shows that on substituting the lateral 8-position of the nucleus of dioxin 1 by Cl atom, the substrate becomes more photolabile (see above); whereas, the additional substitution of the peri 6-position as well as the peri 6- and 9-positions of pollutant 2 with Cl atom(s) renders the substrate less photoreactive. Why rates constants for O_8CDD (4) are greater than those for H_7CDD (3) remains unanswered. Although such trend in the case of k_{sp} is possibly attributable to the fact that the ϵ_λ values for the substrates were measured using different solvent systems (see Table I); the trend in the case of k_p still remains unexplained because the same solvent system was utilized for the determination of k_p's for all dioxins (Table II).

   As expected, the rates of the sunlight phototransformation (k_{sp}) and the corresponding half-lives ($(t_{1/2})_{sp}$) of the PCDDs 1-4 are greatest and smallest, respectively, in the summer season (see Table III). Finally, the greater difference between the estimated sunlight rate constants (and half-lives) for dioxins 4 and 3 in comparison with the difference between the k_p (and $t_{1/2}$) for 4 and 3 may be ascribable to the fact that the former pollutant absorbs more strongly in the region of wavelengths > 295 nm (see Table I).

Conclusions

Our photochemical investigations at 313 nm conducted on the dilute solutions of 1,2,3,4,7-pentachlorodibenzo-p-dioxin (1,2,3,4,7-P_5CDD) (1) (2.805 μM), 1,2,3,4,7,8-H_6CDD (2) (3.328 μM), 1,2,3,4,6,7,8-H_7CDD (3) (2.780 μM) and 1,2,3,4,6,7,8,9-O_8CDD (4) (0.310 μM) in water-acetonitrile (2:3 v/v) mixtures lead us to draw several environmentally significant conclusions. The quantum yields for the PCDD congeners 1-4 amounting to (9.8 ±2.4) x 10^{-5}, (1.10 $\pm$ 0.02) x 10^{-4}, (1.53 ±0.17) x 10^{-5} and (2.26 $\pm$ 0.33) x 10^{-5}, respectively, are rather low, thereby reflecting that pollutants such as polychlorodibenzo-p-dioxins (PCDDs) present in the aquatic environments would photodegrade rather slowly. Similar conclusions can be drawn from both absolute ($t_{1/2}$) and sunlight phototransformation ($(t_{1/2})_{sp}$) documented in Table II and Table III, respectively. Contrary to the previous reports on the photodegradation of PCDDs in organic solvents (2,8, 26) our photolytic studies using H_2O-CH_3CN systems stress that in the environment PCDD contaminants are <u>not</u> likely to photodissipate as rapidly as was concluded by other researchers. Finally, individual isomers of chlorinated dioxins possessing a greater number of lateral Cl substituents are apparently expected to photoconvert faster than those with larger peri Cl contents, when such PCDD isomers are present in water bodies.

Acknowledgment

We appreciate and acknowledge the financial support for this project by Wildlife Toxicology Division, Canadian Wildlife Service, Ottawa, Ontario, Canada.

Literature Cited

1. Buser, H. R. <u>J. Chromatogr</u>. 1976, <u>129</u>, 303.
2. Dobbs, A.J.; Grant, C. <u>Nature</u>. 1979, <u>278</u>, 163.
3. Choudhry, G.G.; Hutzinger, O. <u>Toxicol. Environ. Chem</u>. 1982, <u>5</u>, 1.
4. Choudhry, G.G., Hutzinger, O. "Mechanistic Aspects of the Thermal Formation of Halogenated Organic Compounds Including Polychlorinated Dibenzo-p-dioxins", Gordon and Breach Sci. Publ.: New York, 1983.
5. Choudhry, G.G.; Olie, K.; Hutzinger, O. <u>Pergamon Ser. Environ. Sci</u>. 1982, <u>5</u>, 275.
6. National Research Council of Canada, "Polychlorinated Dibenzo-p-dioxins": Criteria for Their Effects on Man and His Environment", NRCC 18574, Ottawa, 1981.
7. Jones, P.A. "Chlorophenols and Their Impurities in the Canadian Environment", Report EPS 3-EC-81-2, Environment Impact Control Directorate, Ottawa, 1981.
8. Choudhry, G.G.; Hutzinger, O. <u>Residue Rev</u>. 1982, <u>84</u>, 113.
9. Cochrane, W.P.; Singh, J.; Miles, W.; Wakeford, B.; Scott, J. <u>Pergamon Ser. Environ. Sci</u>. 1982, <u>5</u>, 209.
10. Schecter, A. <u>Chemosphere</u> 1983, <u>12</u>, 669.
11. Corbet, R.L.; Muir, D.C.G.; Webster, G.R.B. <u>Chemosphere</u> 1983, <u>12</u>, 523.
12. Choudhry, G.G.; Webster, G.R.B. <u>Chemosphere</u> 1985, <u>14</u>, 9.
13. Choudhry, G.G.; Roof, A.A.M.; Hutzinger, O. <u>J. Chem. Soc. Perkin Trans. I</u> 1982, 2957.
14. Choudhry, G.G.; van den Broeck, J.A.; Hutzinger, O. <u>Chemosphere</u> 1983, <u>12</u>, 487.
15. Dulin, D.; Mill, T. <u>Environ. Sci. Technol</u>. 1982, <u>16</u>, 815.
16. Choudhry, G.G. "Humic Substances: Structural, Photophysical, Photochemical and Free Radical Aspects and Interactions with Environmental Chemicals"; Gordon and Breach Sci. Publ.: New York, 1984.

17. Choudhry, G.G. Toxicol. Environ. Chem. 1983, 6, 231.
18. Zepp, R.G. "Experimental Approaches to Environmental
     Photochemistry" in The Handbook of Environmental Chemistry, ed.
     Hutzinger, O., Vol. 2/Part B, Springer-Verlag: Berlin, West
     Germany, 1982, 19.
19. Mill, T.; Mabey, W.R.; Lan, B.Y.; Baraze, A. Chemosphere 1981,
     10, 1281.
20. Wolfe, N.L.; Zepp, R.G.; Baugham, G.L.; Fincher, R.C.; Gordon,
     J.A. "Chemical and Photochemical Transformation of Selected
     Pesticides in Aquatic Systems", U.S. EPA-600/3-76-067, 1976,
     12.
21. Zepp, R.G.; Cline, D.M. Environ. Sci. Technol. 1977, 11, 359.
22. Choudhry, G.G. "Interactions of Humic Substances with
     Environmental Chemicals", in The Handbook of Environmental
     Chemistry, ed., Hutzinger, O., Vol. 2/Part B; Springer-Verlag:
     Berlin, West Germany, 1982, 103.
23. Leighton, P.A. "Photochemistry of Air Pollution", Academic
     Press: New York, 1961.
24. Koller, L.R. "Ultraviolet Radiation", 2nd ed.; John Wiley: New
     York, 1965.
25. Roof, A.A.M. "Aquatic Photochemistry" in The Handbook of
     Environmental Chemistry, ed. Hutzinger, O., Vol. 2/Part B;
     Springer-Verlag: Berlin, West Germany, 1982, 43.
26. Nestrick, T.J.; Lamparski, L.L.; Townsend, D.I. Anal. Chem.
     1980, 52, 1865.
27. Bunce, N.J. Chemosphere 1978, 7, 653.

RECEIVED June 24, 1986

INORGANIC PHOTOOXIDANTS

Chapter 6

Mechanism of Photolytic Ozonation

Gary R. Peyton[1,3] and William H. Glaze[2,4]

[1]SumX Corporation, Austin, TX 78761
[2]Graduate Program in Environmental Sciences, University of Texas, Dallas, TX 75235

Photolytic Ozonation has been known for over a decade
as a powerful water treatment process for the destruction of organic compounds, but its mode of action has
not been understood. It is shown using kinetic argu-
ments and data from scavenging experiments that
photolysis of aqueous ozone yields hydrogen peroxide,
which then reacts with further ozone in a complex
series of reactions to yield hydroxyl radical. The
proposed mechanism is shown to explain pH behavior of
model compound destruction in earlier data.

Photolytic Ozonation (Ozone/UV) (1-4) has been in use for over a
decade for the destruction in water of compounds which are refractory to ozonation alone. Originally developed for the destruction
of metal cyanide complexes (5), it was soon shown to be effective
for the treatment of a number of organic compounds as well (3,6-10).
There has been considerable speculation (11,12) concerning the
active specie(s) responsible for the degradative power of photolytic
ozonation, but until recently (4,13,14) almost no experimental data
had been offered in support of that speculation.
    In the present study, the mechanism of photolytic ozonation was
investigated in the laboratory by measuring ozone, hydrogen peroxide, and total oxidant levels in purified water as a function of
time in a two-liter stirred tank reactor in which concurrent ozone
sparging and UV irradiation were taking place. Experiments were run
in the presence and absence of various radical scavengers and the
results interpreted in terms of reaction rate constants taken from
the literature. This paper will discuss the mechanism of photolytic
ozonation, show its relationship to other ozonation processes, and

[3]Current address: Aquatic Chemistry Section, Illinois State Water Survey, Department of
 Energy and Natural Resources, Champaign, IL 61820
[4]Current address: Department of Environmental Science and Engineering, School of
 Public Health, University of California, Los Angeles, CA 90024

illustrate why variable and apparently conflicting results for
photolytic ozonation have appeared in the literature.

Background

The production of hydroxyl radical by the gas phase photolysis of
ozone in the presence of water vapor is well documented (15), and is
the basis for most of the speculation concerning hydroxyl radical
production in aqueous solution. In 1957, Taube (16) showed that
irradiation of an aqueous solution of acetic acid through which
ozone was bubbling resulted in an almost stoichiometric and linear
(with time) production of hydrogen peroxide. Through the use of ^{18}O
tracers Taube showed that half of the oxygen content of the peroxide
originated in the water while the other half came from the ozone.
The production of hydrogen peroxide from the 2537Å photolysis of
ozone is consistent with the observed gas-phase photochemistry,
where at wavelengths shorter than 310 nm the products are dioxygen
and $O(^1D)$. In the condensed phase, the latter could either insert
into an O-H bond of water or abstract a hydrogen atom, after which a
geminate recombination of the hydroxyl radicals could occur. The
correct interpretation of Taube's results was made unclear, however,
by the findings of Baxendale and Wilson (17), who demonstrated that
the production of hydroxyl radicals in the presence of acetic acid
resulted in the generation of hydrogen peroxide. Since Taube and
Bray (18) had already published evidence that ozone and hydrogen
peroxide reacted to produce hydroxyl radical, it can be seen from
the literature prior to 1958 that hydroxyl radical is the principal
active species in photolytic ozonation, regardless of whether the
primary step produces hydrogen peroxide or hydroxyl radical.
However, the actual results obtained in the presence of other substances could vary considerably depending on solution composition,
relative concentrations of intermediate products, and in particular,
the nature of the initial photochemical step.
    In 1982, Staehelin and Hoigne (19) showed that reaction of
ozone with peroxy anion (Equation 1), the conjugate base of hydrogen
peroxide (Equation 2), was in many cases faster than with the
undissociated peroxide or the base-catalyzed decomposition of ozone,
even when only very small amounts of peroxide are present.

$$HO_2^- + O_3 \rightarrow O_3^- + HO_2 \qquad (1)$$
$$H_2O_2 \;\rightleftarrows\; HO_2^- + H^+ \qquad (2)$$

    Recent papers by Buhler, Staehelin, and Hoigne (20) and by
Sehested, Holcman, Bjergbakke and Hart (21,22) provided values of
rate constants for reactions between OH and O_3 (Equation 3), HO_2 and
O_3 (Equation 4) the forward and reverse reactions in the protonation
of ozonide ion (Equation 5), and the decomposition of HO_3 to yield
hydroxyl radical, Equation 6.

$$OH + O_3 \rightarrow HO_2 + O_2 \qquad (3)$$
$$HO_2 + O_3 \rightarrow HO + 2O_2 \qquad (4)$$
$$H^+ + O_3^- \;\rightleftarrows\; HO_3 \qquad (5)$$
$$HO_3 \rightarrow HO + O_2 \qquad (6)$$

In addition, Staehelin and Hoigne (23-25), from information in the radiochemical literature, have provided a clear (although in practice, complicated) picture of the radical cycle in the so-called "indirect" ozonation reactions, whereby superoxide is also formed from the reaction of hydroxyl radical with organic compounds in the presence of oxygen.

In 1983, Peyton and Glaze (13) presented experimental evidence which showed that ozone photolysis at 254 nm in aqueous solution resulted directly in the production of hydrogen peroxide. Further studies (4,14), and reexamination of older data (3) have confirmed these conclusions. The resulting mechanism for photolytic ozonation is discussed below.

Experimental

The apparatus used for ozone photolysis studies was similar to that described previously (1,4), and is shown in Figure 1. The two-liter stirred tank reactor was made from pyrex pipe (6" i.d.), with top and bottom heads cut from 1/4" thick PTFE sheet. The reactor contained four baffles and a six-blade paddle-type impeller, made from aluminum using the standard CSTR relative dimensions (6,26,27). All tubing and fittings were glass or PTFE, so that no ferrous materials came in contact with ozone or liquid. Four quartz UV lamp sheaths passed vertically through the reactor, extending through both the top and bottom reactor heads. The sheaths were sealed into the heads using viton o-rings. All work reported in this paper was done using low pressure mercury lamps (model no. G8T5, American Ultraviolet, Chatham, N.J.). These lamps are rated at 8 W power consumption with 1.6 W of 2537Å UV output at 100 hours of life, according to the manufacturer. As the lamps had been used in considerable previous experimentation, intensities were measured radiometrically and averaged cylindrically around the lamp, giving a UV power output of 0.433 W. Stirring speed was set at 550 rpm using a phototachometer. This speed was found by Yocum (26) and Prengle (6) to give good mass transfer performance in larger reactors of this type.

Ozone in the aqueous phase was analyzed by the indigo method of Bader and Hoigne (28,29), using the disulfonate rather than the trisulfonate as originally described by those authors. This method (hereafter called the HBI method) was calibrated in purified water against the iodimetric method of Flamm (30) (BKI) and checked by UV absorbance using the extinction coefficient of Hart et al. (31). The iodimetric method was, itself, calibrated by quantitative iodine liberation using excess iodide and standard iodate solution, prepared using dried iodate as a primary standard. Ozone in the gas phase was measured by UV absorbance, calibrated against the wet methods by absorbing the gas in reagent solution contained in the reactor.

Hydrogen peroxide was measured colorimetrically by complexation with Ti(IV) ("TI4" method) (32) or by the method of Masschelein et al. (33) (MDL method). As ozone appears to interfere negatively with hydrogen peroxide measurement using the TI4 method, ozone was quickly and vigorously sparged from solution before peroxide measurements were made. The MDL method was not used on ozone-containing solutions. Total oxidants were measured iodimetrically by the method of Flamm (30), but with the addition of a small quantity of ammonium molybdate to catalyze the reaction with peroxides (BKI/M method).

Water was purified by a Millipore or equivalent ion-exchange/ carbon filtration system, after which it was distilled from alkaline permanganate. Typical TOC levels of the final product water were 60-100 µg/L as measured by a Dohrman DC-54 low-level carbon analyzer.

Other chemicals were of reagent grade and were used without further purification.

Results

In a typical experiment, ozone, hydrogen peroxide and total oxidants were measured as a function of time, while ozone was bubbled into the reactor which contained the lamp(s). Figure 2 shows peroxide accumulation for these experiments as a function of pH. Figure 3 compares results obtained by replacing acetic acid with sulfuric acid. In Figure 4 are shown the data from two similar experiments where acetic acid was replaced by sodium bicarbonate solution.

The results of similar experiments where ozone is bubbled into distilled water are shown in Figure 5. In all of the results shown, the ozone dose rate (inlet stream) was 4 mg/L-min or 8.3×10^{-5} mol/L·min while the UV flux into the reactor was 0.22 W/L or 2.8×10^{-5} E/L-min.

In addition to the photolytic ozonation experiments described above, hydrogen peroxide photolysis experiments were performed in the presence and absence of hydroxyl radical scavengers. These experiments were run using distilled water (a) as it came from the lab reservoir, (b) after oxygenation, and (c) after sparging with nitrogen to remove oxygen. The results are shown in Table I, in the form of the observed rate constants.

Table I. Observed Hydrogen Peroxide Photolysis Rate Constants in the Absence and Presence of Scavengers

Solution conditions	Apparent rate constant, $min^{-1} \times 10^3$		
	No scavenger	0.1 M bicarbonate	0.1 M acetic acid
Deaerated	10.5	9.8	3.8
"As is"*	9.8	10.2	2.8
Oxygenated	8.2	9.6	1.6

* Meaning neither oxygenated nor deaerated

Discussion

Two cases will be considered:

I) Ozone photolysis in aqueous solution results in the direct production of hydrogen peroxide

$$O_3 + H_2O \xrightarrow{h\nu} O_2 + H_2O_2 \tag{7}$$

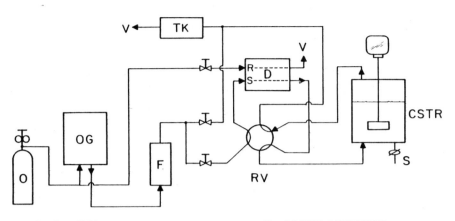

O = OXYGEN
OG = OZONE GENERATOR
V = VENT
TK = THERMAL OZONE KILL UNIT
F = ROTAMETER

D = OZONE DETECTOR
R = REFERENCE SIDE
S = SAMPLE SIDE
RV = ROTARY VALVE
CSTR = STIRRED TANK REACTOR
S = SAMPLE POINT

Figure 1.   Laboratory ozonation system.

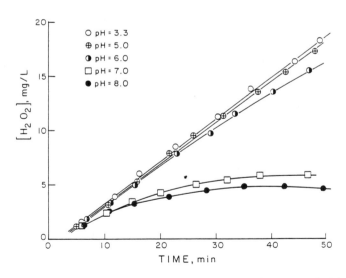

Figure 2.   Effect of pH on hydrogen peroxide accumulation.
Total HOAc/OAc⁻ concentration is 0.015 M.

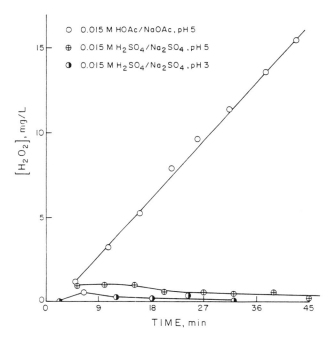

Figure 3.   Hydrogen peroxide accumulation in the presence of acetic and sulfuric acids.

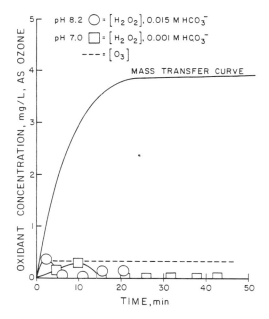

Figure 4.   Ozone photolysis in the presence of bicarbonate.

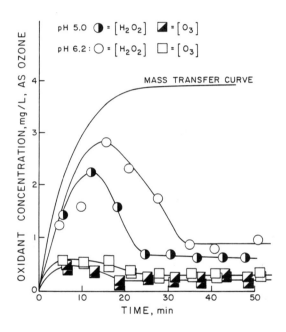

Figure 5. Oxidant concentrations during ozone photolysis in
           distilled water.

   II) Ozone photolysis directly produces two hydroxyl radicals
which are capable of avoiding recombination and leaving the solvent
cage.

$$O_3 + H_2O \xrightarrow{h\nu} O_2 + 2 \cdot OH \tag{8}$$

The case where Equation 8 occurs but geminate recombination is
immediate and complete is indistinguishable from Case I. There may
also exist an intermediate case where Equation 8 occurs, after which
some fraction of the hydroxyl radicals escape while the remainder
recombine to form hydrogen peroxide.
   As inferred in an earlier section, the peroxide accumulation
seen in Figure 2 may be the result of direct peroxide production
(Case I) or a product of hydroxyl radical (Case II) reaction with
acetic acid. Replacement of acetic acid by another acid which is
not a radical scavenger (Figure 3) did not give appreciable peroxide
accumulation, seemingly indicating Case I, where the scavenger pro-
tected accumulating peroxide from hydroxyl radical (produced by
Equations 1, 2, 5 and 6), thereby preventing Equation 9.

$$\cdot OH + H_2O_2 \rightarrow H_2O + HO_2 \cdot \tag{9}$$

Although in the Case II version, one mechanism for peroxide production (reaction of hydroxyl radical with acetic acid) is removed,
direct recombination in the bulk solution is still a possibility

$$2 \cdot OH \rightarrow H_2O_2 \tag{10}$$

However, the high concentrations of ozone present in solution (compared to hydroxyl radical) makes it unlikely that this occurs to a
very great extent, since the hydroxyl radical would be scavenged by
the swamping concentration of ozone.
   Replacement of acetic acid by another hydroxyl radical
scavenger, bicarbonate, resulted in no accumulation of peroxide
(Figure 4), seemingly supporting Case II. Yet the stoichiometry of
the peroxide photolysis experiments (Table I) suggests that the
scavenging product, carbonate radical anion (Equation 11),

$$\cdot OH + HCO_3^- \rightarrow \cdot CO_3^- + H_2O \tag{11}$$

reacts with hydrogen peroxide. This was indeed reported by Weeks
and Rabani (34) and the rate constant later reported by Behard,
Czapski and Duchovny (35) to be $8 \times 10^5 \ M^{-1}s^{-1}$, who unfortunately
did not specify the products of that reaction. However, Equation 12
is a likely possibility and gives stoichiometry consistent with the
hydrogen peroxide photolysis data in Table I.

$$H_2O_2 + \cdot CO_3^- \rightarrow HCO_3^- + HO_2 \cdot \tag{12}$$

In view of this reaction, the lack of peroxide accumulation in
Figure 4 cannot be taken to rule out Case I.
   The most meaningful data seems to come from the distilled water
experiments, Figure 5. If hydroxyl radical were produced directly,
then at steady-state (about 35-50 minutes in Figure 5) the ratio of

hydroxyl radical reaction with ozone, hydrogen peroxide, and hydroxyl radical respectively, would be

$$\frac{k_3 [O_3]}{k_{10} [OH]} : \frac{k_9 [H_2O_2]}{k_{10} [OH]} : \frac{k_{10} [OH]}{k_{10} [OH]} = \frac{1.7 \times 10^{-7}}{[OH]} : \frac{4.5 \times 10^{-8}}{[OH]} : 1$$

Since hydroxyl radical concentrations are more typically 10^{-12} M, reaction of hydroxyl radical with itself is seen to account for only 10^{-5} of the hydroxyl radical reactions. The product of both Equations 3 and 9 is $HO_2\cdot$, which upon dissociation gives superoxide,

$$HO_2\cdot \rightleftharpoons H^+ + O_2^- \quad , \quad \quad (13)$$

which, in turn, reacts with ozone (Equation 14) more quickly than it disproportionates to peroxide (Equation 15)

$$O_3 + O_2^- \rightarrow O_3^- + O_2 \quad \quad (14)$$
$$H_2O + HO_2 + O_2^- \rightarrow H_2O_2 + {}^-OH + O_2 \quad \quad (15)$$

It thus seems unlikely that an appreciable amount of peroxide could be formed in Case II in the presence of so much ozone and hydrogen peroxide. It is therefore concluded that the first step in photolytic ozonation is the production of hydrogen peroxide (Equation 7), followed by reaction of its anion with ozone (Equations 1 and 2) and ensuing Equations 14, 5, and 6. Since dissociation of the HO_2 formed in Equation 1 also results in the production of superoxide, a second hydroxyl radical is also formed from the sequence of Equations 14, 5, and 6, with a net consumption of three ozone molecules.

In the presence of an organic compound (HMH), however, hydroxyl radicals react to give an organic radical (Equation 16)

$$HMH + \cdot OH \rightarrow H_2O + HM\cdot \quad \quad (16)$$

which in the presence of oxygen can quickly add oxygen (Equation 17, Swallow, ref. 36) then in many cases, lose superoxide (Equation 18) to yield a neutral oxidized organic molecule, M:

$$HM\cdot + O_2 \rightarrow HMO_2\cdot \quad \quad (17)$$
$$HMO_2\cdot \rightarrow H^+ + M + O_2^- \quad \quad (18)$$

Thus, when HMH is methanol, M is formaldehyde. When HMH is formaldehyde (hydrated to $HOCH_2OH$), M is formic acid, which similarly leads to carbon dioxide. Since this sequence produces superoxide, it is not necessary to photolyze another ozone molecule to yield an electron-transfer reagent (HO_2^-) for hydroxyl radical production, and the hydroxyl radical yield per ozone molecule consumed approaches unity. This cyclic scheme has been suggested in the context of other ozonation reactions by Staehelin and Hoigne (23-25) and the flow diagram analogous to that given by those investigators is shown in Figure 6 for the photolytic ozonation system, thus unifying it with the body of knowledge concerning aqueous ozone chemistry which has been elucidated by Hoigne and coworkers.

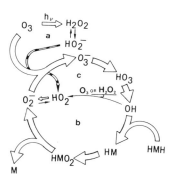

Figure 6.   Chain reaction initiated by photolytic ozonation.

Attempts to use full kinetic calculations to more quantitatively confirm the initiation step in photolytic ozonation encounter difficulty because of the sensitivity of the results to the twenty or so literature values of rate constants which must be used in the calculation. Additional confirmation was thus sought from other experimental results. Previously published ([3]) data on the destruction of chloroform, tetrachloroethylene and bromodichloromethane by ozone and photolytic ozonation show that all three compounds are destroyed more rapidly by ozone at higher pH, in agreement with the accepted base catalyzed ozone decomposition mechanism ([19]). Photolytic ozonation of all three compounds, however, is considerably faster at lower pH. This would not be expected if Equation 8 were the initiation step. Furthermore, the dissociation of both H_2O_2 to HO_2^- and HO_2 to O_2^-, favored at higher pH, would appear to enhance the rate of photolytic ozonation, suggesting that the protonation of ozonide ion (Equation 5), and thus OH production is being facilitated in acidic solution. The observed ([3]) relative reaction rates and pH behavior for chloroform, tetrachloroethylene, and bromodichloromethane are consistent with the value of 6.15 for the dissociation constant of HO_3, reported by Buhler, Staehelin, and Hoigne ([20]).

Conclusions

1) The photolysis of ozone in aqueous solution results in the direct production of hydrogen peroxide.
2) These findings unify photolytic ozonation with the existing body of knowledge concerning aqueous ozonation, as elucidated by Hoigne and coworkers.
3) After initiation by peroxide production, the reaction may proceed with considerably lowered UV input, due to the chain reaction which is carried by superoxide (Figure 6).
4) Results equivalent to those from photolytic ozonation should be obtainable using hydrogen peroxide addition, provided that direct excitation of substrate or intermediates is not important for the substrate in question.

Acknowledgments

This work was funded in part by cooperative agreement CR808825 with the United States Environmental Protection Agency, Drinking Water Research Division, Water Engineering Research Laboratory, Cincinnati, OH. The understanding and cooperation of the project officer, Mr. J. Keith Carswell, was greatly appreciated.

Literature Cited

1. Peyton, G. R.; Huang, F. Y.; Burleson, J. L.; Glaze, W. H.
   Environ. Sci. Technol. 1982, 16, 448.
2. Glaze, W. H.; Peyton, G. R.; Lin, S.; Huang, F. Y.; Burleson,
   J. L.   Environ. Sci. Technol. 1982, 16, 454.
3. Glaze, W. H.; Peyton, G. R.; Huang, F. Y.; Burleson, J. L.;
   Jones, P. C.   "Oxidation of Water Supply Refractory Species by
   Ozone with Ultraviolet Radiation." Final Report,
   EPA-600/2-80-110, August, 1980.

4. Glaze, W. H.; Peyton, G. R.; Sohm, B.; Meldrum, D. A. "Pilot
    Scale Evaluation of Photolytic Ozonation for Trihalomethane
    Precursor Removal." Final Report to USEPA/DWRD/MERL,
    Cincinnati, OH, Cooperative Agreement #CR-808825, J. Keith
    Carswell, Project Officer.
5. Garrison, R. L.; Mauk, C. E.; Prengle, H. W., Jr. Proc. 1st
    International Symposium on Ozone for Water and Wastewater
    Treatment; Rice, R. G.; Browning, M. E., editors; International
    Ozone Institute, Syracuse, N.Y., 1975.
6. Prengle, H. W., Jr.; Hewes, C. G. III; Mauk, C. E. Proc. 2nd
    International Symposium on Ozone Technology; Rice, R. G.;
    Richet, P.; Vincent, M. A., Eds.; International Ozone
    Institute, Syracuse, NY, 1975; p. 211.
7. Prengle, H. W., Jr.; Mauk, C. E.; Payne, J. E. Proc. Interna-
    tional Ozone Institute Forum on Ozone Disinfection, Chicago,
    Illinois, June 2-4, 1976.
8. Fochtman, E. G.; Huff, J. E. Proc. International Symposium on
    Ozone Technology, 2nd, 1975, p. 211.
9. Lee, M. K.; See, G. G.; Wynveen, R. A. Proc. Symposium on
    Advanced Ozone Technology, Toronto, Ontario, Nov. 16-18, 1977.
10. Kuo, P. P. K.; Chian, E. S. K.; Cheng, B. J. Environ. Sci.
    Technol. 1977, 11, 1177 .
11. McCarthy, J. J.; Cowen, W. F.; Chian, E. S. K. Proc. 32nd
    Industrial Waste Conference, Purdue University, 1977, p. 310.
12. Prengle, H. W., Jr. Environ. Sci. Technol. 1983, 17, 743.
13. Peyton, G. R.; Glaze, W. H. Presented at the Sixth World Ozone
    Congress, held by the International Ozone Association,
    Washington, D.C., May 23-26, 1983.
14. Peyton, G. R.; Glaze, W. H. Presented at the Symposium on
    Aquatic Photochemistry, 189th Annual Meeting of the American
    Chemical Society, April 1985.
15. Okabe, H. "Photochemistry of Small Molecules";
    Wiley-Interscience: New York, 1978, p. 244.
16. Taube, H. Trans. Farad. Soc. 1957, 53, 656.
17. Baxendale, J. H.; Wilson, J. A. Trans. Farad. Soc. 1957, 53,
    344.
18. Taube, H.; Bray, W. C. J. Am. Chem. Soc. 1940, 62, 3357.
19. Staehelin, J.; Hoigne, J. Environ. Sci. Technol. 1982, 16,
    676.
20. Buhler, R. F.; Staehelin, J.; Hoigne, J. J. Phys. Chem. 1984,
    88, 2560.
21. Sehested, K.; Holcman, J.; Bjergbakke, E.; Hart, E. J.
    J. Phys. Chem. 1984, 88, 4144.
22. Sehested, K.; Holcman, J.; Bjergbakke, E.; Hart, E. J.
    J. Phys. Chem. 1984, 88, 269.
23. Hoigne, J.; Staehelin, J.; Buhler, R. "Rates of Reactions and
    Decomposition of Ozone in Water: A Few Reasons for Many Miscon-
    ceptions," presented at the Sixth World Ozone Conference, held
    by the International Ozone Association, Washington, D.C. May
    23-26, 1983.
24. Staehelin, J.; Hoigne, J. Vom Wasser, 1983, 61, 337.
25. Staehelin, J.; Hoigne, J. Environ. Sci. Technol. 1985, 19,
    1206.
26. Yocum, F. H. Paper presented to 86th National Meeting of
    American Institute of Chemical Engineers, April 1-5, 1979.

27. Horak, J., and J. Pasek. "Design of Industrial Chemical
     Reactors from Laboratory Data"; Heyden and Sons, Inc.,
     Philadelphia, 1978, p. 358.
28. Bader, H.; Hoigne, J. Water Res. 1981, 15, 449.
29. Bader, H.; Hoigne, J. Ozone: Science and Engineering 1982, 4,
     169.
30. Flamm, D. L. Environ. Sci. Technol. 1977, 11, 978.
31. Hart, E.; Sehested, K.; Holcman, J. Anal. Chem. 1983, 55, 46.
32. Parker, G. A. In "Colorimetric Determination of Nonmetals";
     Boltz, D. R.; Howell, J. A., Eds.; Wiley, 1928, p. 301.
33. Masschelein, W. J.; Davis, M.; Ledent, R. Water and Sewage
     Works, August 1977, 69.
34. Weeks, J. L.; Rabani, J. J. Phys. Chem. 1966, 70, 21.
35. Behard, D.; Czapski, G.; Duchovny, J. J. Phys. Chem. 1970, 74,
     226.
36. Swallow, A. J. Prog. Reaction Kinetics, 1978, 9, 195.

RECEIVED May 27, 1986

Chapter 7

Consequences of OH Radical Reaction in Sea Water: Formation and Decay of Br_2^- Ion Radical

Oliver C. Zafiriou[1], Mary B. True[1], and E. Hayon[2]

[1]Department of Chemistry, Woods Hole Oceanographic Institution, Woods Hole, MA 02543
[2]Chemistry Department, Queens College of the City University of New York, Flushing, NY 11367

The interaction of OH radical with seawater yields oxidized bromine species. The identity of the oxidized bromine species and its subsequent reactions have been studied by extensive flash photolysis experiments and also by pulse radiolysis. OH appears to give a nearly quantitative yield of the dibromide ion-radical in seawater. This radical decays by parallel first- and second-order reactions, the latter process being well-known but irrelevant in nature. The former involves reaction with some components of the carbonate system in seawater, resulting in decay rates for the dibromide ion-radical of roughly 2000–3000 s^{-1} in seawater at pH 8 (halftimes of ca 300 microseconds).

The concept that free radicals are important intermediates in photo-chemical and other redox interactions of oxygen, organic compounds and heavy metals in natural waters has received considerable support recently ((1-3) and references therein; this volume). Some of the major primary radicals expected are: hydroxyl (OH), superoxide (O_2^-), and various organic moieties (R, RO, ROO). Of these, OH is of interest because of its extremely high reactivity, significant formation rate from a known source (nitrite photolysis, among others) and the analogy of its known key role in tropospheric chemistry.

The purpose of this study is to explore the fate of OH radicals and the identity and chemistry of their progeny in seawater. This paper presents some of the experimental evidence concerning radical formation and behavior in seawater and artificial seawater obtained by the fast-reaction kinetics technique of flash photolysis-kinetic spectrophotometry (4) supplemented by pulse radiolysis (5). The companion paper which follows presents results on related reactions and rates observed in media simpler than seawater and applies them to partially explain the data reported here using a simple reaction-mechanistic model.

Known OH reaction rate constants and the major-ion composition of seawater combine to imply that OH should react in seawater almost exclusively with bromide ion, with a small amount of side-reaction

0097-6156/87/0327-0089$06.00/0

with the carbonate system and dissolved organic matter (DOM) (6).
Table I estimates OH reactivity towards seawater components; similar
conclusions were reached by Hoigné (7), although he took the first
product to be Br_2^- rather than $BrOH^-$.

TABLE I. Expected Reactions of OH with Constituents of Seawater
(pH 8.1, S = 35°/∘∘)

Reactant	Concentration ($\underline{M}$)	Rate Constant $\underline{M}^{-1}$ s^{-1}	% of Total OH Reaction	Initial Products
Br^-	$8x10^{-4}$	[d]$1.06x10^{10}$	97.7	$BrOH^-$
Total CO_3^{2-} (9.3% Free)	[a]$3x10^{-4}$	[e]4.2 $x10^8$	1.5	$CO_3^- + OH^-$
Total HCO_3^- (72.3% Free)	[a]$2.02x10^{-3}$	[e]1.5 $x10^7$	0.3	$CO_3^- + H_2O$
NO_2^-	[b]$4x10^{-6}$	[f]5 $x10^9$	0.2	$NO_2 + OH^-$
Dissolved Organic Matter	[c]$2x10^{-5}$	[g]10^9	0.2	?
Cl^-	0.55	[h]<200	0.01	$ClOH^-/Cl_2^-$?

a) Calculated from our model for speciation of CO_2 in seawater (16).
b) An upper limit for surface nitrite concentrations.
c) Dissolved Organic Matter (DOM) was assumed to consist of 20 micro-
   moles of 5-carbon subunits, with total DOM = 1.2 mg/Kg of seawater.
d) Zehavi and Rabani (10), Zafiriou (6) and Hoigné (7) used the upper
   limits for Br_2^- formation.
e) We assume that ion pairs are as reactive as the free ions; rate
   constants are for the free ions (22).
f) Upper limit of values given in Anbar and Neta (23).
g) Mean of rates for 130 organic compounds in the pH range 7-9, given
   by Anbar and Neta (23).
h) (18,20,24,25).

    In this study our objectives were (1) to confirm that bromide
oxidation is the major pathway for OH reaction, (2) to validate our
method for generating the radical Br_2^- in seawater, and (3) to use
this method to study the fate of the oxidized bromine species in seawater, emphasizing processes that would dominate under low intensity
light (nonflash conditions). A preliminary qualitative report of
some of this work has been presented (6).

Methods

Since the methods used in this study are not standard in marine science and the precision and accuracy of the results depend on numerous

factors, we describe them below, with fuller documentation in the
Appendix; see also (8).

Chemical Basis. Our working hypothesis is that OH reacts predominantly with Br^- in seawater, yielding the dibromide ion-radical,
Br_2^-. In simple salt solutions this reaction proceeds via a multi-
step process (9):

$$R1 : OH + Br^- = BrOH^-$$
$$R2 : BrOH^- = Br + OH^-$$
$$R3 : BrOH^- + H^+ = Br + H_2O$$
$$R4 : BrOH^- + Br^- = Br_2^- + OH^-$$
$$R5 : Br + Br^- = Br_2^-$$

R1 forms $BrOH^-$, which then reacts via three parallel processes, R2-
R5, R3-R5, and R4, to yield Br_2^-. In aerated pH 8 aqueous solutions
containing the seawater concentration of bromide, $8 \times 10^{-4}M$ Br^-, R3
is negligible and R2 predominates over R4 by 10^3-fold and is complete
within the flash (10).
     The value of the equilibrium constant K_5 for R5 is in doubt.
Values as high as 2.2×10^5 were measured by pulse radiolysis (11);
and as low as 3.3×10^3 measured in flash studies (12). The ratio of
$[Br_2^-]$ to $[Br]$ in seawater should nevertheless be in the range of
2.6 - 180 to 1. Thus, even if the smallest value of K_5 is correct,
only 25% of the oxidized Br would be present as the free atom (spec-
troscopically transparent at accessible wavelengths) while higher
values would reduce the stoichiometric importance of this species to
negligible proportions. However, the facile equilibrium R5 ensures
that monitoring the ion-radical concentration also monitors the
effect of reactions of the free atom and other species in fast equilibrium with it (see (9) for discussion).
     Thus, our approach has been (a) to make the Br atom by direct
photolysis in seawater; (b) to study the spectral and kinetic consequences of the oxidized Br species via the observable ion-radical
formed in R5, and then (c) to make OH in seawater to see if it also
yields species operationally resembling Br_2^-.

Techniques

A. Flash Photolysis Studies.

We used the flash photolysis facilities of the Physical Chemistry
Group, Pioneering Research Laboratory, U.S. Army Natick Laboratory.
The apparatus has been described in Dogliotti and Hayon (4) and
Zafiriou (6), and technical details of this study are given in
Zafiriou and True (8). The salient features are that the system has
sufficient shortwave UV intensity to excite simple anions, a ca 30 μs
flash, and a 20 cm optical path cell surrounded by a solution-filter
jacket of ~1 cm path.
     Kinetic data from flash experiments were fit initially to first-
or second-order rate laws by least-squares analyses at the U.S. Army
Natick Laboratory. These fits were merely used to locate appropriate
conditions for intensive experiments gathering data for detailed
analysis by mixed first- and second-order kinetics by the program,

MIXKIN ($\underline{8}$). The database for the MIXKIN-analyzed results reported here comprises several hundred flash experiments, frequently in triplicate and monitored by oscilloscope on two different timescales. These have been selected solely on the basis of technical quality and relevance of conditions from over one thousand flash experiments.

MIXKIN finds suitable values for three kinetic parameters, α, β and A_0 by successive approximation to the integrated equation ($\underline{13}$):

$$A = \text{Absorbance} = F(\alpha, \beta, A_0, t) = \qquad (1)$$
$$\{(1/A_0)\exp(\alpha t) + (\beta/\alpha)[\exp(\alpha t)-1]\}^{-1}$$

Our α = K_1 (in Reference $\underline{13}$); our β = K_2 (in Reference $\underline{13}$). α is an exponential rate constant characterizing true or pseudo first-order processes and β = $k(2)/\varepsilon$ is a second-order rate constant divided by molar extinction coefficient[1] characterizing radical-radical decay processes important at high intensities, but not under low-intensity illumination conditions. A_0 = initial optical density.

The photolyzing flash was used to excite $\underline{\text{selectively}}$ the bromide ion in seawater ($\underline{12,14}$):

R6: $Br^- + h\nu = Br + e_{aq}^-$

followed immediately by

R7: $Br + X^- = BrX^-$ (X = halogen)

Since, despite searches by ourselves and others, there is no strong evidence for the production of $BrCl^-$ or BrI^- in fluid systems, R7 reduces to R5.

We photolyzed seawater saturated with either air or N_2O. In aerated seawater

R8: $e_{aq}^- + O_2 = O_2^-$

yields superoxide ion-radical so one mole of Br_2^- is produced for each mole of Br^- photolyzed via R6. N_2O-saturated seawater generates one primary Br product, and additionally one OH radical ($\underline{15}$):

R9: $e_{aq}^- + N_2O + N_2 + O^-$

R10: $O^- + HOH = OH + OH^-$

B. Pulse Radiolysis Studies.

We also used pulse radiolysis ($\underline{15}$) in a brief series of experiments to confirm the main conclusions of the extensive flash photolysis studies by producing OH in seawater without photooxidizing bromide ion. Although the pulse radiolysis approach is a more direct way to study OH chemistry, it is complicated by the "prompt effect," whose contribution via Cl_2^- to the UV transient must be evaluated (see Appendix). Pulse radiolysis experiments/data analysis were done at the Center for Fast Kinetics Research (CFKR) at the University of

---

[1] Note that k(2) refers to second-order kinetics; k_n refers to the rate constant in the forward direction for the nth reaction. Texas at Austin.

Water Samples. Precautions were taken to minimize metal or organic
contamination in seawater sampling and in artificial seawater preparation. Sargasso seawater samples for early experiments (Tables II
and III) were pumped from 15 m through a polypropylene-Teflon system

TABLE II.   Doubling of Transient Yield from
Seawater upon Addition of N_2O.

Seawater + N_2O λ (nm)	Seawater + Air
340	1.76
350	1.94
360	1.88
370	1.92

Mean Ratio = 1.88 $\pm$ .08

Notes:
    Sargasso seawater samples at pH 8.0 $\pm$ 0.1
    saturated with air or nitrous oxide (N_2O);
    ratios are of optical densities measured
    100 μs after the flash; bandpass 3-6 nm;
    baseline recorded 2-3 ms after the flash.

containing preleached 0.2 μ cellulose acetate Gelman filters into
autoclaved Pyrex jugs and stored in the dark for 1-10 months before
use. Later, Sargasso seawater samples were collected from 30-liter
Niskin casts at 10 m below the surface just SE of the Gulf Stream,
stored in the dark in Pyrex or high-density polyethylene containers,
used within 3 days, or frozen and used within 3 weeks. Artifical
seawater preparation was described in Zafiriou (6). Vineyard Sound
seawater was collected in an enamel pan, stored in the dark in preleached polyethylene bottles, and passed through precleaned fine
sintered-glass filters just prior to use. Copenhagen seawater was
IAPSO Standard Seawater, Batch P (6/8/72) with a chlorinity of
19.377°/∘∘.
    Analytical reagent grade chemicals and Millipore "Super-Q" water
were used. pH was measured to about $\pm$0.05 units using a standard
glass electrode on a Beckman Model 15 pH meter; adjustments in the
pH of natural and artificial seawaters were made with additions of
diluted high-purity HCl and/or KOH (not carbonate-free). Total CO_2
was assumed to be 2.3 m$\underline{M}$ for natural seawater based on a few spot
measurements, or was estimated from known amounts of added bicarbonate and/or carbonate salts. CO_2-free seawater was prepared by acidifying samples (pH <5), purging with N_2, then readjusting the pH.

Methods Testing and Evaluation. An extensive evaluation of our flash
photolysis techniques and of the MIXKIN program are given in Zafiriou
and True (8). The results of the most powerful or relevant tests are
summarized in Figure 1 and Table III and discussed in the Appendix.

TABLE III. Summary of Flash Photolysis Methods Validation

Test	Comparison	Conclusion	Refs.
A. Flash Excitation Selectivity	Compare the size of the 360-nm transient with photolysis cell surrounded by filter solutions with various wavelength cutoffs.	No appreciable contribution to the 360-nm transient from excitation of species absorbing above 220 nm. Seawater excitation is predominantly via R6.	8
B. Identity of 360-nm transient	Compare shape of UV transient spectrum in air- and N_2O - saturated seawater to published spectra of Br_2^-, Cl_2^-, and I_2^-	Spectrum of UV transient from seawater identical to Br_2^- spectrum within experimental error. We cannot rule out small contributions from such species as $BrCl^-$ and BrI^-.	10,14,18
C. Decay Kinetics	Compare β of 360-nm seawater transient to β in pure Br^- solutions.	In the absence of CO_2, the decay of the 360-nm seawater transient is predominantly second-order and β varies with ionic strength as expected.	8,11,12 26-30
D. MIXKIN 1. Fitting real data	Compare fit by MIXKIN to that of program in 13 for a real data set.	Fits almost identical identical in all parameters	Section 2.4 of 8
2. Fitting simulated data with added random noise.	Compare fit of data sets by MIXKIN and 13.	Good fit by both programs as long as noise is <6% of A_0.	Section 2.4 of 8
3. Fitting "Artificial Seawater Data Set"	Probe effects of baseline location errors on the fit by MIXKIN of a "mean" seawater set.	Baseline offset has larger effect on α than on β.	Section 2.5 of 8

TABLE III.   Continued

Test	Comparison	Conclusion	Refs.
E. Validity of Kinetic Data			
1. Detect Baseline Shifts	Plot α versus β for individual kinetic determinations.	Points should group in one area. Outliers can be rejected.	8
2. Probe variance in kinetic rates.	Compare the variance in our kinetic data to that measured by others using similar techniques.	Variance in our β's similar to variance measured for Br_2^- decay. Our α shows more variance than our second-order rates.	29

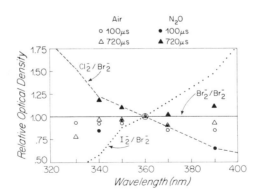

Figure 1.   Comparison of the UV-region transient spectra.
Literature data: —— Br_2^- spectrum (15), --- Cl_2^- spectrum (18),
··· I_2^- spectrum (14); Points: Seawater, pH 8.1, this study.

Figure 2 shows the second-order decay rate constant and its
scatter for Br_2^- as found by a variety of other studies using different methods, as well as our own data using MIXKIN. This decay is
caused by the extremely well-studied (see Fig. 2 notes for references) self-decay of the dibromide ion-radical:

$$R11: \quad 2\,Br_2^- = Br^- + Br_3^-$$

Our values and scatter for the second-order decay parameter for β,
which we assign as $k(2)/\varepsilon$ for R11, are very similar to the values for
the second-order decay process R11 found by other authors, even
though MIXKIN has available an additional free parameter, α, to which
it correctly assigns near-zero values. The entire data set is fairly
well accomodated by the expected relationship between ionic strength
and activity, as approximated by the Davies equation (17).
    In air-saturated seawater samples with small α terms (low pH or
CO_2-free removal, hence giving the best constraints on the β term),
$k(2)/\varepsilon$ values are very similar to those for pure bromide solutions
(stippled area in Fig. 2). This consistency strongly supports the
identity of the major transient: Br_2^-. The close comparability
between the kinetic parameters fit to the data by the flash photolysis of aerated seawater (no OH generated) and those fit to transients
initiated by pulse radiolysis (no direct Br oxidation, OH the initiating radical) strongly buttresses this conclusion. Finally, the
α values obtained in flash experiments using air or nitrous oxide at
constant pH near 8 are virtually identical to each other and to those
from pulse radiolysis.
    The data presented in this paper are not all completely consis-
tent with this simple picture; many results presented in this paper
involve MIXKIN solutions giving β parameters less similar to the
values of Figure 2. As explained in the table notes and in Figure 3
of the Appendix, these deviations are most likely due to baseline
uncertainties and the smaller relative importance of the β term.
However, we cannot entirely discount the less likely explanation that
there is a kinetic difference between the transient from dibromide
ion-radical and the seawater UV transient.

Results

Spectral Identity of the Seawater Transient.

Initial survey work
showed a single transient in the UV region, with no other detectable
absorptions in the range 300-700 nm. Figure 1 compares the spectra
of the UV-absorbing transients formed in seawater under various conditions with one another and with the literature spectra of dihalide
ion-radicals. All spectra have been divided by that of authentic
dibromide ion-radical and normalized to 1.00 at 360 nm. With the
exception of the 390 nm point at 100 μs in nitrous oxide-saturated
seawater, the data are consistent with the dibromide ion-radical
rather than the other species. Similar comparisons (not shown) of
the UV transient generated in seawater using pulse radiolysis lead
to the same conclusion.
    Since at constant flash intensity transient size should double
without changing shape in nitrous oxide saturated seawater vs. air-
saturated samples (see Methods), we determined this ratio at several

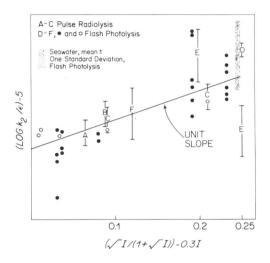

Figure 2.   Ionic strength dependence of ß for the decay of Br_2^- at 360 nm.   Errors estimated by referenced investigators. A - (11), B - (26), C - (27), D - (28), E - (30), F - (12), o - this work, Br^- + Cl^- solutions.   Stippled region shows mean ± 1 s.d. of seawater experiments.

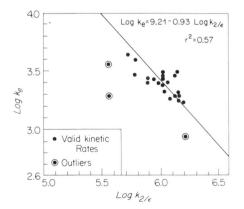

Figure 3.   Covariation of α and ß for the decay of the 360-nm transient in air-saturated seawater near pH 8.

wavelengths 100 μs after the flash. The expected doubling is found
(Table II). At 100 μs, a small amount of transient decay has occurred, biasing the reported ratios on the low side. Thus, the spectral evidence confirms clean formation of dibromide ion-radical in
air by the direct path, and is consistent with its being the major
product of OH reaction with seawater as well.

Transient Decay - General. The outstanding features of the decay of
the UV transient in seawater are: (1) it yields no sizeable product
grow-in absorptions in the 300-750 nm range, (2) in seawater it fits
poorly to either first- or second-order decay kinetics, but very well
to parallel exponential and second-order decay reactions, (3) the
exponential decay term varies as a function of pH and total CO_2 content of the water.

We carried out many experiments to derive the kinetic parameters
and their dependence on pH, CO_2 content, water source, and wavelength
to characterize the behavior of the OH-daughter radicals in seawater.
Table IV shows the results of MIXKIN fits of the data derived from
Sargasso seawater at pH 8 with or without concurrent generation of OH
radical via N_2O. The first order rate constants are remarkably similar in all cases, showing that the UV transient decays monolithically
in the operational sense that the OH-daughter product behaves like
Br_2^- in its interactions with seawater constituents. The second-
order rate parameters at 360 nm are likewise consistent with those
expected from the pure bromide decay and the decay in CO_2-free seawater (Fig. 2 regression line and stippled area), though in the presence of significant first- and second-order components this parameter
is less tightly constrained. This series of experiments utilized a
different time registration and baseline-location method than the
principal experimental series discussed later, which is probably responsible for the inconsistencies in ß values between the two data
sets.

The data can be used to test whether the UV transient is spectrally similar to the dibromide ion-radical in the course of its decay by converting ß to k(2) by multiplying it at each wavelength by
the epsilon values for the Br_2^- radical, as shown in the last column
of Table IV. For both air- and N_2O-saturated samples, the constancy
of these k(2) values again shows the spectral similarity of the seawater transient to the dibromide ion-radical. The absolute values of
k(2) in air- and N_2-saturated samples are in reasonable agreement
with those expected (Fig. 2); the imperfect agreement probably reflects the poorer constraints on k(2) in the presence of a substantial α term. Possibly there is a real difference between the two
conditions. However, this supposed spectral difference is not reflected in the interpretationally more important exponential decay
terms.

Table V presents fits to a variety of seawater types adjusted to
various pH values. Here the ß values are uniformly higher than in
Table IV and quite unstable for technical reasons (Appendix, Fig. 3).
It is not possible to select objectively the "better" data, and the
relatively small discrepancies in the α terms do not drastically
affect our interpretation. The most important trends of Tables IV
and V are that the seawater pseudo first-order rate constant, α,
appears to be independent of seawater source (hence, of trace constituents), to be simulated well by artificial seawater, and to be pH

TABLE IV. Decay of the UV - Transient from Flash Photolysis of
           pH 8.0 Sargasso Seawater as a Function of Wavelength

λ (nm)	Number of Determinations	$^a\alpha$ (s^{-1})	$^b\beta$ $(10^5 \times cm\ s^{-1})$	$^c k(2)$ $(10^9 \times \underline{M}^{-1}\ s^{-1})$
Air-Saturated:				
320	1	2780	18.2	7.83
340	3	3220	10.05	7.04
350	3	3190	8.66	6.41
360	3	3210	8.63	6.73
370	3	3220	8.58	6.44
390	4	2810	13.6	8.16
410	2	3920	15.6	6.24
	Mean $\pm$ S.D.:	3193 $\pm$ 376		6.98 $\pm$ 0.75
N_2O-Saturated:				
320	2	3210	8.13	3.50
340	3	3300	5.25	3.68
350	4	3550	5.09	3.77
360	3	3940	5.21	4.06
370	3	3500	5.46	4.10
390	3	3930	4.73	2.84
410	2	3580	12.3	4.92
	Mean α = 3573 $\pm$ 281		Mean $k(2)$ = 3.84 $\pm$ 0.64	

Notes: pH 8.0 $\pm$ 0.1, saturated with air or N_2O. Bandpass 3-6 nm;
baseline recorded 2-3 ms after flash; data prior to 80-100 μs deleted
due to scattered light distortion. (a) α = mean exponential rate
determined by MIXKIN for individual runs; (b) β =Mean second order
rated for Rll divided by moler extinction coefficient for Br_2^- radical as determined by MIXKIN for individual runs; (c) Multiplied by
extinction coefficient for Br_2^- as a function of wavelength (10).

dependent, with smaller values being observed at lower pH's. As stated earlier, this exponential term nearly vanishes in CO_2-stripped seawater, leaving the expected second-order decay term unaffected.

TABLE V.   Decay Kinetics for the 360-nm Transient from Flash
           Photolysis of Air-Saturated Seawater

Seawater Type	Number of Replicates	pH Range	$10^{-3} \alpha$ (s^{-1})	$10^{-5} \beta$ $(cm\ s^{-1})$
Sargasso	5	6.1 - 6.5	0.68 ± 0.45	8.76 ± 1.31
	3	7.1 - 7.5	1.17 ± 0.23	9.93 ± 1.11
	10	8.0 - 8.1	2.57 ± 0.54	12.14 ± 3.22
Copenhagen	7	7.6	1.45 ± 0.81	10.19 ± 2.59
	3	8.3	3.42 ± 1.32	8.47 ± 1.08
Vineyard Sound	3	8.1	2.03 ± 0.25	12.80 ± 1.95
Buzzards Bay	1	8.1	2.73	10.50
Artificial	4	8.1 - 8.2	2.48 ± 0.25	9.50 ± 1.31

Discussion

In an initial survey of the expected behavior of OH in seawater (6) we presented qualitative results implying that the expected dibromide ion-radical could be formed in seawater by flash photolysis and that its decay appeared to involve the carbonate system, rather than being dominated by such a priori more likely reactions as recombination of radicals, metal and/or inorganic (nitrite, iodide, etc.) redox interactions, or reaction with DOC.

The quantitative validation of the methods, though generally successful, leaves some vexing uncertainties. While the bromide excitation technique works cleanly and the major product from OH radical in these systems is the expected dibromide ion-radical, the remaining smaller discrepancies, probably experimental errors, could alternatively be significant. N_2O experiments may generate in part some species spectrally and kinetically different from the dibromide ion-radical. For this reason, we focussed on experiments in aerated seawater to minimize the chance of unexpected complexities. Even a relatively small percentage of some additional "mystery" species, while hardly detracting from the importance of the dibromide ion-radical pathway in seawater, could compromise the kinetic parameters derived from assuming a one-species, two-process decay scheme.

Despite this cautionary note, we emphasize that two pieces of evidence that became available later strongly support the concept that the N_2O experiments are also valid indicators of the geochemically important exponential decay reactions. The first is that the terms that will dominate in seawater in sunlight (exponential decay) are extremely similar (Table IV), so that the OH-derived transient behaves kinetically like the dibromide ion-radical. The second is that pulse radiolysis experiments generating OH (without direct bromide oxidation) at 360 nm in pH 8 coastal and Sargasso seawater gave transients whose decays were fitted by a ß of 5.2 and 6.3 x 10^5 s^{-1}, respectively and by exponential decay rate constants of 3800 and 3700 s^{-1}, in good agreement with the exponential decays from the flash experiments (Tables IV and V) and expected second-order decays (Fig. 2). These transients were spectrally most similar to the dibromide ion-radical as well, and again no other absorptions could be found.

Thus the formation of OH in seawater seems on careful examination to lead to very rapid oxidation of bromide, but this reactivity is in turn dissipated within a millisecond by reactions with other seawater constituents, apparently involving the carbonate system in a pH-dependent manner. This process, not the second-order self-decay due to R11 observed at high light intensities, undoubtedly predominates in natural sunlight. However, no reactions of the dibromide ion-radical with carbonate species have been reported, and the nature of this interaction is not clear. The simplest plausible reaction might be:

$$R12 \quad Br_2^- + CO_3^{2-} = 2\ Br^- + CO_3^-\ ?$$

However, R12 generates the carbonate radical, which absorbs in the 600 nm region, free of interference from the UV transient. In a large number of experiments, we sought to detect the grow-in of absorption in the 600 nm region during aerated seawater flash photolysis. Although we found a very small, variable-intensity transient increasing in size during the early part of the 360 nm decay, the feature was on the borderline of detectability.

Thus, the empirical characterization of the UV transient produced from OH in seawater leads to a chemical mystery: the UV transient definitely interacts with seawater in a pH and CO_2-dependent process that occurs in waters of different origin, including artificial seawater. Hence, the effect would appear to be due to the carbonate system itself, not some trace impurity. The following paper takes up the challenges of finding such an interaction in simpler media than seawater and of explaining the pseudo first-order decay of seawater in terms of these interactions and carbonate system speciation (16).

Acknowledgments

This work was assisted by numerous colleagues, especially Drs. Ed Black and John Connolly at Natick. We acknowledge useful discussions with Drs. John Endicott, Mort Z. Hoffman, M. A. J. Rodgers, and Rod Zika. This work was funded by the National Science Foundation grants GA-35401, DES 72-1553, OCE-79-09381, and OCE 84-17770. Flash photolysis studies were carried out at the U.S. Army Natick Laboratories. Pulse radiolysis studies and data reduction were carried out at the Center for Fast Kinetics Research. The CFKR is supported jointly by the Biomedical Research Technology Program of the Division of Research Resources of NIH (RR 00886) and by the University of Texas at Austin.

This is Contribution Number 6019 from the Woods Hole Oceanographic Institution.

APPENDIX

Methods Validation

Flash Photolysis Experiments

A. Optical Filter Tests (Table IIIA)

We checked that the principal detectable process occurring in the
sample was excitation of bromide rather than other chromophores.
For most experiments, a saturated NaCl solution filter jacketed the
photolysis cell to minimize excitation of Cl^-. When 0.54 $\underline{M}$ NaCl
alone was photolyzed while surrounded by this filter, the 360 nm signal was less than 10% of the signal produced by photolysis of seawater or bromide solutions at seawater ionic strength. Therefore,
the excitation of Cl^- in seawater must be much less than 10% of the
total observed reaction, since in mixtures bromide competes very
efficiently with chloride for excitation. A filter solution containing 0.1 $\underline{M}$ KBr eliminated the signal from seawater entirely, suggesting that all species absorbing above 220 nm are not contributing
observable transients.

B. Tests of Spectral Identity (Table IIIB)

See Figure 1 and text discussion. Dihalide ion radical spectra are
from the known spectra of Br_2^- (15), Cl_2^- (18), and I_2^- (14). The
data are normalized so that the spectrum of Br_2^- is a horizontal
line at 1.00. Such a line is a reasonable approximation of the data
for air-saturated and N_2O-saturated samples measured 100 microseconds
after the flash between 330 and 390 nm.

C. Tests of Decay Kinetics (Table IIIC)

If weakly-absorbing transients not detectable by optical filter tests
are formed and react in our system, they should be detectable by
their subsequent reactions with Br_2^-. However, in CO_2-free seawater
Br_2^- showed a clean self-decay reaction and negligible first-order
decay constants (Table VI) as summarized for the second-order component in Figure 2.

D. Tests of MIXKIN (Table IIID)

MIXKIN was tested for ability to reproducibly fit simulated and real
data. For simulated data with added random noise, MIXKIN achieved
good fits for first- and second-order cases (α and β, respectively)
as long as the added noise was less than 6% of the optical densities
at the beginning of the decay (Table IIID). Although MIXKIN achieved
satisfactory fits of α and β for an artificial data set with several
standard deviations of added baseline variation (Fig. 6 in 8), α, the
more interesting term, was more heavily affected by baseline shifts
than was β, the mathematically dominant term at short times after the
flash.

TABLE VI. Decay of the 360-nm Transient from
Flash Photolysis of Seawaters with no CO_2

Seawater Type	pH	$10^{-3} \alpha$ (cm s^{-1})	$10^{-5} \beta$
[a]Sargasso	7.0	0.52	9.53
	7.0	1.10	8.30
	7.3	1.02	3.86
	7.3	0.96	4.06
	8.1	0.47	9.59
	8.1	1.61	4.72
Mean $\pm$ 1 S.D. =		0.95 $\pm$ 0.42	
[b]Artificial	6.7	0.33	7.34
	6.7	0.12	9.07
	8.2	0.89	8.87
	8.2	0.52	8.10
	8.2	1.90	5.40
	8.2	0.74	9.13
	8.3	1.04	7.21
	8.3	0.61	8.25
Mean $\pm$ 1 S.D. =		0.77 $\pm$ 0.54	

Notes:
  a) Sargasso S.W. stripped of CO_2 by acidifying,
     purging with N_2 or air, then readjusting pH.
  b) Artificial seawater with no carbonate added.

E. Tests of Rate Constants (Table IIIE)

The first source of uncertainty affecting these results is the placement of the experimental baseline on the oscilloscope photographs for
each kinetic run. After minimizing the effects of random error in
baseline placement, we screened computer fitted rates of individual
kinetic determinations for outliers indicative of non-random electrical noise. An example is shown in Figure 3. We have plotted the
logarithm of the exponential rate constants (α's) for all the individual seawater experiments at pH's between 8 and 8.3 versus the
logarithm of the second-order rate constants (β's) for the same runs.
The entire data set, including four seawater types, yields a mean α
of $2.54 \pm .79 \times 10^3$ s^{-1} and a mean β of $10.74 \pm 3.95 \times 10^5$ l m^{-1} s^{-1}.
The three circled points are outliers sufficiently different from the
rest to be rejected.

Mean rates for the remaining points are $\alpha = 2.60 \pm .71 \times$
10^3 s^{-1} and $\beta = 11.16 \pm 3.23 \times 10^5$ l m^{-1} s^{-1}. With the elimination
of the outliers, the variance for both exponential and second-order
rates is less than $\pm$ 30%. The line is a regression through all but
the rejected points with a coefficient of variation = 0.57, explaining about one-half of the variation as being due to uncertainty in
baseline placement, which strongly affects the relative weights
assigned to the two decay modes by MIXKIN.

Pulse Radiolysis Experiments. The well-known technique of pulse
radiolysis in aqueous solutions is complicated in seawater by the
so-called "prompt yield" (19-21), that in neutral concentrated salt
solutions yields some dichloride ion-radical which is independent of
the chemistry of the water fragmentation products in neutral solution. At 0.54 $\underline{M}$ [Cl$^-$], the seawater value, this effect in nitrous-
oxide saturated solutions will produce about 11% Cl$_2^-$ in the transient, while about 89% will be due to OH reactions, and neglecting
the transient involvement of ClOH$^-$, will be Br$_2^-$. Although complete
kinetic analysis of the system is not feasible, presumably this Cl$_2^-$
decays primarily by oxidation of Br$^-$ on a short timescale, thus having no effect on longer-timescale observations. We found using short
(100 ns) pulses that almost all of the 360 nm transient in sodium-
bromide-sodium chloride solution at the seawater concentrations
"grows in" after the pulse, with a halftime of about 270 ns. Actual
measurements during the pulse were not reliable with the system used,
precluding direct quantification of the "prompt yield." However, we
also found that the transient grow-in in the seawater concentration
of bromide, but with 0.54 $\underline{M}$ fluoride instead of chloride is slower,
with a halftime of 966 ns for the rise. This result suggests some
involvement of Cl-derived species in the initial interactions of OH
and seawater, as is well-known in more acid solution (9,18).

References

1. Zika, R. Marine organic photochemistry. In "Marine Organic
   Chemistry"; Duursma, E. K.; Dawson, R., Eds., Elsevier:
   Amsterdam, 1981.

2. Zafiriou, O. C. In "Chemical Oceanography"; Riley, J. P. and Chester, G., Eds.; Academic Press, 1983; Vol. 8, pp. 339-379.
3. Zafiriou, O. C.; Joussot-Dubien, J.; Zepp, R. G.; Zika, R. G. Environ. Sci. Technol. 1984, 18, 358A-371A.
4. Dogliotti, L.; Hayon, E. J. Phys. Chem. 1967, 71, 2511-2516.
5. Ebert, M.; Keene, J. P.; Swallow, A. J.; Baxendale, J. H., Eds. "Pulse Radiolysis"; Academic Press: London, 1965; 319 pp.
6. Zafiriou, O. C. J. Geophys. Res. 1974, 79, 4491-4497.
7. Hoigné, J. Reactions of ozone and inorganic radicals in natural waters. Extended Abstract for NATO-ARI Workshop "Photochemistry of Natural Waters," Woods Hole, MA, September 1983.
8. Zafiriou, O. C. and M. B. True. WHOI Tech. Memorandum I-77, 1977.
9. Fornier de Violet, Ph. Polyhalide radical anions as intermediates in chemistry. Revs. Chem. Intermeds. 1981, 4, 121-169.
10. Zehavi, D.; Rabani, J. J. Phys. Chem. 1972, 76, 312-319.
11. Matheson, M. S.; Mulac, W. A.; Weeks, J. L.; Rabani, J. J. Phys. Chem. 1972, 70, 2092-2099.
12. Wong, D.; B. DiBartolo, B. J. Photochem. 1975, 4, 249-268.
13. Gorman, D. S.; Connolly, J. S. Int. J. Chem. Kinetics 1973, 5, 977-989.
14. Grossweiner, L. I.; Matheson, M. S. J. Phys. Chem. 1957, 61, 1089-1095.
15. Zehavi, D.; Rabani, J. J. Phys. Chem. 1971, 75, 1738-1744.
16. True, M. B.; Zafiriou, O. C. ACS Symposium Series, this volume.
17. Stumm, W.; Morgan, J. J. "Aquatic Chemistry"; John Wiley & Sons: New York, 1981, 2nd ed., 780 pp.
18. Jayson, G. G.; Parsons, B. J.; Swallow, A. J. J. Chem. Soc. Faraday Trans. 1973, 1, 1597-1607.
19. Fisher, M.; Hamill, W. H. J. Phys. Chem. 1973, 77, 171-177.
20. Ogura, H.; Hamill, W. H. J. Phys. Chem. 1973, 77, 2952-2954.
21. Huang, T.; Hamill, W. H. J. Phys. Chem. 1975, 79, 2465-2469.
22. Weeks, J. L.; Rabani, J. J. Phys. Chem. 1966, 70, 2100-2106.
23. Anbar, M.; Neta, P. Int. J. of Applied Radiation and Isotopes 1967, 18, 493-523.
24. Ward, J. F.; Myers, L. S., Jr. Radiation Res. 1965, 26, 483-492.
25. Anbar, M.; Thomas, J. K. J. Phys. Chem. 1964, 68, 3829-3835.
26. Cercek, B.; Ebert, M.; Gilbert, C. W.; Swallow, A. J. In "Pulse Radiolysis"; Ebert, M.; Keene, J. P.; Swallow, A. J.; Baxendale, J.H., Eds.; Academic Press: London, 1965, pp. 83-98.
27. Sutton, H. C.; Adams, G. E.; Boag, J. W.; Michael, B. O. In "Pulse Radiolysis"; Ebert, M.; Keene, J. P.; Swallow, A. J.; Baxendale, J. H., Eds.; Academic Press: London, 1965, pp. 61-81.
28. Thornton, A. T.; Laurence, G. S. J. Chem. Soc. (Dalton), 1973, 804-813.
29. Malone, S. D.; Endicott, J. F. J. Phys. Chem. 1972, 76, 2233-2229.
30. Langmuir, M. E.; Hayon, E. J. Phys. Chem. 1967, 71, 3808-3814.

RECEIVED June 24, 1986

Chapter 8

Reaction of Br_2^- Produced by Flash Photolysis of Sea Water with Components of the Dissolved Carbonate System

Mary B. True and Oliver C. Zafiriou

Department of Chemistry, Woods Hole Oceanographic Institution, Woods Hole, MA 02543

Br_2^- produced by flash photolysis of seawater decays by parallel first- and second-order reactions. The environmentally important exponential decay is a pseudo first-order reaction of Br_2^- with the carbonate/bicarbonate system in seawater. A chemical speciation model for the free ions and ion-pairs in seawater and in solutions at seawater ionic strength allowed us to measure the dependence of the pseudo first-order rate term, α, on individual CO_2-containing species. A predictive equation based on reaction of Br_2^- with free CO_3^{2-} and the $MgCO_3^0$, $NaCO_3^-$ and $CaCO_3^0$ ion pairs accounts for the mean seawater α at pH 8.1 within experimental uncertainty. The reaction product(s) are unknown.

The preceding paper ([1]) showed that Br_2^- is produced in the UV flash photolysis of seawater and that some previously unknown reaction between Br_2^- and carbonate species is environmentally important. The mean pseudo first-order rate for this reaction in a variety of natural seawaters near pH 8.1 is $2.47 \pm 0.52 \times 10^3$ s^{-1}.

The purpose of this paper is to examine this reaction in simple solutions to determine rates and possible reactants. In order to explore the relative reactivities of free CO_3^{2-}, free HCO_3^- and the important carbonate ion pairs towards Br_2^-, we flashed aqueous solutions of bromide with KCl, NaCl and $MgCl_2$ at seawater ionic strength over a range of carbonate concentrations and pH's. The measured rates for the reaction of the relevant carbonate species with Br_2^- in simple solutions were combined with a model for the speciation of carbonate in seawater to see whether this reaction can account for the observed seawater kinetics.

Methods. We used UV flash photolysis to form Br by selective direct excitation of Br^-:

$$R1: \quad Br^- + h\nu = Br + e_{aq}^-$$

0097-6156/87/0327-0106$06.00/0
© 1987 American Chemical Society

The bromine atom reacts predominantly with bromide ions in solution to yield Br$_2^-$ (1-3).

Solutions were made using analytical reagent grade chemicals in Millipore "Super-Q" water. Artificial seawater was prepared as previously described (2).

We monitored the decay of Br$_2^-$ at 360 nm and fit data from this decay to Equation 1:

$$-d\ [Br_2^-]/dt\ =\ \alpha[Br_2^-]\ +\ k(2)\ [Br_2^-]^2 \qquad (1)$$

with a computer program (MIXKIN) which finds values for α and β ($\beta = k(2)/\varepsilon$ where $\varepsilon = 7800$ $\underline{M}^{-1}$ cm^{-1} ($\underline{M}$ = moles/ℓ) for Br$_2^-$ according to Zehavi and Rabani (4) and initial optical density (A_0) based on an integrated form of Equation 1 (1)[1]. This paper examines the environmentally significant exponential process involving components of the carbonate system in seawater. The second-order process is discussed in detail in the preceding paper (1).

In order to investigate the dependence of α on dissolved CO_2 and pH, we prepared solutions of simpler composition in which the concentrations of several important free ions and ion-pairs were maximized. In order to do this, we calculated the chemical speciation of carbonate/bicarbonate in seawater and in solutions of KCl, NaCl, MgCl$_2$ and mixtures of these salts as a function of pH in the range 6.0 to 8.9. Ion strengths were kept equivalent to those of natural seawater ($\mu \approx 0.7$ at S = 35°/$\circ\circ$). For the seawater calculations, we assumed the concentrations of major cations given by Culkin (5) and a total CO_2 concentration of 2.333×10^{-3} $\underline{M}$. We used an iterative computer program to solve a series of simultaneous equations based on thermodynamic association constants and estimated activity coefficients at ionic strengths of solutions for free carbonate and bicarbonate, and for the carbonate/bicarbonate ion-pairs with Mg^{2+}, Ca^{2+} and Na$^+$ (6). Our calculations did not consider the reduction in available cations due to ion-pairing with SO$_4^{2-}$ (7), nor any potential contributions from ion triplets such as MgCaCO$_3^{2+}$ or Mg$_2$CO$_3^{2+}$ (8). These limitations are not expected to have important influences on the results. Examples of the resulting distributions of the various carbonate/bicarbonate species for seawater at pH 6.0 and pH 8.1 are given in Figure 1.

The carbonate speciation of the KCl, MgCl$_2$ and NaCl solutions are given in Table I. The dependence of α upon one or several major forms of bicarbonate/carbonate was investigated for each of these solutions.

Results

The decay of Br$_2^-$ in the various inorganic solutions studied follows the expected second-order kinetics when no aqueous CO_2 is present (Fig. 2, 1). In the presence of CO_2, there is a small pseudo-first-order component (α) which can be quantified even in the presence of the much larger β term. However, the presence of multiple decay pathways results in substantial uncertainties in the value of the α and β terms, resulting in the rather large scatter of the data.

---

[1] Note that k(2) refers to second-order kinetics.

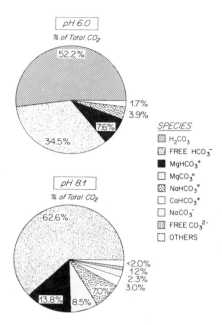

Figure 1.   Carbonate speciation in seawater at pH 6.0 and 8.1.
The percent of H_2CO_3 pictured for pH 6.1 includes dissolved CO_2.

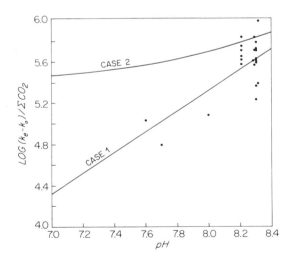

Figure 2.   [CO_2]-normalized values of α in solutions of 0.65 $\underline{M}$ KCl
with 8 x 10^{-4} $\underline{M}$ Br^- and added K_2CO_3/$KHCO_3$ as a function of pH.
● Individual kinetic determinations; ——— Case 1:   Fit of data if
CO_3^{2-} is only contributor to Y in Equation 2 in KCl solution;
——— Case 2:   Fit of data if Equation 2 is: $(\alpha-C) = \sum k_y$
($[CO_3^2] + 1/30$ $[HCO_3^-]$) where k_y was determined as in Case 1.

TABLE I.   Chemical Speciation of Carbonate and Bicarbonate as a Function of pH and Total CO$_2$ in Aqueous Solutions of Some Metal Ions

Metal Ion (Me^{n+})	$[Me^{n+}]$ (M)	pH	Free $[CO_3^{2-}]$ (M)	$[MeCO_3^{n-1}]$ (M)	Free $[HCO_3^-]$ (M)	$[MeHCO_3^{n-1}]$ (M)	Total CO_2 (M)
Na^+	1.3	8.21	1.40×10^{-4}	7.40×10^{-4}	5.70×10^{-3}	1.37×10^{-3}	8.0×10^{-3}
K^+	0.65	7.00	2.32×10^{-5}	0	1.53×10^{-2}	0	17.7×10^{-3}
		7.6	1.02×10^{-4}	0	1.70×10^{-2}	0	17.7×10^{-3}
		8.0	2.60×10^{-4}	0	1.72×10^{-2}	0	17.7×10^{-3}
		8.3	5.15×10^{-4}	0	1.71×10^{-2}	0	17.7×10^{-3}
		8.3	6.11×10^{-5}	0	2.02×10^{-3}	0	2.1×10^{-3}
		8.3	1.27×10^{-4}	0	4.21×10^{-3}	0	4.4×10^{-3}
		8.3	2.55×10^{-4}	0	8.43×10^{-3}	0	8.8×10^{-3}
Mg^{2+}	0.25*	7.5	4.24×10^{-6}	1.43×10^{-4}	8.87×10^{-4}	9.24×10^{-4}	2.0×10^{-3}
		7.5	1.71×10^{-5}	5.67×10^{-4}	3.57×10^{-3}	3.67×10^{-3}	8.0×10^{-3}
		8.0	1.17×10^{-5}	3.94×10^{-4}	7.75×10^{-4}	8.06×10^{-4}	2.0×10^{-3}
		8.0	4.73×10^{-5}	1.57×10^{-3}	3.13×10^{-3}	3.21×10^{-3}	8.0×10^{-3}
		8.1	9.88×10^{-6}	3.33×10^{-4}	5.19×10^{-4}	5.41×10^{-4}	1.41×10^{-3}
		8.1	2.59×10^{-6}	8.72×10^{-4}	5.42×10^{-4}	5.66×10^{-4}	2.0×10^{-3}
		8.1	2.83×10^{-6}	9.49×10^{-4}	1.49×10^{-3}	1.54×10^{-3}	4.0×10^{-3}
		8.2	6.72×10^{-5}	2.23×10^{-3}	2.80×10^{-3}	2.88×10^{-3}	8.0×10^{-3}
		8.3	7.88×10^{-5}	2.61×10^{-3}	2.61×10^{-3}	2.68×10^{-3}	8.0×10^{-3}

* Highly supersaturated MgCO$_3$ solutions are very slow to form precipitates, making it possible to do these experiments. Thermodynamically, MgCO$_3$(s) should precipitate.

In seawater near pH 8.1, the α term, as determined by UV flash photolysis, is 2470 $\pm$ 520 for a variety of natural seawaters. In pH 8.1 seawater <u>free bicarbonate and bicarbonate ion pairs</u> with magnesium, sodium and calcium together account for 86.40% of the total dissolved CO_2. Magnesium carbonate ion pair (8.5% of total CO_2) is the most abundant carbonate form in seawater; sodium carbonate ion pair and free carbonate together account for 3.5% of the total CO_2. However, since for the well-documented reactions of hydroxyl radical with the carbonate/bicarbonate system, CO_3^{2-} is about 30 times more reactive than HCO_3^- (<u>9</u>), we expected that reactions between Br_2^- and the carbonate system in seawater would be even more selective, hence dominated by Br_2^-/<u>carbonate</u> interactions. Since there were no published rates for the reactivity of <u>carbonate ion pairs</u> toward inorganic radicals, we determined the reactivity of the major carbonate ion pairs, $MgCO_3^0$ and $NaCO_3^-$, by examining the rate of disappearance of Br_2^- as a function of added CO_2 in solutions in which Mg^{2+} and Na^+ were the major cations (Table I). We measured the reactivity of free carbonate and bicarbonate towards Br_2^- in solutions in which K^+ was the major cation. We assumed that the reactivity of $CaCO_3^0$ was the same as that of $MgCO_3^0$.

The exponential decay of Br_2^- in the various salt solutions proved to be a function of pH-dependent and pH-independent factors. The pH dependent term varied with total CO_2, while the pH independent term was constant over a wide range of total CO_2 concentrations. Therefore, we expressed the exponential rate, α, as in Equation 2:

$$\alpha = C + \sum k_y [Y] \qquad (2)$$

where Y denotes the reaction partners of Br_2^- involving CO_2-containing species. The constant, C, is of uncertain origin.

In the simple case of pure solutions of 0.65 $\underline{M}$ KCl with 8 x 10^{-4} $\underline{M}$ KBr near pH 8.1, added K_2CO_3 and $KHCO_3$ are present as free HCO_3^- (97%) and free CO_3^{2-} (3%) (see Table I). We fitted our data to two extreme cases (Fig. 2). For Case 1, we assumed that free CO_3^{2-} was the sole species contributing to Y (Equation 2) and calculated a regression on the α's versus [CO_3^{2-}] for the individual sample determinations. From this calculation we determined that $k_{CO_3^{2-}}$ = 1.43 x 10^7 $\underline{M}^{-1}s^{-1}$, with a regression coefficient, r^2 = 0.73. For the other extreme case (Case 2), we fitted the experimental k's to Equation 2, assuming that $k_{HCO_3^-}$ is 1/30 of $k_{CO_3^{2-}}$ (a maximum based on the values for the more reactive, less selective OH radical), and obtained a $k_{CO_3^{2-}}$ = 6.50 x 10^6 $\underline{M}^{-1}$ s^{-1} and $k_{HCO_3^-}$ = 2.17 x 10^5 $\underline{M}^{-1}$ s^{-1} with a regression coefficient, r^2 = 0.60. Plotting the log of the measured α's (corrected for the constant rate, C, measured when no CO_2 is present) versus pH gives the individual points in Figure 3. The solid line represents a Case 1 fit (small bicarbonate reactivity) versus pH, whereas the dashed line represents a Case 2 fit (small bicarbonate contribution). At pH 8.1, either assumption fits the data well, while at lower pH's, Case 1 represents the data better.

In Figure 4 the measured exponential rate constants for decay of Br_2^- in 0.25 $\underline{M}$ $MgCl_2$ are plotted versus concentration of magnesium carbonate ion pair, [$MgCO_3^0$]. Closed circles represent points obtained when MIXKIN was allowed to find a three-parameter fit (α, β

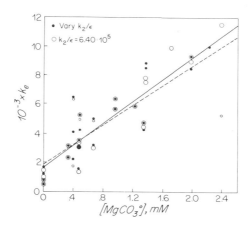

Figure 3. Dependence of α upon concentration of MgCO$_3^0$ in 0.25 <u>M</u> MgCl$_2$ with 8 x 10^{-4} <u>M</u> Br$^-$ and added K$_2$CO$_3$/KHCO$_3$. ● Three parameter (A$_0$, α, ß) fit to individual kinetic determinations. Solid line is a least-squares regression through the points, r^2 = 0.74; o Two parameter (A^0, α) fit to individual kinetic determinations, ß = 6.40 x 10^5 cm s^{-1}; --- Dashed line is a least squares regression through the points, r^2 = 0.65.

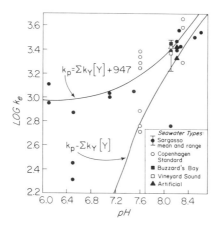

Figure 4. Variation in the pseudo-first-order rate, α, for the decay of Br$_2^-$ in seawater as a function of pH. Lines are from our model, Equation 3, based upon k$_y$'s measured in ionic solutions. The upper line includes the mean value of C (947 s^{-1}) found for seawater experiments with CO$_2$ removed (see text discussion).

and A_o) to the data. Forcing MIXKIN to use the mean β from all the kinetic determinations with a three-parameter fit gives the rates shown as open circles. The solid line is a least squares fit to the closed circles, the dashed line a least squares fit to the open circles. Forcing MIXKIN to use the "correct" β value did not improve the quality of the kinetic determinations. Therefore we used a $k_{MgCO_3}^o$ obtained from the solid line of 3.68×10^7 M^{-1} s^{-1} with a regression coefficient, $r^2 = 0.74$ for our seawater model.

However, in 0.25 M $MgCl_2$ solution free bicarbonate and magnesium bicarbonate ion pair account for a total of 76% of the dissolved CO_2, whereas the combined concentration of $MgCO_3^o$ and free CO_3^{2-} is only 24% of the total. We therefore investigated the dependence of α on total carbonate and total bicarbonate in aqueous $MgCl_2$. A calculation of α versus total added carbonate, assuming negligible bicarbonate reactivity yields a k_{TC} (TC = total carbonate) of 3.57×10^6 M^{-1} s^{-1} with a regression coefficient, $r^2 \approx 0.74$. Adding a total bicarbonate reactivity term (k_{TB}) equal to 1/30th of the carbonate reactivity, we calculated that $k_{TC} = 3.30 \times 10^6$ M^{-1} s^{-1} and $k_{TB} = 1.10 \times 10^5$ M^{-1} s^{-1} with a regression coefficient of 0.75. In this case, the fit of the data is very slightly improved with a small bicarbonate contribution. Since the improvement is marginal (r^2 to 0.75 from 0.74), and since the KCl data show that bicarbonate is not the major reactive species, we excluded a bicarbonate term from our seawater model.

In a similar manner we calculated that $k_{NaCO_3}^-$ is 9.11×10^6 M^{-1} s^{-1} ($r^2 = 0.74$) in solutions of 0.54 M or 1.3 M NaCl with added carbonate/bicarbonate, but this rate term is based on only four kinetic determinations. We assumed that $k_{CaCO_3}^o$ would be similar in size to $k_{MgCO_3}^o$ and therefore set $k_{CaCO_3}^o = 3.68 \times 10^6$ M^{-1} s^{-1} in our model.

The reaction of Br_2^- with CO_3^{2-} is not a known process. We speculate that the carbonate radical, CO_3^-, would be the product:

$$R2: \quad Br_2^- + CO_3^{2-} \rightarrow 2\ Br^- + CO_3^- \ (?)$$

The CO_3^- radical absorbs at 600 nm ([10]), but in seawater no clear signal at this wavelength was evident. In $MgCO_3^o$ solutions, there is a definite absorption grow-in at 600 nm that accompanies the Br_2^- decay at 360 nm. However, we were unable to quantify the relationship between the two absorptions and so cannot prove that the stoichiometry of R2 is correct. Qualitatively, it appears that the size of the 600 nm transient is too small to account for all of the Br_2^- decaying by the pseudo-first-order pathway.

We also showed by pulse radiolysis that CO_3^{2-} accelerates the decay of Br_2^- (formed from OH + Br^-), but further work is required to characterize the rate constant, stoichiometry, and product spectrum of the $Br_2^- + CO_3^{2-}$ interaction (R2).

Discussion

Our flash photolysis studies of seawater and related simpler solutions show that Br_2^- is produced in these experiments ([1]), and that it decays through a combination of first- and second-order processes (Equation 1). In this paper we have examined a previously

unknown, but environmentally important reaction between Br_2^- and
carbonate which occurs in seawater. In aqueous solutions of KCl,
NaCl and $MgCl_2$ we have measured the rates of reaction of Br_2^- with
the relevant carbonate species.

Our data show that there is no stoichiometrically significant
reaction of CO_2, H_2CO_3, free bicarbonate or bicarbonate ion pairs
with Br_2^-. Therefore Equation 2 can be applied to explain the
pseudo-first-order decay of Br_2^- in seawater by substitution of the
relevant k_y's for the various <u>carbonate</u> species measured in simple
ionic solutions in Equation 3:

$$k_p = (1.43 \times 10^7) \ [CO_3^{2-}] + (3.68 \times 10^6) \ [MgCO_3^0] \qquad (3)$$
$$+ \ (3.68 \times 10^6) \ [CaCO_3^0] + 9.11 \times 10^6 \ [NaCO_3^-] + C$$

The rate terms measured in ionic solutions multiplied by the seawater
concentrations of the relevant carbonate species (Table II) predict a
pseudo-first-order decay rate, $\alpha = 1.69 \times 10^3$ s^{-1} at pH 8.1 in seawater with a total CO_2 content of 2.333 mM. In seawater, however, as
in the ionic solutions studied, there is a small pH and CO_2-indepen-
dent term, C, contributing to α. The mean value of this term, as
determined in six Sargasso seawater experiments with no CO_2 present,
is 947 s^{-1}. When this average C is included in the predictive equation, then $k_p = 2.64 \times 10^3$ s^{-1} at pH 8.1. The mean measured seawater α at pH 8.1 lies between the two predicted values at 2.47 $\pm$
0.52 $\times 10^3$ s^{-1}.

TABLE II. The Exponential Decay of the 360 nm Transient in Seawater
and Various Salt Solutions

Solution	[a]Rate Term k_y [Y], for Y =				
	$10^{-3} \ \alpha$ (s^{-1})	CO_3^{2-}	$MgCO_3^0$	$NaCO_3^-$	$CaCO_3^0$
		------------(10^{-3} s^{-1})---- ---------			
Coastal Seawater	2.21$\pm$0.41				
Sargasso Seawater	2.57$\pm$0.54				
Artificial Seawater	2.48$\pm$0.25				
[b]0.65 M KCl		0.40			
[c]0.25 M MgCl$_2$			0.73		[d]0.08
[e]0.54 M or NaCl				0.48	

Natural seawaters and artificial seawater pH $\approx$8.1$\pm$0.1.
All artificial seawater and salt solutions contained 8x10^{-4} M KBr.
a: Rate term based upon the concentration of the relevant carbonate
    species in pH 8.1 seawater containing 2.333x10^{-3} M total CO_2.
b: pH 7.05 - 8.3; regression coefficient, $r^2 = 0.73$, n = 21
c: pH = 7.5 - 8.5; regression coefficient, $r^2 = 0.74$, n = 31
d: Rate constant $k_{CaCO_3^0}$ assumed = $k_{MgCO_3^0}$
e: pH 8.0 - 8.2; regression coefficient, $r^2 = 0.74$, n = 4.

A visual examination of the pH dependence of the exponential rate term (Fig. 4) shows that inclusion of the mean C in Equation 3 explains the full pH range of experimental values better. The origin of this constant term is uncertain. Although it might be due to impurities in the "pure" chemicals used to make ionic solutions, the presence of a constant term of essentially the same size in natural seawaters argues against reagent contamination as the source. We believe that this term may be an indirect result of the manner in which MIXKIN fits the kinetic data. Since the program forces a three parameter fit, there is a tendency for the fit of the "least important parameter" to contain more error than the fit of the parameter of interest ($\underline{3}$). In the case where the decay of Br_2^- is almost exclusively second-order (no CO_2 present), the relative errors in α are large at the same time that the absolute value of α is small. Thus the true value of α in CO_2-stripped seawater may be close to 0 even though MIXKIN finds a mean value of 947 s^{-1}.

An alternative explanation for the small pH-independent portion of the seawater α's is that some side reactions are occurring which affect the fitted parameters.

Thus, in summary, most of the fast exponential decay, α, of Br_2^- observed in seawater is due to an interaction with carbonate species in which CO_3^{2-}, $NaCO_3^-$ and $MgCO_3^0$ are all important reactants. The reaction product is unknown and the significance (if any) of the term C is also unclear.

It is interesting to note that in fresh water OH reacts with the carbonate/bicarbonate system directly ($\underline{11}$). In seawater, OH initially gives rise to Br_2^-, which then reacts with carbonate species in an unknown reaction. Efforts are underway to study this reaction in more detail using pulse radiolysis, since the products are currently unknown, though CO_3^- seems likely. If CO_3^- is the product, the principal effect of Br^- in seawater is just to act as an intermediate in converting OH to CO_3^-.

Acknowledgments

We gratefully acknowledge the assistance of Drs. Elie Hayon and Ed Black for access to the excellent Natick facilities and technical guidance; Drs. John Connolly and Jim Bell for access to relevant computer programs for the kinetic analyses of the flash results; Dr. M. A. J. Rodgers for assistance at CFKR; and Drs. Woolcott Smith and Derek Spencer for guidance in modifying the computer programs for our use at Woods Hole. This work was funded by the National Science Foundation grants GA-35401, DES 72-1553, OCE-77-09381 and OCE 84-17770. Flash photolysis studies were carried out at the U. S. Army Natick Laboratories. Pulse radiolysis studies and their data reduction were carried out at the Center for Fast Kinetics Research. The CFKR is supported jointly by the Biomedical Research Technology Program of the Division of Research Resources of NIH (RR 00886) and by the University of Texas at Austin.

This is Contribution No. 6035 from the Woods Hole Oceanographic Institution.

Literature Cited

1. Zafiriou, O. C.; True, M. B.; Hayon, E.   ACS SYMPOSIUM SERIES, this volume.
2. Zafiriou, O. C.   J. Geophys. Res. 1974, 79, 4491-4497.
3. Zafiriou, O. C.; True, M. B.   "Flash photolysis - kinetic spectrophotometry of seawater and related solutions: Data acquisition, processing, and validation," WHOI Tech. Memo. I-77, Woods Hole Oceanographic Institution, 1977.
4. Zehavi, D.; Rabani, J.   J. Phys. Chem. 76, 1972, 312-319.
5. Culkin, F.   In "Chemical Oceanography"; Riley, J. P.; Skirrow, G., Eds.; Academic: London, 1965; Vol. 1, pp. 121-161.
6. Millero, F. J.   Ann. Rev. Earth Planet. Sci. 2, 1974, 101-149.
7. Stumm, W.; Morgan, J. J.   "Aquatic Chemistry," 2nd ed., John Wiley & Sons: New York, 1981; 780 pp.
8. Pytkowicz, R. M.; Hawley, J. E.   Limnol. Oceanogr. 19, 1974, 224-234.
9. Weeks, J. L.; Rabani, J.   J. Phys. Chem. 70, 1966, 2100-2106.
10. Behar, D.; Czapski, G.; Duchovny, I. J. Phys. Chem. 74, 1970, 2206-2210.
11. Hoigné, J.   "Extended Abstracts of NATO-ARI Workshop "Photochemistry of Natural Waters," Woods Hole Oceanographic Institution, 1983.

RECEIVED June 24, 1986

Chapter 9

Photochemistry of Copper Complexes in Sea Water

James W. Moffett and Rod G. Zika

Rosenstiel School of Marine and Atmospheric Sciences, Division of Marine and Atmospheric Chemistry, University of Miami, Miami, FL 33149

The photochemistry of copper in seawater has been studied to assess the role sunlight plays in the speciation and redox chemistry of copper in the upper water column of the ocean. A variety of photo- chemically induced redox reactions involving Cu(I)/Cu(II) interconversion have been studied at elevated copper concentrations in the laboratory. To evaluate the net effect of these processes at natural copper levels, Cu(I) and $[Cu(II)]_{free}/[Cu(II)]_{total}$ were measured as a function of sunlight irradiation and depth in the water column. The results indicate that sunlight has an important influence on copper speciation in the upper water column.

There is now considerable evidence that a variety of photo- chemically induced redox processes occur in natural water systems. At the present time however, little is known about how these processes influence redox equilibria of minor elements such as copper or other transition metals in the water column. A variety of elements exist in the upper water column in valence states which are unstable with respect to the O_2/H_2O couple. However, since little kinetic data is available for probable photoredox processes involving these elements, it is impossible to assess the importance of photochemistry in relation to biologically mediated processes.

The chemistry of copper has been studied extensively in recent years because of its toxicity to aquatic organisms and possible role in limiting primary productivity under certain conditions (1,2). These studies indicate that the speciation of copper determines the extent of its toxicity in aqueous solution. Unfortunately, the parameters which influence its speciation are poorly understood, in part because of its strong chelation by poorly characterised organic chelators in seawater. Most studies have focused on the complexation chemistry of Cu(II). However, the chemistry of Cu(I)/Cu(II) interconversion has been studied extensively in chemical and biological systems and there is

0097-6156/87/0327-0116$06.00/0
© 1987 American Chemical Society

considerable evidence that similar reactions occur in natural
waters.

   In this work, the photochemistry of copper complexes in
seawater has been investigated with the following goals in mind;

a.   To identify probable primary and secondary photochemical redox
     reactions involving copper complexes and to evaluate their
     potential significance in the marine environment.
b.   To study the overall effect of such reactions on copper
     speciation in seawater by measuring Cu(I) and $[Cu(II)]_{free}$/
     $[Cu(II)]_{total}$ in seawater at natural levels.
c.   Examine the implications of this work for the bioavailability
     of copper and the degradation of organic chelators.
d.   Examine the implications of this work for the chemistry and
     fate of H_2O_2 in seawater.

Methods

Potentially significant reactions were studied in model systems at
elevated copper levels, following Cu(I) formation or decay using a
selective, sensitive procedure involving colorimetric determination of a Cu(I) complex with bathocuproine disulfonic acid
(2,9,-dimethyl,-4,7,-diphenyl 1,10-phenanthroline disulfonic acid).
The method is described in detail elsewhere (3) and has a limit of
detection of 1×10^{-8} mol L^{-1}. The addition of ethylenediamine has
been shown to effectively mask Cu(II) interference. The procedure
was extended to studies at natural levels by using a similar
ligand, neocuproine (2,9-dimethyl,1,10-phenanthroline), which forms
a solvent extractable Cu(I) complex. The complex is extracted into
methylene chloride and back extracted with 10% HNO_3. The limit of
detection is 0.02×10^{-9} mol L^{-1}. Ethylenediamine is again used
as a masking ligand (4).

   The ratio $[Cu(II)]_{free}$/$[Cu(II)]_{total}$ was determined using a
ligand exchange, liquid liquid partition technique. Acetylacetone
was added to seawater, forming a copper acetylacetonate complex.
Determination of the distribution of copper between that complex
and natural complexes enabled calculation of $[Cu(II)]_{free}$/
$[Cu(II)]_{total}$. The procedure is described in detail elsewhere(5).

   Studies at the laboratory were carried out in synthetic media
or in seawater collected at the RSMAS dock, Biscayne Bay, Florida.
Most water was filtered through 0.2 μm Nucleopore filters, althouqh
systematic differences between filtered and nonfiltered waters were
not observed. Shipboard samples were collected using teflon coated
Go Flo bottles (General Oceanics) and were not filtered. All
determinations at sea and in the lab at natural copper levels were
carried out in a laminar flow hood. Go flo bottles were racked in
a clean area of the ship and samples transferred directly to the
hood via teflon tubing. All sampling locations referred to in this
study are shown in Figure 1.

   Organic material isolated from Biscayne Bay, Florida, by
ultrafiltration was used in some experiments at higher copper
levels. An Amicon ultrafiltration apparatus with Amicon PM10
filters was used.

Photoreduction processes involving Cu(II)

Primary Processes. The most common primary photochemical processes involving copper(II) complexes are ligand to metal charge transfer (LMCT) reactions (6,7), also referred to as charge transfer to metal (CTTM) reactions. LMCT reactions occur when light absorbed in an LMCT absorption band of the Cu(II) complex leads to reduction of the metal and oxidation of the ligand.

$$Cu(II)-L \xrightarrow{h\nu} Cu(II)-L*$$
$$Cu(II)-L* \longrightarrow Cu(I) + L^+$$

Where L is an organic ligand, oxidation generally results in the destruction of the ligand.

LMCT reactions have been observed for many Cu(II) complexes, which are listed in Table 1.

Table 1. Photoreactive Copper(II) Complexes

Complex	Products Detected*	References
$CuCl_x^{(2-x)}$	Cl_2^-	7
$CuBr_x^{(2-x)}$	Br_2^-	7
$CuOCOCH_3^+$	Cu^+, CH_3OH, C_2H_6	7
$Cu(malonate)_2^{2-}$	CO_2	7
$Cu(oxalate)_2^{2-}$	CO_2, Cu^+	7, this work
$Cu(glutamate)_2^{2-}$	CO_2, Cu^+	7
$Cu(\beta-alanine)_2^{2-}$	CO_2, Cu^+	7, this work
$Cu(glycine)_2^{2-}$	CO_2, Cu^+	7, this work
$Cu(en)_2^{2+}$	NH_3, CO_2, Cu_2O	7
$Cu(NTA)_2^{2-}$	CO_2 Cu^+	8, this work

* Other products detected for many of these processes but not listed here.

The list indicates that most ligands with carboxylate and amino functional groups form Cu(II) complexes which are photoreactive. For complexes where the LMCT band extends above 300nm the reaction should proceed in sunlight irradiated seawater. This has been demonstrated in this laboratory by using Cu(II) complexes with NTA, oxalate, glycine and alanine in seawater exposed to sunlight and monitoring the formation of Cu(I).

Copper(II) is the predominant valence state of copper in oxygenated marine waters and forms a variety of complexes with inorganic and organic ligands. Considerable attention in recent years has been focused on Cu(II) organic chelators and their importance in Cu(II) speciation is now firmly established. Since oxygen and nitrogen donor functional groups such as carboxylate and amine groups are probably involved in Cu(II) chelation by natural organic chelators (9,10) it is reasonable to expect that they are photoreactive. Spectral data indicate that Cu(II) complexes with organic matter isolated by ultrafiltration from seawater absorb significantly above 300nm (Figure 2). Since this absorption is probably an LMCT band it indicates the potential for these processes in sunlight illuminated seawater.

In addition, phenolic or salicylate type sites may be important in the chelation of copper by dissolved organic matter (11,12). In this work irradiation of Cu(II) salicylate in 0.7 molL^{-1} Cl$^-$ at 296.7 nm and 313nm led to the formation of Cu(I). However it was not clear that a LMCT process was responsible and indeed some reduction occured after cessation of irradiation, indicating a second order process was involved. The observation that irradiation leads to the formation of a relatively long lived reductant is interesting, but renders salicylate less useful as a model for primary reactions.

Irradiation of CuCO$_3$ in 0.7 M NaCl solution at 313nm leads to Cu(I) formation, probably via

$$CuCO_3 \xrightarrow{h\nu} Cu^+ + CO_3^-$$

The reaction is potentially important because the complex absorbs significantly above 300nm and CuCO$_3$ is the major inorganic copper complex in seawater (12). Cu(I) production was extremely slow, negligible in sunlight and probably not significant in the environment. The low quantum yield may be due to back reaction of Cu$^+$ with CO$_3^-$, although addition of 10^{-3} mol L^{-1} 2-propanol to react with the CO$_3^-$ radical did not lead to an increase in rate.

<u>Secondary Reactions.</u> The reduction of a Cu(II) complex by a photochemically generated reducing agent constitutes a secondary photochemical reaction. Reductants such as O$_2^-$, H$_2$O$_2$ and organic radicals are potentially important in this process (13). At the present time, concentration data is available only for H$_2$O$_2$, the concentration in surface seawater being about 10^{-7} mol L^{-1} (14,15). Therefore we have studied the reduction kinetics of Cu(II) by H$_2$O$_2$ to assess its environmental importance.

A general mechanism for this process has been postulated by numerous workers (16).

$$H_2O_2 \rightleftharpoons H^+ + HO_2^- \qquad (1)$$

$$HO_2^- + Cu^{2+} \longrightarrow Cu^+ + HO_2 \qquad (2)$$

$$HO_2 \rightleftharpoons H^+ + O_2^- \qquad (3)$$

$$O_2^- + Cu^{2+} \longrightarrow Cu^+ + O_2 \qquad (4)$$

The reaction has been studied in a variety of aqueous media but not in chloride media (17-19). Therefore we investigated the

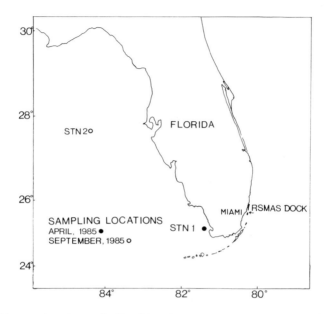

Figure 1.   Map of Florida showing sampling locations.

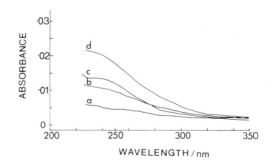

Figure 2.   Spectra of Cu(II) complexes formed by the addition
of Cu(II) to a carbonate free solution of marine organic matter
isolated   from   Biscayne   Bay   water   by   ultrafiltration.
Preconcentrated x 100. (a), $[Cu(II)] = 2 \times 10^{-8}$ mol L^{-1}; (b),
$[Cu(II)] = 4 \times 10^{-8}$ mol L^{-1}; (c) $[Cu(II)] = 8 \times 10^{-8}$ mol L^{-1},
no ultrafiltrate; (d) $[Cu(II)] = 8 \times 10^{-8}$ mol L^{-1}.

reaction in simple chloride media and in seawater to establish the reaction rate and determine which Cu(II) species are kinetically important. The effect of pH, [Cl$^-$] and [CO$_3^{2-}$] on the reaction rate in chloride media was studied. The results, which are described in detail elsewhere (20) showed the reaction has a first order dependence on chloride concentration and a second order dependence on hydroxide. These observations are consistent with the following mechanism.

$$CuL \rightleftharpoons Cu^{2+}_{(aq)} \tag{5}$$

$$Cu^{2+}_{(aq)} + OH^- + Cl^- \rightleftharpoons CuOHCl \tag{6}$$

$$CuOHCl + HO_2^- \longrightarrow CuOHCl^- + HO_2 \tag{7}$$

In this mechanism CuL represents the major Cu complexes in solution which are relatively unreactive towards peroxide. Steps (5) and (6) represent ligand exchange processes which maintain equilibrium steady state concentrations of CuClOH. Reaction (7) is the rate determining step. The reaction pathway of the HO$_2$ formed in reaction (7) in seawater is not known. However in the model systems at elevated Cu levels it was assumed that it reacted via reactions (3) and (4) above.

This mechanism is consistent with expectations from charge transfer theory which indicates that the rate of the charge transfer step is proportional to the free energy change on going from the Cu(II) complex to the Cu(I) complex. Reduction of CuClOH leads to formation of the very stable CuClOH$^-$ species. Reduction of Cu$^{2+}_{(aq)}$ or CuCO$_3$ does not lead to direct formation of a stable Cu(I) species. This simple explanation does not explain why other species such as CuCl$_2^o$ are relatively unreactive in spite of the high stability of the corresponding CuCl$_2^-$ complex. A more complex, inner sphere charge trasfer mechanism is probably involved, as suggested in previous studies with other Cu(II) complexes (17-19).

The overall second order rate constant for Cu(II) reduction by H$_2$O$_2$ in organic free seawater is $6.3 \pm 0.2 \times 10^2$ mol^{-1}Ls^{-1}. Cu(II) complexes with marine organic matter are unlikely to be reactive towards H$_2$O$_2$ because Cu(II) complexes with carboxylate and amine ligands are generally more stable than their Cu(I) counterparts. Therefore, in seawater, the importance of Cu(II) reduction by H$_2$O$_2$ is a function of the fraction of inorganically complexed Cu(II), deetrmined by the stability constants and concentrations of organic chelators, and the lability of these Cu(II) organic complexes.

The importance of O$_2^-$, generated in this reaction or by other pathways is difficult to assess because there is no data for its concentration in seawater. The concentrations are undoubtedly low, but it is very reactive with Cu^{2+}. The rate constant for the reaction

$$Cu^{2+} + O_2^- \longrightarrow Cu^+ + O_2 \tag{8}$$

has been reported as 1.9×10^9 mol^{-1}Ls^{-1} (21). From this data we can calculate a minimum steady state concentration of O$_2^-$ required for the reaction to be comparable with $Cu(II)$ reduction by H_2O_2. The concentration obtained is about 10^{-12} mol L^{-1}, well below estimates of the upper concentration limit of 10^{-8} mol L^{-1} (22).

Irradiation of concentrated humic solutions and ultrafiltrate in seawater leads to $Cu(I)$ formation. $Cu(II)$ was added to ultrafiltrate which had been irradiated for 1 hour at 313 nm. Initially about 5% of the total added copper was reduced but then a steady state was reached with no further reduction occuring even in deoxygenated solution. $Cu(I)$ yields were small in these experiments as $Cu(I)$ oxidation occured simultaneously, by photochemically generated oxidants in these concentrated solutions. This experiment indicates the problem in working in a preconcentrated media where sources sinks and steady state concentrations of reactive transients may be much different than in seawater and are not readily characterizable. Such rapid $Cu(I)/Cu(II)$ interconversions are less probable at seawater concentrations where transients involved probably react rapidly with more abundant species than copper.

Cu(I) Oxidation in Seawater

Probable oxidative pathways for $Cu(I)$ in seawater have been investigated by this group to assess its potential to accumulate at significant steady state levels. The oxidation of $Cu(I)$ by O_2 has been studied elsewhere (14). The overall second order rate constant in seawater for the reaction

$$Cu^+ + O_2 \longrightarrow Cu^{2+} + O_2^- \tag{9}$$

is 6.1 mol^{-1} Ls^{-1}. The rate of oxidation by H_2O_2 has also been investigated in seawater and the overall second order rate constant for the reaction

$$Cu^+ + H_2O_2 \longrightarrow Cu^{2+} + OH + OH^- \tag{10}$$

is $1.0 \pm 0.1 \times 10^2$ mol^{-1} Ls^{-1}. This indicates that oxidation by O_2 is the most significant process since peroxide concentrations are at least three orders of magnitude lower in surface waters. Extrapolation of this rate data to natural concentrations is simpler for $Cu(I)$ than for $Cu(II)$ because interactions with organic ligands are unlikely to be significant and chloride complexation dominates. Therefore speciation in these model systems at elevated levels is representative of speciation at natural levels. Studies of the chloride and pH dependence of both these reactions indicate that Cu^+ and $CuCl^0$ are the most rapidly oxidized species. The major species, $CuCl_2^-$ and $CuCl_3^{2-}$ are relatively inert to oxidation, accounting for the stability of $Cu(I)$ in seawater.

The predominant $Cu(I)$ species in seawater is $CuCl_3^{2-}$ (14) which undergoes photolytic oxidation via a charge transfer to solvent (CTTS) reaction (7).

$$CuCl_3^{2-} \longrightarrow CuCl^+ + 2Cl^- + e^- \tag{11}$$

A quantum yield of 0.23 was determined at 296nm and 313nm.

However, the complex absorbs only weakly above 300nm and so does not react significantly in sunlight. Calculations of photolysis rates using a modified version of the Zepp and Cline photochemical model (23) indicate that at surface seawater under optimum sunlight conditions the half life of Cu(I) is >6 hours assuming this is the only sink.

The results of these studies indicate that Cu(I) oxidation by O_2 is the major oxidative pathway but that oxidation by H_2O_2 is also significant. Other oxidants may be involved, but no concentration or kinetic data is available. In particular, O_2^- may be important as an oxidant here in addition to its role as a reductant outlined previously.

These results indicate that a variety of reactions may lead to Cu(I)/Cu(II) interconversions in seawater. The results are summarised schematically in Figure 3 to demonstrate how copper redox cycling probably occurs. The basic features are a dynamic redox cycle involving the relatively minor but kinetically reactive species which react with oxygen and hydrogen peroxide as described previously. They are probably reactive with ohter photochemically generated oxidants and reductants, such as O_2^- and organic radicals. $CuCl_2$ reduction may also be important despite its negligible reaction with H_2O_2 as it is rapidly reduced by other reductants such as ferrous cytochrome C (24). The major Cu(I) and Cu(II) species, indicated in the boxes, do not participate in these reactions but do undergo primary photolysis. The above studies indicate that the photolysis of $CuCl_3^{2-}$ and $CuCO_3^{o}$ are not significant but photolysis of Cu(II) organic complexes may be, based on the model ligands.

This scheme is highly qualitative at the present time. The speciation of Cu(I) is probably dominated by chloride even at natural levels so extrapolation of the laboratory data is valid. However, for Cu(II) there is still widespread disagreement about the nature, concentrations and stability constants of natural organic Cu^{2+} chelators, resulting in estimates for the fraction of free Cu^{2+} (i.e. $[Cu(II)]_{free}/[Cu(II)]_{total}$) which vary by two orders of magnitude (12,25,26). This makes it difficult to estimate in situ rates of secondary reduction reactions involving minor Cu(II) species which are proportional to this fraction. And there is no direct evidence that LMCT reactions investigated using model ligands actually occur in seawater. A further complication is that steady state concentration and rate data are unavailable for many potentially important reactive species involved in copper redox cycling, such as O_2^-.

In order to determine the overall effect that these processes might have without having quantitative data for every potentially important reaction involved procedures were developed to measure two important parameters in the copper system at natural levels; Cu(I) and $[Cu(II)]_{free}/[Cu(II)]_{total}$.

Measurement of Cu(I) in Seawater

The formation of Cu(I) in coastal waters exposed to sunlight was investigated. Seawater collected from Biscayne Bay was stored in the dark for 2 weeks and exposed to sunlight in round bottomed quartz flasks. The results, shown in Figure 4, indicate that photochemical formation of Cu(I) occurs and correlates with the photochemical production of H_2O_2. In a second experiment, all flasks were exposed to 5 hours of sunlight and the decay in the Cu(I) signal monitored (Figure 5).

Cu(I) formation observed here is probably the result of a combination of primary and secondary processes. Primary processes may be important in destroying Cu(II) complexes which are inert to secondary reactions, thereby making secondary processes more important. The decay of Cu(I) after irradiation is much slower than the expected, since its half life in the presence of O_2 is under 6 minutes. Therefore, the presence of relatively long lived reductant species such as H_2O_2 must be invoked. Artificial seawater containing ultrafiltrate also produced Cu(I) upon solar irradiation, but chloride free media did not (4), in agreement with kinetic expectations based on the extremely rapid oxidation of Cu(I) in chloride free media.

Cu(I) was measured in the water column off the Florida Coast on the SOLARS III cruise. Results from a cast taken at a station west of Tampa are shown in Figure 6. The cast was made at 1400 on a sunny, flat calm day; optimal conditions for photochemical activity. Hydrographic data, obtained during a CTD cast immediately afterwards indicated a well stratified water column. The profile indicates that Cu(I) is present at the surface where it constitutes about 15% of the total copper. The concentration declines with depth and is below the limit of detection at 90m. The H_2O_2 profile shows similar characteristics, with a surface maximum.

A study of the diurnal variability of Cu(I) was made at a coastal site containing high DOC, off the Florida Everglades (Station 1). The results indicate virtually no Cu(I) above the limit of detection despite high daytime peroxide levels shown in Figure 7. This may be a result of more extensive Cu(II) chelation by organic matter in this highly productive coastal site. Or Cu(I) lifetimes may be extremely short because of a high photochemical production of short lived radical oxidants. The results indicate that, apart from the coastal site, there is a general correlation between Cu(I) levels and H_2O_2 concentration. This agreement may be coincidental because other reductants of photochemical origin may have a similar distribution to peroxide.

Measurement of $[Cu(II)]_{free}/[Cu(II)]_{total}$

Measurements of $[Cu(II)]_{free}/[Cu(II)]_{total}$ in seawater were carried out to calculate in situ rates of secondary reactions such as the reduction of Cu(II) by H_2O_2 and to look for evidence of primary photoreactions involving Cu(II) organic complexes. The acetylacetone liquid-liquid partition procedure was used to measure $[Cu(II)]_{free}/[Cu(II)]_{total}$ as a function of depth off the coast of Florida at station 2 during the SOLARS III cruise. Data are shown in Figure 6, along with peroxide and Cu(I) data. Profiles of the three parameters have similar characteristics. $[Cu(II)]_{free}/[Cu(II)]_{total}$ profiles are characterised by a surface maxima and decreasing values with depth to relatively uniform low values from

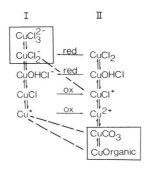

Figure 3. Summary of processes involved in Cu(I)/Cu(II) cycling in seawater.

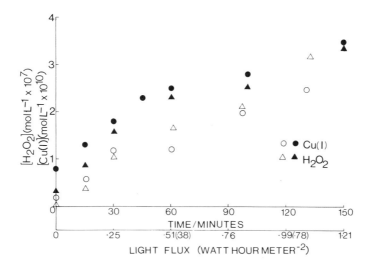

Figure 4. Photochemical formation of Cu(I) in seawater exposed to sunlight in February, O , and April, ● , 1985. Light flux values in brackets are for February, 1985.

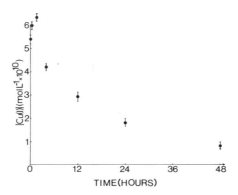

Figure 5. Dark decay of Cu(I) signal in seawater exposed to 5 hours sunlight irradiation.

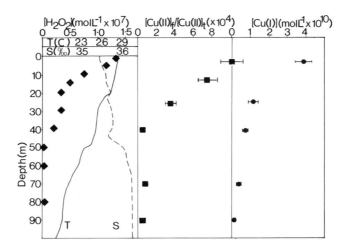

Figure 6. Depth profile of Cu(I), $[Cu(II)]_{free}/[Cu(II)]_{total}$ and H_2O_2 with accompanying hydrographic data, station 8, September 1985.

50m to the deepest depths sampled. There was about a twentyfold increase between the deep values and the surface values. To determine if the increase in free Cu^{2+} towards the surface is photochemically induced, samples of seawater collected in Biscayne Bay were exposed to sunlight in quartz flasks maintained at 25° in a water bath and $[Cu(II)]_{free}/[Cu(II)]_{total}$ measured with irradiation time. The results, in Figure 8, demonstrate that sunlight does lead to an increase, probably as a result of photo-destruction of the ligand and/or copper complex, possibly involving LMCT reactions. The minimum was located at the base of the mixed layer and coincided with what is generally the zone of maximum productivity. An explanation for the observed speciation trends is the biological production of chelators in the zone of maximum productivity (i.e. lower photic zone) which are degraded photo-chemically as they mix upward. Further investigation is necessary to confirm this hypothesis.

An in situ rate of reduction for Cu(II) by H_2O_2, calculated from this data and the kinetic data, indicates that only 5% to 10% of the Cu(I) measured can be accounted for by this source. Therefore, other pathways not considered in the simple model must be important.

Conclusions

A variety of reactions are involved in Cu(I)/Cu(II)interconversion in seawater. Several important reactions have been studied and rate constants determined at elevated copper concentrations. The system cannot be completely characterized by this data base at present because the nature and steady state concentrations of many potentially important species such as O_2^- have not been determined. Nevertheless, measurement of Cu(I) and $[Cu(II)]_{free}/[Cu(II)]_{total}$ at natural copper levels indicates the net effect of these sunlight induced processes has considerable influence on copper speciation in seawater. Measurement of Cu(I) indicates up to 15% of copper is present as Cu(I) in surface seawater under optimum conditions. Depth profile characteristics indicate a surface maxima which is consistent with a photochemical reduction mechanism. This is supported by the measurement of Cu(I) formation in seawater exposed to sunlight. Profiles of $[Cu(II)]_{free}/[Cu(II)]_{total}$ indicate that sunlight influences Cu(II) organic interactions.

This work has important implications for the role of copper in seawater. The uptake characteristics of Cu(I) by organisms may be very different than those for Cu(II) which may affect the bioavailability and toxicity of copper in seawater. The detection of a twenty fold increase in free Cu^{2+} between 50m and the surface is important as numerous investigations have established that toxicity is related to free Cu^{2+} and not total. This study demonstrates that H_2O_2, which is generally considered as an oxidant, also functions as a reductant in some systems, such as this one. Hydrogen peroxide is generally unreactive with organic compounds unless catalysed by transition metals and therefore reaction with transition metals could be an important degradative pathway. The low ambient concentrations of transition metals in seawater could explain the long lifetime of H_2O_2 in seawater.

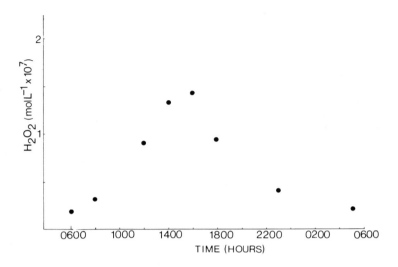

Figure 7. A diel study of H_2O_2 at a coastal station off the
Florida west coast, April 1985.[2]

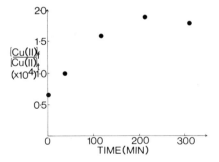

Figure 8. Sunlight induced increase in $[Cu(II)]_{free}$/
$[Cu(II)]_{total}$ for a sample collected from Biscayne Bay,
Florida.

However, reduction of Cu(II) is unlikely to be important in H_2O_2 degradation because oxidation of the resultant Cu(I) leads back to H_2O_2 via O_2^- formation. The oxidation of Cu(I) by H_2O_2 is probably not important either because of the low Cu(I) concentrations in seawater; calculations indicate that H_2O_2 would have a half life of at least 100 days if this was the sole degradative pathway. This is considerably longer than present estimates.

Acknowledgment

This work was supported by the Office of Naval Research under contract N00014-85C-0020.

Literature Cited

1. Sunda, W.G.; Guillard, R.R.L. J. Mar. Res. 1976, 34, 511-9.
2. Sunda, W.G. and Ferguson, R.F. In "Trace Metals in Seawater"; Wong, C.S. Ed.; Plenum: New York, 1983; pp. 871-91.
3. Moffett, J.W.; Zika, R.G.; Petasne, R.G. Anal. Chim. Acta. 1985, 175, 171-9.
4. Moffett, J.W. and R.G. Zika. Determination of Cu(I) at subnanomolar levels in seawater. (submitted)
5. Moffett, J.W., and R.G. Zika. Solvent extraction of copper acetylacetonate in studies of copper speciation in seawater. (submitted).
6. Balzani, V.; Carassiti, V. "Photochemistry of Coordination Compounds"; Academic: London, 1970. 430pp.
7. Ferraudi, G.; Muralidharan, S. Coord. Chem. Rev. 1981, 36, 45-88.
8. Langford, C.H.; Wingham, M.; Sastri, V.S. Environ. Sci. Tech. 1973, 7, 820-2.
9. Mantoura, R.F.C.; Dickson, A.; Riley, J.P. Estuar. Coast. Mar. Sci. 1978, 6, 387-408.
10. Mills, G.L.; Hanson, A.K.; Quinn, J.G.; Lammela, W.R.; Chasteen, N.D. Mar. Chem. 1982, 11, 355-78.
11. Gamble, D.S.; Underdown, A.W.; Langford, C.H. Anal. Chem. 1980, 52, 1901-8.
12. Zuehlke, R.W.; Kester, D.R. In "Trace Metals in Seawater"; Wong, C.S., Ed.; Plenum: New York, 1983; pp. 773-88.
13. Zika, R.G. In "Marine Organic Chemistry"; Duursma, E.K.; Dawson, R. Ed.; Elsevier: Amsterdam, 1981; pp. 299-325.
14. Moffett, J.W.; Zika, R.G. Mar. Chem. 1983, 13, 239-251.
15. Zika, R.G.; Moffett, J.W.; Cooper, W.J.; Petasne R.G.; Saltzman, E.S. Geochim. Cosmochim. Acta. 1985, 49, 1173-84.
16. Gray, R.D. J. Amer. Chem. Soc. 1969, 91, 56-62.
17. Sigel, H.; Flierl, C.; Griesser, R. J. Amer. Chem. Soc. 1969, 91, 1061-4.
18. Davies, G.; Higgins R.; Loose, D.J. Inorg. Chem. 1976, 15, 700-3.
19. Otto, M.; Lerchner, J.; Pap, T.; Zuanziger, H.; Hoyer, E.; Inczedy, J.; Werner, G. J. Inorg. Nucl. Chem. 1981, 43, 1101-5.
20. Moffett, J.W.; Zika, R.G. Reaction of hydrogen peroxide with copper and iron in seawater. (submitted)

21. Klug-Roth, D.; Rabani, J. J. Phys. Chem. 1976, 80, 588-91.
22. Zafiriou, O.C.; Joussot-Dubien, J.; Zepp, R.G.; Zika, R.G. Environ, Sci. Tech. 1984, 18, 358A-71A.
23. Zepp, R.G.; Cline, D.M. Environ. Sci. Tech. 1977, 11, 359-66.
24. Yandell, J.K. Aust. J. Chem. 1981, 34, 99-106.
25. Van den Berg, C.M.G. Mar. Chem. 1984, 15, 1-18.
26. Waite, T.D.; Morel, F.M.M. Anal. Chem. 1983, 55, 1268-74.

RECEIVED June 24, 1986

PHOTOSENSITIZATION IN NATURAL WATERS

Chapter 10

Time-Resolved Fluorescence Measurements on Dissolved Marine Organic Matter

P. J. Milne, D. S. Odum, and Rod G. Zika

Rosenstiel School of Marine and Atmospheric Sciences, Division of Marine and Atmospheric Chemistry, University of Miami, Miami, FL 33149

The fluorescence decay rates of samples of dissolved organic matter of marine and terrestrial origin have been measured. The lifetimes were all closely similar (2-2.4 ns) despite their widely different origins and histories. Implications of this similarity to other physical and chemical properties of humic/fulvic substances is discussed as is the interpretation of the deactivation pathways of the excited states of marine chromophores.

Quantitative measurement of the photophysics of the dissolved organic chromophores found in natural water is needed to better understand the rates of energy transfer from their excited states and to provide information as to the kinetics of excited state reactions they may undergo. Specific areas of interest in natural water chemistry are the kinetics of quenching interactions and energy transfer processes to other chemical species; the effect of such interactions on the initiation of secondary photochemical reactions is particularly important (1).

These measurements may also aid in the characterization of the physical and chemical properties of the humic and fulvic acid fractions of dissolved organic matter. The present study describes an experimental setup for determination of luminescence lifetimes and presents values obtained for some natural organic materials.

Fluorescence Decay Rates

Time resolved fluorescence measurements of simple organic molecules are regularly used to analyze a wide range of chemical and biological processes (2). This is possible by virtue of the ways in which a number of phenomena can influence the rate at which a molecule fluoresces, that is undergoes an electric dipole transition from an excited electronic state to a lower, usually the ground, state of the same multiplicity. The kinetic parameter that is measured reflects the sum of the rates of processes depopulating the excited state of the fluorophore being monitored. On a molecular level, the intrinsic rate of de-excitation of a given fluorophore is subject to a number of factors including symmetry requirements, the frequency of the fluorescent radiation, the integrated area under the absorption curve as well as on spatial restrictions imposed by the necessity of molecular orbital overlap of the excited and ground states. Typically, values of the rate constant for fluorescence are in the range of $10^5 - 10^{10}$ s^{-1} (3).

The intensity of fluorescence from an excited molecule will be dependent on the fluorescent decay rate and other non-radiative processes such as intersystem crossing to the triplet state, internal conversion to the ground state, and any photochemical reactions. In condensed media, vibrational relaxation from upper vibrational levels of excited states is ultrafast ($>10^{12}$ s^{-1}) so that vibronic relaxation is complete before electronic relaxation can take place. Internal conversion is a process that is also very fast (picoseconds) at high excess energies, but less important for lower lying levels of the first excited singlet state. In this way, the main competing process to fluorescence is often intersystem crossing to the triplet manifold of energy levels.

Writing equations for these processes allows definition   of the fluorescence quantum yield, $\emptyset$, and the fluorescence decay time, t_f, in terms of sums of the various first order rate constants (nb. other possible deactivation pathways also exist).

Pathway	Rate Constant
$M + h\nu \longrightarrow {}^1M^*$	I
${}^1M^* \longrightarrow M + h\nu$	k_f
${}^1M^* \longrightarrow {}^3M^*$	k_{isc}
${}^1M^* \longrightarrow M + \Delta$	k_{ic}
${}^1M^* \longrightarrow$ (products)	k_p

Using the steady state approximation leads to:

$$\emptyset_f = k_f / (k_f + k_{isc} + k_{ic} + k_p)$$

and

$$t_f = (k_f + k_{isc} + k_{ic} + k_p)^{-1}.$$

From this framework it can be seen that the fluorescence intensity of a molecule is dependent upon the magnitude of k_f relative to the sum of all other deactivation path rates. It is also clear that lifetime measurements themselves do not give the individual rate constants for the processes of interest, however in conjunction with the emission and product quantum yields, they do provide a way in which this can be calculated.

Experimental Methods

The experimental setup employed in this work used conventional
right angled viewing of the time course of the fluorescence
intensity of a sample contained in a small volume (0.2 ml) flow
cell. The fluorescence flow cell was filled from a separate
reservoir via a peristaltic pump. Solution parameters such as pH
could be monitored directly from this larger reservoir, as could
the oxygen partial pressure by blanketing or bubbling the cell
contents with nitrogen or oxygen.

The excitation source was a N_2 laser (PAR 2100 Dyescan,
modified to allow use of the primary line) at a wavelength of
337.1nm. The fluorescent emission was detected by a modified
side-on photomultiplier (PMT Hammamatsu R928), after passage
through a monochromator (ISA HR 320). Particular attention was paid
to the wiring of the voltage divider network of the anodes of the
PMT to ensure fastest possible response and least distortion of the
fluorescent photon flux. The signal from the PMT was amplified
through a high-speed, wide-band (to 0.5GHz) single trace amplifier
(Tektronix 7A29) and monitored on a transient waveform digitizer
(Tektronix 7912AD). The digitizer was interfaced to a laboratory
computer (Tektronix 4502) for data acqusition, control and
processing of the experimental results. A fast photodiode (EG&G
Electro-optics FND-100Q) monitored the firing of the laser pulse
(usually at a repetition rate of 2Hz) and provided an external
trigger signal for the digitizer.

Deconvolution of the observed decay pulse was necessary
because of the finite width (approx. 1.9ns FWHM) of the excitation
pulse. This was carried out using a Fourier transform method (4).
Despite the non-trivial computational requirements and the need to
filter out the high frequency components of the Fourier division
before taking the inverse transform (5) it was felt that this
method was the most direct way of generating the true impulse
response function of the system. The resulting fluorescence decay
curves were fit to a single (or double) exponential. The phase
plane plot method of Demas (6) and others (2), was also used for
deconvolution but with less success.

Two tests of the reliabilty of the deconvolution procedure
used in this study were carried out. In the first of these,
analytic functions of the form

$$y = a * \exp^{(-b*t)}$$

were generated and convolved, by complex multiplication of the two
Fourier transforms in the frequency domain, with experimentally
determined instrument response curves. The instrument response
curves were approximated as the time course of laser pulse flashes
recorded from the same cell and cell geometry, at an intense Raman
scattering frequency of the solvent, which for water at our
excitation frequency was 380.6 nm. This approximation was based on
consideration of the time course of the off-resonance Raman scatter
as being the same as the exciting light pulse on a time scale
significantly shorter than the fluorescence time scale under
investigation (7). The resulting synthetic decay curves,

corresponding to a convolution of the instrument response function and exact fluorescent decays of various known lifetimes, were then deconvolved. For known lifetimes down to 500ps, the calculated values were within 5%, the error growing to some 30% for known lifetimes of 100ps. These estimates then, are the lower limits of measurement attainable with our observation system. The main limitation of the system is seen to be the pulse width of the laser flash.

In the second test, a number of fluorescent compounds of relatively well known lifetimes in the nanosecond time range (8,9) were used as standards, allowing evaluation of both the instrumental and computational aspects of the measurement. Table I shows the values obtained for 2,5-diphenyloxazole (PPO), anthracene and quinine bisulphate. All chemicals were analytical grade and not further purified before use. Anthracene and PPO were dissolved in cyclohexane, quinine in $0.1N$ H_2SO_4; solvents were not degassed. The case of quinine is of interest because of its common use as a standard for fluorescence measurements, despite its complex decay kinetics (10). In agreement with previous work (10) we found satisfactory fits of our deconvolved data to a biexponential rather than a single exponential model.

TABLE I. Fluorescence decays of standard substances

Compound	l(nm)	t(ns)	solvent	reference
PPO	440	1.2	cyclohex.	(this work)
	440	1.3	cyclohex.	(Lampert et al,8)
	400	1.4	ethanol	(Zuker et al,9)
Anthracene	420	4.1	cyclohex.	(this work)
	410	4.1	cyclohex.	(Lampert et al,8)
	415	4.0	cyclohex.	(Rayner et al,11)
	380	5.3	ethanol	(Zuker et al,9)

Quinine*	l(nm)	t_1(ns)	t_2(ns)	reference
	400	5.0	17.2	(this work)
	450	5.0	19.7	
	500	5.2	21.2	
	550	5.4	21.9	
	400	2.6	18.2	(O'Connor et al,10)
	450	3.6	19.1	
	500	10.3	19.7	
	550	–	–	

* solvent used was $0.1N$ H_2SO_4

Sample Preparation

A number of samples of dissolved organic material were used in this investigation. The first of these was a commercial preparation of "humic acid" (Aldrich) which was dissolved (1mg/100ml) in dilute

base (0.01M NaOH). This substance is derived from a peat like
material. These solutions were ultrasonicated (30sec) to speed
dissolution and filtered through 0.2um polycarbonate (Nuclepore)
membrane filters to ensure homogeneity of the solution.

Two other samples were marine material isolated by
ultrafiltration of natural seawater samples through a Nuclepore 500
MWCO membrane, which has a nominal retention of all compounds of
molecular weight greater than 500 Daltons (see however Staub et
al,12). Ultrafiltration was carried out in an Teflon coated
ultrafiltration cell (Amicon 2000B) under a nitrogen pressure of
50psi. The two samples were chosen to represent two quite different
light regimes of the ocean. One sample was taken offshore from
Whitewater Bay (13) and represents a near shore, terrestrially
influenced surface water. This sample was concentrated from an
initial volume of approximately 17 liters to a final volume of
1000ml (x17). The second sample was taken from deep (1500m) water,
well below the photic zone, at a site in the Tongue of the Ocean,
Bahamas and represents a sample of marine organic matter that has
not been exposed to sunlight for some time. This sample, which was
kept in the dark throughout sampling and preparation, was
concentrated from approximately 17 liters to 900ml (x19). Further
concentration of these samples was deliberately avoided to guard
against any aggregation of the organic matter.

The final two samples investigated consisted of a marine
fulvic acid isolated by XAD-2 resin absorption (14) of a bulk
sample of near surface seawater collected from a site in the Gulf
of Mexico (15) and also a soil fulvic acid extracted from an
horizon B podsol (16). These samples were dissolved in filtered
Gulf Stream seawater and deionized (MilliQ) water respectively,
with the addition of sufficient 0.1M NaOH to effect dissolution of
the solid soil fulvic acid.

Results

Single exponential fluorescence decay times for the different
dissolved organic chromophores are tabulated in Table II. Replicate
determinations of the lifetimes of these samples was generally
better than 5%. Despite the diversity of the sources of these
materials, their fluorescent lifetimes are similar.

It was not found necessary to model any of the decay functions
with more than a single exponential, perhaps indicating some
underlying similarity in the nature of the fluorophores to be found
in these molecules. This is in disagreement with the work of Lapen
and Seitz (17) who suggested that the lifetime of a soil fulvic
acid they investigated was best fit by a double exponential, (with
components lifetimes of 1.0 and 6.0ns) reflecting the heterogeneity
of a complex mixture. Recent work (Langford personal communication)
on the fluorescence lifetimes of a well characterized Armedale
horizon B soil fulvic acid material has suggested that material to
have three components contributing to the overall fluorescence of
the sample. While it is uncertain, with the time resolution
attainable with our measurement system, that a component of the
order of 100ps could be adequately time resolved, the non-

TABLE II. Fluorescence lifetimes of dissolved organic matter (seawater samples) and humic acid (Aldrich) measured under different solution conditions

Sample	l(nm)	lifetime(ns)	soln. cond.
Whitewater Bay	460	2.4	pH 8.0 S= 33.62
Tongue of the Ocean	460	2.3	pH 8.2 S= 34.65
Fulvic acid	460	2.4	alk.
Yucatan (XAD-2)	460	2.1	alk. S=35
Humic acid	460	2.0	pH 8
Humic acid	460	2.3	pH 11
Humic acid	460	1.8	pH 1
Humic acid	460	2.0	pH 8 1atm O_2
Humic acid	460	1.9	pH 8 0.1M KI

observation of a longer (6-7 ns) decay in the samples measured in this work is of interest. Work to further elucidate the number of identifiable components in the same samples is clearly indicated.

In another report of the measurement of lifetimes of humic materials (18) a similar constancy of t_f for samples of apparently widely different sources was also noted.

The effects of some important solution variables on fluorescence lifetimes of (Aldrich) humic acid were also briefly investigated. Values obtained as a function of pH indicated that the lifetime was somewhat longer at pH 11 than at either pH 8 or pH 1. It is perhaps interesting to speculate on the the possible involvement of ionizable functional groups, which ionize at high pH, being part of the chromophore. Phenols for instance, ionize at higher pH values and are known to be present as part of the complex structure of these molecules.

Temperature variations may have an effect on the lifetimes and yields of luminescence processes. Measurements made here were carried out at room temperature (22+ 2C) for the most part. Some limited temperature runs over the range of 5-60 C, gave linear Arrhenius plots of relative fluorescence intensity versus temperature.

Oxygen

Molecular oxygen is an efficient quencher of the fluorescence of
aromatic hydrocarbons (19) especially in non-aqueous solvents where
the solubility of oxygen and its diffusion coefficient are
proportionately higher than in aqueous solution. In these systems
quenching by oxygen approaches a diffusion controlled process,
wherein each encounter of an oxygen molecule with an excited
fluorophore results in quenching. It is known to quench both the
singlet and triplet excited states, and quenching can be both
chemical or physical in nature (3). The photochemical production of
singlet oxygen species from terrestrial humic materials has been
noted (20,21,22).

Measurement of the decay times for solutions of humic acid
that were saturated (1atm) with oxygen did not show any reduction
over those at equilibrium with air or saturated with nitrogen.
Given that the maximum oxygen concentration in solution obtainable
under 760mm O_2 is of the order of 10^{-2} M, and assuming a 100%
efficiency of quenching at a diffusion controlled limit of 10^{10}
s^{-1}, then the product of the diffusion coefficient and the quencher
concentration will be less than or equal to $10^8 s^{-1}$, so that either
singlet or triplet states having lifetimes of the order of
nanoseconds will at best only be slightly quenched in even oxygen
saturated solutions. It appears then that there is little
interaction, either physical or chemical, of oxygen with the
excited singlet states produced by irradiation of organic matter,
at least at this excitation wavelength.

Work on oxygen quenching in protein systems (23) has shown
that fluorophores attached to protein molecules may be inaccessible
to the diffusion of a small, uncharged and not particularly
hydrophilic molecule such as oxygen. These workers used elevated
pressures (up to 100atm) of oxygen to achieve significant
quenching, and pointed out that since oxygen does not form any
complexes with the molecules they studied, quenching would require
actual short-range interaction with the fluorophore. Quenchers
which do form complexes with the fluorophore, or other parts of the
molecule, should be expected to have a wider radius of action for
energy transfer.

The only other potential quencher besides oxygen measured in
this study was iodide ion, which at a solution concentration of
0.1M did show a small reduction in fluorescent lifetime. Further
work on the static and dynamic quenching of these molecules is
under investigation.

Conclusion

Initial measurement of the fluorescence lifetimes of samples of
marine organic matter and a terrestrial humic acid have suggested
an underlying similarity in this physical property of all of these
molecules. This is in accord with the apparent homogeneity of
certain other of the spectral properties (fluorescence and
absorption spectra , photosensitizing characteristics etc) observed
for a number of natural water chromophores. At the same time this
is at variance with observations of other properties, such as metal

ion complexation, structural determinations based on degradative studies etc which seem to imply much greater heterogeneity at a molecular level (24).

The question of how sensitive a parameter the time resolved fluorescence properties of these chromophores can be to both structural differences and photochemical reactivity of these molecular assemblages remains unclear. The observation that oxygen, at natural levels, is not likely to be a significant quenching agent for the excited singlet states of these chromophores is of interest to the interpretation of the photosensitizing ability and direct photoreactivity of this important class of materials.

Acknowledgments

This work was carried out with the support of the Office of Naval Research under Navy Grant N00014-85C-0020. We thank Dr. G.R.Harvey for kindly supplying some of his humic extracts. We also thank Dr. C.H.Langford for making the results of his studies available to us and for his helpful comments on the manuscript.

Literature Cited

1.   Zika, R.G. In "Marine Organic Chemsitry"; Duursma, E.K. and Dawson, R., Eds.; Elsevier: Amsterdam, 1981.

2.   Demas, J.N. "Excited state lifetime measurements"; Academic Press: New York, 1983.

3.   Turro, N.J. "Modern Molecular Photochemistry"; Benjamin Cummings: Menlo Park, CA., 1978.

4.   Andre, J.C.; Vincent, L.M.; O'Connor, D.; Ware, W.R. J. Phys. Chem. 1979, 83, 2285.

5.   Wild, U.; Holzworth, A.; Good, H.P. Rev. Sci. Instrum. 1977, 48, 1621.

6.   Demas, J.N.; Adamson, A.W. J. Phys. Chem. 1971, 75, 2463.

7.   Kinoshita, S.; Kushida, T. Rev. Sci. Instrum. 1982, 52, 469.

8.   Lampert, R.A.; Chewter, L.A.; Phillips, D.; O'Connor, D.; Roberts, A.J.; Meech, S.R. Anal. Chem. 1983, 55, 68.

9.   Zuker, M.; Szabo, A.G.; Bramall, L.; Krajcarski, D.T.; Selinger, B.K. Rev. Sci. Instrum. 1985, 56, 14.

10.   O'Connor, D.V.; Meech, S.R.; Phillips' D. Chem. Phys. Lett. 1982, 88, 22.

11.   Rayner, D.M.; McKinnon, A.E.; Szabo, A.G.; Hackett, P.A. Can. J. Chem. 1976, 54, 3246.

12.   Staub, C.; Buffle, J.; Haerdi, W. Anal. Chem. 1984, 56, 2843.

13.   Moffett, J.W.; Zika, R.G. 1986, (this volume).

14.   Stuermer, D.H.; Harvey, G.R. Deep Sea Res. 1977, 24, 303.

15   Harvey, G.R.; Boran, D.A.; Chesal, L.A.; Tokar, J.M. Marine Chemistry. 1983, 12, 119.

16.   Gamble, D.S.; Schnitzer, M. In "Trace Metal and Metal Organic Interactions in Natural Water"; Singer, P.S., Ed.; Ann Arbor Science: Ann Arbor, 1973.

17.   Lappen, A.J.; Seitz, W.R. Anal. Chim. Acta. 1982, 134, 31.

18.   Fischer, A.M. Ph.D. Thesis, University of California, Santa Cruz, 1985.

19. Berlman, I.B. "Handbook of Fluorescence Spectra of Aromatic
     Molecules"; Academic Press: New York, 1965, p. 35.
20. Zepp, R.G.; Wolfe, N.L.; Baughman, G.L.; Hollis, R.C. Nature
     1977, 267, 421.
21. Woolf, C.J.M.; Halmans, M.T.H.; van der Hiejde, H.B.
     Chemosphere 1981, 10, 59.
22. Haag, W.R.; Hoigne, J.; Gassman, E.; Braun, A. Chemosphere
     1984, 13, 641.
23. Lakowicz, J.R.; Weber, G. Biochemistry 1973, 12, 4161.
24. Aiken, G.R.; McKnight, D.M.; MacCarthy, P. "Humic Substances
     in Soil, Sediment, and Water"; Wiley-Interscience: New York,
     1985.

RECEIVED June 24, 1986

Chapter 11

Primary Photochemical Processes in Photolysis Mediated by Humic Substances

Anne M. Fischer[1,4], John S. Winterle[2], and Theodore Mill[3]

[1]Department of Chemistry, University of California, Santa Cruz, CA 95064
[2]Syntex Research, Institute of Pharmaceutical Sciences, Palo Alto, CA 95064
[3]Department of Physical Organic Chemistry, SRI International, Menlo Park, CA 94025

Natural water samples and humic substance solutions were probed for their phototransient behavior. Laser flash kinetic spectroscopy was used to study two transients common to most samples. One transient with a maximum around 720 nm was quenched by decreasing pH and nitrous oxide. It was present in all waters with DOC and had a spectrum which resembled that of a solvated electron. The signal was linear with laser power. The quantum yield for this transient was measured. Samples with higher ground state absorbance yielded a transient with a maximum at 475 nm that was quenched by oxygen. This transient seemed to be a photophysical hybrid with triplet and radical cation character. Additional work done to characterize these transients and predict their environmental fates is discussed.

Aquatic photochemistry has become a discipline that now interests more than just a handful of scientsts. Recent reviews (1-3) have chronicled a trend toward an interest in kinetics and mechanisms from initial work which relied on the analytical chemistry of final products of aquatic photoreactions.

Some of the better understood aquatic photoprocesses have involved reactive oxygen species such as hydrogen peroxide (4,5) singlet oxygen (6,7) peroxyl radicals (8), and superoxide radical anion (9). Humic substances have been implicated as the precursor or initiator of the photoprocesses in all of these studies.

Humic substances are polymeric oxidation products of biological detrital materials. They are variable in structure depending on the environment of their origin and residence. Humic substances are probably the most variable substance to have a generic chemical name. They have been characterized to vary from

[4]Current address: Rosenstiel School of Marine and Atmospheric Sciences, Division of Marine and Atmospheric Chemistry, University of Miami, Miami, FL 33149

0097-6156/87/0327-0141$06.00/0

500 to 200,000 in molecular weight and contain conjugated olefinic and aromatic functional groups, as well as carboxyl and hydroxyl and a small percentage of nitrogenous functional groups. Several monographs have been published very recently which describe the characterzation of terrestial and marine humic substances (10,11). One unifying feature of humic substances is that that they have a featureless ground state absorption with a dramatically increasing optical density below 375 nm. Thus humic substances can absorb sunlight and cause indirect photoreactions with organic compounds that do not absorb solar radiation.

Various studies have been undertaken in an attempt to elucidate the primary processes and photochemical transients generated immediately after light is absorbed by humic substance solutions and natural waters. Earlier work (12-14,6) used steady state studies in phosphoresence, illuminated ESR, and a kinetic analysis of photoproducts to probe humic substance photochemistry and photophysics. This work has suggested that the humic substance phototransient is an excited state of a conjuganted organic system containing oxygen and nitrogen and may be a triplet. These suggestions have interested several groups (15-18) in using excited state laser absorption spectroscopy to directly observe and characterize the humic substance.

The objectives of the study presented in this paper were to observe and characterize phototransients produced by laser excitation of natural waters and humic substance (HS) solutions. The photosystems were studied on two scales. On the laboratory scale pulsed laser flash photolysis was used to study the time resolved and spectral behavior of the photochemical transients. Studies to identify and quantify the transients included adding energy and electron acceptors and model compounds to the solution and varying parameters such as pH, metal, and oxygen content. On the field scale laboratory data taken at solar actinic wavelengths is extrapolated using published solar photon fluxes to predict environmental effects of the phototransients studied in this work. This paper thus contains an overview of many experiments performed over four years (16).

Methods and Apparatus

Three types of samples were examined. Natural waters (NW) were sampled from several freshwater lakes, an aquifer, and a coastal seawater sample from a kelpbed. NW samples were filtered and sterilized with a 0.22 micron filter which was prewashed (by rinsing with 500 ml double diltiled deionized (DDI) water and stored at 4°C and subjected to photochemical analysis within 24-48 hours after sampling. Minimal storage time was necessary to minimize photolyis and adsorption of the low concentrations of dissolved organic compounds (DOC) which were found to be the precursors to the phototransients.

The second kind of samples were concentrated natural waters (CNW). These samples were concentrated by rotary evaporation to give a ground state O.D. greater than 0.1 at 355 nm, the laser excitaton wavelength in the solar actinic range. All other handing of CNW samples was identical to that described for NW samples.

The third kind of sample was a humic substance extract (HSX) into DDI. The humic substance usually was an untreated soil provided by Aldrich as "Humic Acid", a peat soil mined in Germany and packaged without treatment. Other humic substances were homogenized untreated peat, leonardite, and topsoil purchased from the International Humic Substance Society. These samples were prepared by neutral water extraction with rolling or stirring for 24-60 hours. The proportion of bulk to water was 20-40g/l. Double distilled acids and bases were used to adjust the pH during preparation and analysis. After extraction the humic substance extract samples were centrifuged at 15,000 rpm for 20 minutes and filtered through a clean 0.22 micron filter. Another type of humic substance extract analyzed for phototransients was solutions of purified humic and fulvic acids. These solids had been stripped of metals and separated into humic and fulvic fractions by the methods of (19). The samples most thoroughly analyzed were the HSX prepared from Aldrich "Humic Acid" and the NW samples from Searsville Lake, Stanford, CA.

During sample preparation reagents such as the extraction water were examined for contamination by UV-Vis, fluorescence spectroscopy, and excited state absorption after laser excitation. Also the samples were checked for changes in the above spectral characteristic before storage and immediately prior to analysis. If there were significant changes the sample was disgarded as unsuitable for futher photochemical analysis.

The flash photolysis apparatus was a Quanta Ray DCR-1 Nd:YAG pulsed laser exciting source (FWHM = 7 ns, frequency tripled to 355 nm or quadrupled to 266 nm) and a flash lamp monitoring light source (E. G. & G. high pressure xenon arc lamp FWHM = 50 us). The laser power was usually 5 mj/pulse unless the effect of laser power variation was under study. The laser power was monitored and kept as stable as possible by measurement with a laser power meter between every series of analyzing pulses. The laser itself had a pulse to pulse variation of +5% and a single shot noise level of 0.05 ΔD. However most of the data had less error and a lower detection limit decreasing by the square root of the number of pulses in each measurement. Thus the signal to noise ratio was enhanced greatly by signal averaging 30 to 150 pulses and repeating each of these measurements at least three times. The laser was focused to about 4 mm onto a 1 cm cuvette or flow cell with a repetition rate of 5 Hz. The apparatus was electronically tuned so the laser would fire at the maximum of the flash lamp pulse. See Figure 1 for a schematic of the flash photolsis apparatus.

After passing through the sample the xenon arc probe beam was directed through a 0.45 m monochromator and detected with an EMI D279 or EMI 9876B photomultiplier tube set to 1200-1500 V. The signal was then digitized by a Biomation 6500 transient recorder (2 or 5 or 10 ns per point) and sent to a Z-80 microcomputer for signal averaging and analysis. The apparatus and data analysis routines are further described in the literature (20).

The data analysis provided for the plotting of time versus transmitted flashlamp intensity or time versus excited state absorption as ΔD at a given excitation and monitoring wavelength. To take a ΔD excited state absorption spectrum measurements were made separately for each monitoring wavelength. Photolysis of the sample from prolonged exposure to laser pulses was monitored by checking ΔD at 475 nm or 720 nm after every few measurements. If transient absorbance decreased, fresh sample was used.

A flow cell system, Figure 2 was developed to make it more convenient to study dilute samples or take spectra with a minimum of photolysis. The sample volumes circulated were large, from 200 to 1000 ml. The flow cell had a filter flask as the sample reservoir. The purging gas entered through the vacuum outlet. Inserted in the mouth of the cell was the electrode of a pH meter and the inlet tubing leading to the flow cell, and the outlet tubing leading from the flow cell. The sample reservoir was kept homogenous by stirring with a magnetic stirrer as well as purging with the gas. The flow was maintained by a peristaltic pump which circulated 1-5 ml/min through 3mm O.D. tygon tubing. The tubing was rinsed with water and the washings were tested for organic contaminants by UV-Vis, fluorescence, and excited state spectroscopy. The washings produced no absorbance, fluorescence or transient absorbance signal. Thus the tubing contributed no photochemically active or detective contaminants to the samples.

Quenching rate constants were measured by examining the extent and rate of decay of the phototransient under study at several concentrations of the quencher. A Stern-Volmer analysis of the change of lifetime of the transient with changing quencher concentration yielded a dynamic quenching rate constant k_q. A Stern-Volmer analysis of the change in excited state absorption with increasing quencher concentration was used when there was a combination of lifetime and concentration quenching. If the extent of dynamic vs. static quenching was not known, then the rate constant calculated was an empirical or apparent rate constant k_{app}.

Detection and Characterization of a 720 nm Absorbing (T720) Phototransient in Dilute Waters

A transient with an excited state absorption ΔD maximum at 720 nm was detected in dilute natural waters (adjusted to a pH of 7) irradiated with 266 nm laser light. The ΔD spectrum plotted 400-450 ns after the laser flash resembled that of the solvated electron in water (21). Nitrous oxide is known to react specifically with the aquated electron, Reaction 1.

$$N_2O + e^- + H_2O \longrightarrow N_2 + O^- \qquad (1)$$

Nitrous oxide was found to attenuate the T720 signal in dilute NW. The rate constant for nitrous oxide quenching of T720 was measured to be $k_q = 5 \times 10^{+9} M^{-1} s^{-1}$. The measured rate constant agrees well with that in the literature $k_q = 7.5 \times 10^{+9} M^{-1} s^{-1}$. The T720 signal was linear with increasing laser power from 0.5 mj/pulse to 10 mj/pulse passing through the origin. These data suggested that T720 was an aquated electron, formed from a single photon process in waters containing dissolved organic matter. DDI water produced no ΔD signal when irradiated under the conditions employed in this study. Dilutions of NW and concentrated NW showed the excited

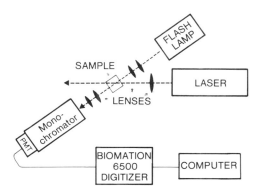

Figure 1.   Schematic diagram of the laser flash apparatus.

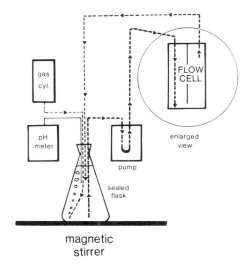

Figure 2.   Flow cell apparatus.

state absorption signal to be proportional to concentration of organic matter measured as light absorbed in the ground state at the laser excitation wavelength which implied that the electron was generated from the DOM.

Figure 3 shows the ΔD spectrum of dilute natural waters as a three dimensional surface of wavelength vs. time vs. ΔD. Figures 3 and 4 were prepared as composites of much experimental data. Figure 3 shows the decay of the transient in NW to be exponential. The lifetime of T720 varied directly with increasing pH. T720 reaction with various concentrations of oxygen was also measured. The quenching rate constant was experimentally determined to be 7 x 10^{+9} $M^{-1} s^{-1}$, this was also in fair agreement with the literature value of the rate constant of the reaction of aquated electrons with oxygen, k_q = 1.8 x 10^{+10} $M^{-1} s^{-1}$. The quenching reactions discussed here were dynamic, i.e. the lifetime of the excited state decreased with increasing acidity, oxygen content, and nitrous oxide content. Copper also was found experimentally to quench T720 and an apparent rate constant of k_{app} = 2 x 10^{+10} $M^{-1} s^{-1}$ was calculated from the data. The literature value, k_q = 3.5 x 10^{+10} $M^{-1} s^{-1}$, was close to the measured value. However this probably was fortuitous since the value in the literature was reported as a dynamic quenching rate constant, in contrast to the empirical data. The laser data taken in this study on copper and other metals suggested that the mechanism of copper quenching of T720 was static, i.e. the amplitude of the D signal decreased with increasing copper concentration, but the lifetime was not affected. All literature values of quenching rate constants with aquated electrons are from (22).

Detection and Characterization of a 475 nm Absorbing Transient in Humic Substance Extracts (HSX) and Concentrated Natural Waters (CNW).

The excited state absorbance spectra of HSX and CNW were monitored from 350 to 800 nm 400-450 ns after the 355 nm laser pulse. All HSX and CMW samples measured produced excited state spectra which had broad maxima at about 475 nm. Figure 4 shows a three dimensional surface of time vs. wavelength vs. excited state absorption typical of data taken on HSX and CNW samples. The three dimensional profile of T475 in Figure 4 illustrates several contrasts between T475 and T720, Figure 3. T475 had a greater excited state absorbance than T720 overall by at least 2-3x. Also T720 showed an exponential decay in time, while T475 has more complex kinetics. Additionally T475 had a short lived decay below 600 nm which followed the laser flash. Because of its short lifetime a singlet assignment was suggested. These same HSX and CNW solutions all were measured to have a fluorescent lifetime of about 3 ns (16). These data could be due to the emission and absorption of light by the same transient. Above 600 nm the kinetics of T475 become exponential again. Below 600 nm the decay appears to be bi-exponential.

Experiments to characterize T475 showed a dynamic quenching by oxygen. The quenching rate constant calculated from these data was k_q = 7 x 10^{+8} $M^{-1} s^{-1}$. A survey of quenching of T475 with water

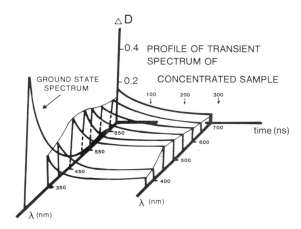

Figure 3. Time vs. wavelength vs. excited state absorption of Searsville Lake water monitored from 400 nm to 800 nm from t = 0 to 300 ns after 266nm pulsed laser excitation, 5 mj/pulse.

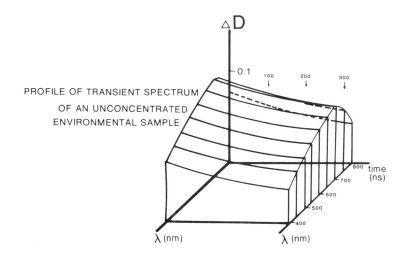

Figure 4. Time vs. wavelength vs. excited state absorption of Aldrich humic substance extract excited at 355 nm and monitored from 350 nm to 700 nm from the time of the laser flash to 300 ns.

soluble triplet energy acceptors with various E_T from 30 to 70 kcal/mole gave complex results which were difficult to interpret (16). No sensitizer except oxygen gave dynamic quenching of the T475 time trace. The quenchers with E_T above 57 kcal/mole showed a combination of static and dynamic quenching. These results suggested that T475 has partial triplet character, but that there are other additional processes. These processes probably involve electron and proton transfer that are mediated by T475. A survey a set of triplet sensitizers (23) in HSX solutions with experiments in sunlight suggested an operational (black box mechanism) triplet energy level of 57 kcal/mole. This agreed with the HS triplet energy measured earlier by phosphorescence (12). This suggests that pollutants (dissolved in sunlit waters containing humic substances) with triplet energy levels below 57 kcal/mole are likely to undergo secondary photoysis by an energy transfer mechanism.

Most of the experiments for T475 and T720 were performed under argon saturation to eliminate oxygen. Air and oxygen saturation of samples was utilized during experiments to determine the effect of oxygen on the transient, and nitrous oxide was used to characterize T720 in dilute solutions and to resolve T720 from T475 in HSX solutions excited by 355 nm laser pulses.

Resolution of T720 from under T475 Signal in HSX Using Argon and Nitrous Oxide Saturation

Spectra of nitrous oxide saturated samples of Aldrich HSX having a ground state absorbance of 1.0 at 355 nm showed an increase in absorbance at 475 nm and a decrease in absorbance at 720 nm compared to argon saturated samples, see Figure 5. Each point in the figure is a result of at least 5 measurements of 50 pulses so the signal to noise in Figure 5 is about 0.01   D in this experiment. Subtraction of the nitrous oxide spectrum from the argon spectrum in Figure 5 showed a negative band at 475 nm and a positive band at 720 nm.

This consistently repeated experiment with Aldrich HSX suggested that the 720 nm absorbing transient existed in all types of samples studied. This experiment also showed that T720 could be produced by laser excitation at 355 nm, a solar actinic wavelength as well as by UV radiation at 266 nm. The quenching of the long wavelength tail of the spectrum indicated that the spectrum with an apparent single maximum at 475 nm (T475) also had a component due to the absorbance of T720 proposed to be the aquated electron. The increase in intensity under nitrous oxide saturation of the 475 nm signal probably was due to the fact that argon and oxygen have about the same solubility, and nitrous oxide is thirty times more soluble than either (24). Nitrous oxide would be more effective in ridding an initially air saturated sample of residual oxygen which quenches the 475 nm transient, while argon would be less effective.

Another explanation would be that nitrous oxide inhibits the back reaction between the solvated electron and its partner radical cation by scavenging the back reaction of the radical cation with the solvated electron. Then the solvated electron absorbance would be quenched and the absorbance of the radical cation would appear

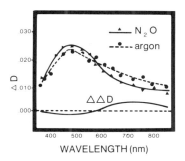

Figure 5. Excited state spectra of Aldrich soil extract taken under nitrous oxide and argon saturation. The difference between the two signals shows a band at 720 nm which was quenched by nitrous oxide.

to increase since it was less likely to react with an aquated
electron. Furthermore if the radical cation were a component of
the long lived absorbance at 475 nm found in HSX and CNW the
absorbance of the 475 nm transient would be larger. A simple
reaction scheme that qualitatively explains the effect shown in
Figure 4 is shown below in Reaction 2 and Reaction 3. This scheme
does not include organic radicals and anions, which were also
suspected to be present in the system.

$$HS + h\nu \; <--> \; HS^{+\bullet} + e^-_{(aq)} \tag{2}$$

$$N_2O + HS^{+\bullet} + e^-_{(aq)} \; ---> \; HS^{+\bullet} + N_2 + O^- \text{ or } OH^- \tag{3}$$

Quantum Yield for Production of Red 720 nm Transient and
Extrapolation to Field Situation

After T720 was tentatively characterized as an aquated electron
with nitrous oxide and electron transfer studies, the quantum yield
for the production of the aquated electron in dilute natural waters
containing dissolved organic matter and in humic substance extract
was measured by the comparision method. In this method the
literature value for the extinction coefficient of the solvated
electron at 720 nm was used (21). The excited state absorption of
T720 was measured. These were used in algebraic ratio to an
actinomter for which a quantum yield had already been thoroughly
determined.

All trans-retinal was used as an actinometer to calculate the
number of photons reaching the humic substance chromophore
producing the solvated electron. The ground state absorbance of
all-trans retinal in methanol was adjusted to that of the NW sample
at the exciting wavelength 266 nm, and the HSX sample at 355 nm.
The values for the retinal triplet quantum yieds and extinction
coefficients in methanol excited by 266 nm and 355 nm laser pulses
and monitored at 450 nm were those determined previously (25). The
excited state absorption of the actinometer and humic substance
solution were measured immediatly after photolysis by averaging the
first ten nanosecnds of D_t after the peak of the laser flash.

Each time the experiment was run three excited state optical
densities D were meaured: (1) All-trans retinal in methanol,
argon saturated, (2) Humic substance solution sample, argon
saturated , and (3) Humic substance solution, nitrous oxide
saturated. Since nitrous oxide is an electron scavenger, the
signal with nitrous oxide saturation was thought to be caused by
transients other than aquated electrons. The D under nitrous
oxide sturation was subtracted from the D under argon saturation
to calculate a signal generated by the solvated electron. This
calculation assumes that nitrous oxide reacted with nearly all of
the solvated electrons at the time of measurement, this calulation
and more details of the experimental conditions are given in detail
elsewhere (16).

The quantum yield for the production of aquated electrons by
355 nm laser excition of Aldrich HSX (with ground state absorbance
of 1.0 at 355 nm) was determined to be 0.014. The quantum yield
for the production of aquated electrons by 266 nm excitation of

Searsville Lake NW (with ground state absorbance 0.125 at 266 nm) was determined to be 0.07 by the same method.

The quantum yield for Aldrich HSX was significantly lower than that for Searsville Lake.   The HXS quantum yield was lower in part because other phototransients, such as T475 were simultaneously produced in the more colored humic substance extract samples.   Thus a given amount of absorbed photons created several transients from the absorbed photons measured by the actinometer.   It would be useful to have an estimated extinction coefficient for T475 to better understand the fate of photons absorbed by HSX solutions with ground state optical densities near 1.0 at 355 nm.   Then the value calculated for the aquated electron quantum yield would also be a better estimate.

Waters from Searsville Lake had fewer interferences with T720. The nitrous oxide saturated blank solutions gave a signal at noise level, and nitrous oxide quenched the NW signal to just above noise level indicating few or no phototransients competing with the aquated electron for the absorbed photons.   Also the quantum yield for the production of aquated electrons may be wavelength dependent.   Quantum yield studies with melanins and similar model humates have quantum yield values in the same range with wavelength dependence, increasing with photon energy.

Spiking Experiments with Melanin

Fungal melanin samples provided as a gift from Dr. James Martin of the University of California at Riverside were neutral water extracted by the same method as the humic substance extracts.   An Aldrich HSX was prepared in parallel.   Both solutions and a 1:1 combination were adjusted to a ground state optical density of 1.0 at 355 nm the laser excitation wavelength.   Ground state and fluorecence spectra taken of melanin and HS solutions were similar. Both samples had fuorescence emission maxima near 460 nm with excitation at 355 nm.

Excited state absorption spectra of the three solutions taken under experimental conditions as described in previous sections gave excited state spectra that were proportional to the spectrum shown in Figure 4, the time vs. wavelength vs. ΔD for HSX and CNW solutions.   The excited state spectra were also similar in shape and with a broad ΔD maximum around 475 nm as shown in Figure 6. The results of this work tend to validate previous work showing that melanins have structural as well as functional similarities, as also shown by NMR, IR, ESR, and transient ESR (11,26-28).   Most significanty melanin is also known to generate a solvated electrons with a quantum yield close to that found for humic substances (29-30).   These studies have also found melanin to generate superoxide anions and hydrogen atoms using transient ESR and spin traps.

Although extrapolation of melanin work to humic substances seems valid, the structures found in melanins are as diverse as those found in humic substances, so this model gives us little more insight into the actual structure of humic substance chromophores.

Reduction of Paraqat (Methyl Viologen) with HSX

A 10^{-4} M solution of methyl viologen (MV^{+2}) did not have significant ground or excited state absorbance from 350 nm to 750 nm. A 10^{-4} M solution of methyl viologen in Aldrich HSX had ground state spectra characteristic of humic substances before and after laser irradiation. A transient absorption spectrum of the above solution measured under the standard experimental conditions described previously showed a spectrum similar to that of MV^{+1} reported in the literature (31). See Figure 7. These data show evidence of interaction between MV^{+2} and the humic substance via a photoprocess.

The excited state absorption spectra show that HS excited state absorption at 475 nm and 720 nm (thought to be in part due to a solvated electron), are significantly quenched. This leads to the conclusion that an electron transfer reaction has taken place generating an MV^{+1} ion spectrum in the excited state. A kinetic trace of D_t monitored at 390 nm (16) showed the 390 nm absorbance attributed to MV^{+1} concentration increasing in the first few hundred nanoseconds after the laser flash. Simultaneous quenching of portions of the humic substance spectrum are consistent with the humic substance donating an electron and forming a charge-transfer complex with humic substances.

This is the first known observation of such a herbicide-humic substance charge transfer interaction with flash photolysis. The results shown in this section and the nitrous oxide quenching of T720 seem to be good evidence for the generation of HS charge-transfer complexes involving an aquated electron upon irradiation of HS solutions.

Summary and Conclusions: Environmental Significance of Observed Phototransients

The quantum yield calculated from laser data for solvated electron production by Aldrich HSX excited at 355 nm was extrapolated to a day averaged surface steady state concentration of solvated electrons in sunlit waters. In direct sunlight an average rate of $1.62 \times 10^{+17}$ photons per second impinging on a square centimeter of surface water was calculated from solar photon fluxes (32-33). Using absorptivities of HS from 299 to 800 nm (with an O.D. of 0.1 at 355 nm) and a solvated electron production quantum yield of 0.014 (16), a rate of 3.50×10^{-8} moles of solvated electrons produced per second was calculated. Based on a lifetime of 0.25 microseconds for solvated electrons in air saturated natural waters, the surface steady state concentration in the top cobic centimeter of water was calculated to be about 10^{-14} M.

This concentration wass within the range of calculated for reactive oxy organic radicals in natural waters by (23,8). The details of this and further calcuations which extrapolated the laser data to field conditions were described in detail elsewhere (16).

To gauge the significance of the transients observed in this laser study in surface waters, the speciation of the various oxy anions and cations, and of the relative populations of the various

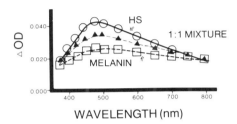

Figure 6. Excited state absorption was measured for melanin, 1:1 HS:melanin, and a control HS solution, and monitored at 400-450 ns after the 355 nm laser flash.

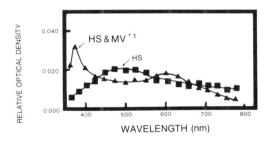

Figure 7. Excited state spectra of an Aldrich humic substance control solution spiked with 10^{-4} M methyl viologen.

oxidation states of metals must be taken into consideration. For instance recent evidence for a mechanism for the production of hydrogen peroxide from the dismutation of superoxide ions and for the existence of reduced metal species in surface waters has been partially explained by the solar flux and the quantum yield for the solvated electron.

If the operational triplet energy level for excited states of humic substances is indeed around 57 kcal/mole, then pollutants which have triplet energy levels below this value are likely to photoreact by an energy transfer mechanism mediated by humic substances or DOM. If a redox potential of an environmentally reactive transient produced by humic substances is higher than that of a xenobiotic, then the xenobiotic may be oxidized, etc. if the reaction is also kinetically favorable.

Just as the bicarbonate buffer system stabilizes natural waters to a significant extent against radical changes in pH, it is possible that humic substances in natural waters buffer within a narrow range of redox potential, and also subject contaminants to photolytic processes if they have an E_T below that of humic substances. This conjecture is supported by photochemical studies of oil spills containing polyaromatic hydrocarbons, which are degradable mainly by photolytic processes in field studies (34).

Work done here documunting a photochemically induced electron transfer from HS to methyl viologen was promising. Studies using flash photolysis as an aid in understanding the mechanisms of electron donating herbicides are underway. Also thiocarbamate pesticides are known to be degraded by an indirect photolytic mechanism mediated by HS (35). Thus HS phototransients that act as energy donors and electron acceptors have been shown to have environmental significance in field studies by other workers as well as by extrapolations of laser data taken in this study.

All of the humic substance solutions and natural water samples discussed in the materials and methods section of this paper were shown to have common phototransients, T475 and T720. This implies a global common energy sink in natural waters that contain dissolved organic matter, with quantifiable energy and electron transfer capabilities. It is expected that continued laser studies of this system backed up by complementary field studes will enable us to better understand the human ecology of natural waters when solar flux and HS photochemistry is taken into perspective consideration.

Acknowledgments

A. Fischer wishes to thank J. Winterle, J. Moffett, P. Milne, R.G. Zika, and W.J. Cooper for their valuable comments and assistance in the task of this paper.

Literature Cited

1. Zafiriou, O. C.; Joussot—Dubien, J.; Zepp, R. G.; Zika R.; Environ. Sci. Technol. 1984, 18, 358—371.
2. Zafiriou, O. C.; In "Chemical Oceanography"; Riley, J. P.; Chester, R., Eds.; Academic: London, 1983; Vol. 8, p. 339.

3. Zika, R. G. In "Marine Organic Chemistry: Evolution, Composition, Interactions, and Chemistry of Organic Matter in Seawater"; Duursma, E. K.; Dawson, R., Eds.; Elsevier: Amsterdam, 1981; p. 299.
4. Cooper, W. J.; Zika R. G. Science 1983, 220, 711.
5. Draper, W. M.; Crosby, D. G. Arch. Environ. Contam. Toxicol. 1983, 12, 121.
6. Zepp, R. G.; Baughman, G. L.; Schlotzhauer, P. F. Chemosphere 1981, 10, 119.
7. Haag, W. R.; Hoigne, R. J.; Gassman, E.; Braun, A. Chemosphere 1984, 13, 641.
8. Hill, T.; Hendry, D. G.; Richardson, H. Science 1980, 207, 886–887.
9. Baxter, R. M.; Carey, J. H. Freshwater Biol. 1982, 12, 285.
10. Rashid, M. A. "Geochemistry of Marine Humic Compounds"; Springer-Verlag: New York, 1985.
11. Christman, R. F.; Gjessing, E. T. "Aquatic and Terrestrial Humic Materials"; Ann Arbor Science: Ann Arbor, 1983.
12. Ziechman, W. Z. Pflanzeneraehr. Bodenkd. 1977, 140, 133–57.
13. Slawinska, D.; Slawinski, J.; Sarna, T. J. Soil Sci. 1975, 26, 93.
14. Rabek, J. F.; Ranbey, B.; Polymer Eng. Sci. 1975, 15, 40.
15. Mill, T.; Davenport, J. E.; Winterle, J. S.; Fischer, A.; Maybe, W. H.; Tse, D.; Baraze, A.; Conference on Gas- Liquid Chemistry of Natural Waters, Brookhaven National Laboratories, April 1984. BNL 51757, Vol 1 and 2. p. 25–1.
16. Fischer, A. Ph.D. Thesis, University of California, Santa Cruz, 1985.
17. Power, J. F.; Sharma, D. K.; Langford, C. H.; Bonneau, R.; Joussot-Dubien, J.; In Press.
18. Braun, A., Personal Communication.
19. MacCarthy, P.; Peterson, M. J.; Malcolm, R. L.; Thurman, E. M. Anal. Chem. 1979, 51, 2041.
20. Horwitz, J. Ph.D. Thesis, University of California, Santa Cruz, 1983.
21. "Optical Spectra of Nonmetallic Inorganic Transient Species in Aqueous Solution," U. S. National Bureau of Standards Reference Data Series 69, 1973.
22. "Selected Specific Rates of Reactions of Transients from Water in Aqueous Soluton. 1. Hydrated Electron," U.S. National Bureau of Standards Reference Data Series 49, 1973.
23. Zepp, R. G.; Schlotzhauer, P. F.; Sink, R. M. Environ. Sci. Technol. 1985, 19, 462.
24. Green, D. W. "Perry's Engineering Handbook"; McGraw Hill: New York, 1984.
25. Bensasson, R. V.; Land, E. J.; Truscott, T. G. "Flash Photolysis and Pulse Radiolysis"; Pergamon: Oxford, 1983.
26. Rabek, J. F.; Ranbey, B. Photochem. Photobiol. 1978, 28, 557.
27. Slawinski, J.; Puzyna, W.; Slawinska, D. Photochem. Photobiol. 1978, 28, 459.
28. Slawinski, J.; Puzyna, W.; Slawinska, D. Photochem. Photobiol. 1978, 28, 459.
29. Kalyanaraman, B.; Felix, C. C.; Sealy, R. C. Photochem. Photobiol., 1982, 36, 5.

30. Kalyanaraman, B.; Felix, C. C.; Sealy, R. C. J. Am. Chem. Soc. 1984, 106, 7327.
31. Kosower, E. M.; Cotter, J. L. J. Am. Chem. Soc. 1964, 86, 5524.
32. Mill, T.; Hendry, D. G.; and Richardson, H. Science 1980, 207, 886.
33. Davenport, J. E.; Winterle, J.; Mabey, W. R.; Mill T. USEPA Report, Contract #68-03-2981.
34. Payne, J. R.; Phillips, C. R. Environ. Sci. Technol. 1985, 19, 7.
35. Crosby, D. G. In "Pesticide Chemistry: Human Welfare and Environment", Miyamoto, J.; Kearney, P. C., Eds.; Pergamon: Oxford, 1983, Vol. 2., p. 339.

RECEIVED July 1, 1986

Chapter 12

Laser Flash Photolytic Studies of a Well-Characterized Soil Humic Substance

Joan F. Power[1], Devendra K. Sharma[1], Cooper H. Langford[1], Roland Bonneau[2], and Jacques Joussot-Dubien[2]

[1]Department of Chemistry and Canadian Center for Picosecond Flash Photolysis, Concordia University, Montreal, Quebec, Canada
[2]CNRS Laboratoire de Chimie Physique A, Universite de Bordeaux I, 33405 Talence Cedex, France

Laser flash photolysis studies of the well characterised soil humic substance, Armadale Fulvic Acid (P.E.I., Canada), have been carried out with excitation at 355 nm on picosecond and nanosecond time scales. Three principal transient absorption signals have been observed in aqueous solution: a component with a maximum absorption at 675 nm and a lifetime of about 1 microsecond (at pH = 7.0), a second component with a maximum absorption at 475 nm and a lifetime of 1-10 microseconds, and a third component with a broad, featureless transient absorption spectrum and a lifetime in excess of 100 microseconds. The 675 nm signal is believed to be a solvated electron on the basis of lifetime and quenching data, and is observed 20 ps after excitation. The 475 nm signal is believed to be a radical cation on the basis of its concurrent appearance with the electron at 20 ps. The third featureless component emerges nanoseconds after excitation and is believed to correspond to the triplet states of the humic material.

The role of dissolved humic materials in initiating the photochemical transformations of organic compounds in natural waters has been a subject of increasing study over the last decade. This subject shows great promise of providing a detailed understanding of the multiple

0097-6156/87/0327-0157$06.00/0

mechanisms by which many organic substances are degraded
in natural systems under the action of sunlight.

A number of studies have yielded evidence for the
participation of a wide variety of transient species in
the photolysis initiated by absorption of light by humic
substances. These include ·OH radicals ($\underline{1}$), $^1O_2$ ($\underline{2}$),
ROO· ($\underline{3}$), and O_2^- ($\underline{4}$). Their presence in natural
systems suggests multiple photopathways including $^1O_2$
oxidations, O_2^- reductions, light initiated free radical
decompositions, and H_2O_2 chemistry. Sunlight may also
influence the speciation of metal ions in surface waters
through photoredox reactions of the humic ligands ($\underline{5}$).

The need for photophysical studies in this area is
indicated by the diversity of the photochemistry
observed. Flash photolysis experiments in the early
time domain may identify precursors to later transient
species, as well as provide general information on
mechanisms.

One laser photophysical study ($\underline{6}$) has already been
reported by Fischer et al, in which a variety of natural
water samples and solutions of humic substance standards
were excited at 355 nm (near the absorption maximum for
excitation of humic substance fluorescence). Extensions
of their work appear in this symposium. They resolved
two components of transient absorption common to all the
samples studied: a component with maximum absorbance at
475 nm with a lifetime of several microseconds and a
signal at 700 nm which was attributed to a solvated
electron on the basis of is its sensitivity to N_2O and
on its absorption spectrum.

In this work, we have carried out laser flash
photolysis studies on a well characterized sample of
fulvic acid (Armadale, P.E.I., Canada), for which the
physicochemical data are well established ($\underline{7}$, $\underline{8}$, $\underline{9}$).
Our studies have extended from picosecond to microsecond
domains and include studies of pH effects, O_2 and metal
ion quenching. Our objective has been to link the
photophysical events of the nanosecond time scale where
transients decay, with those of the earlier scale, where
they appear, and to study the evolution of the observed
transient species over the entire time scale. On this
basis we hope to identify the multiple pathways of the
photophysics of this complex natural mixture which can
account for the diversity of consequent photochemistry.

Experimental Section

Sample. The well characterized fulvic acid used in our
studies is the Armadale fulvic acid described by Hansen
and Schnitzer ($\underline{7}$) and Gamble ($\underline{8}$). It was extracted from
the Bh horizon of a P.E.I. podzol and its physicochemi-
cal properties have been well summarized by Gamble and
Schnitzer ($\underline{9}$) and Langford et al ($\underline{10}$). The number
average molecular weight of this material has been

determined at 951 g/mol (7, 10). Functional group analysis of the material has yielded the following composition basis: 3.3 meq/g phenolics, 7.7 meq/g carboxylate, 3.6 meq/g aliphatic alcohol, 2.5 meq/g ketone, and 0.6 meq/g quinoid (9).

Preparation.   Fulvic acid stock solutions were prepared in Millipore ultrapure water or glass distilled water which had been previously adjusted to pH 2.0. Samples were prepared by dilution of stock solutions, and pH was adjusted by addition of 0.1 M HCl or NaOH (precision = + 0.15 units). Sample concentration was 200–250 mg/l of FA. The optical density of the samples was determined in a 1 cm or 1 mm quartz cell at 355 nm on a Beckman UV-Vis or Perkin Elmer absorption spectrophotometer. Millimolar stock solutions of metal ions were prepared directly from available metal chlorides (reagent grade).

Picosecond $\triangle A$ spectra were run on aerated samples while nanosecond spectra were run on Ar or N_2 degassed solutions except as otherwise indicated.

Flash Photolysis Spectrometers.   Picosecond timescale measurements were carried out at 355 nm (3rd Harmonic, Nd:YAG) with 20 ps half width pulses from the passively mode locked laser system at the Canadian Center for Picosecond Laser Flash Photolysis (11). The pulse energy was 3 mj and the wavelength range of the probe pulse used for observation of spectra extended from 400 to 700 nm.

Nanosecond timescale measurements were recorded on a mode locked Nd:YAG laser system located in the CNRS Laboratoire de Chimie Physique A, Universite de Bordeaux I, Talence, France. The pulse energies ranged from 10–40 mj at 355 nm. Pulse duration was 300 ps. Details of the system design are provided elsewhere (12).

Results and Assignments

Kinetic Overview.   The observations may best be introduced in summary by the kinetic map depicted in FIGURE 1. The kinetic behavior of the sample may be resolved into four distinct regions, temporally.   Two (II, III) have been spectrally characterized and match those observed by Fischer et al (6).   Third, there emerges (IV) a featureless "black" background transient absorbance, which may be traced from its origin in early nanosecond to its decay in the later microsecond domain. The final component (I) remained inaccessible to detailed study on both flash photolysis systems used owing to its appearance in an awkward time domain.

Time resolved spectra for components (II) and (III) are reported at pH 4.0 and 7.0 in the presence and absence of N_2O, a widely used electron scavenger (See FIGURE 2). As expected (6, 16), the 675 nm peaked spectrum is quenched in the presence of N_2O, consistent with the behavior of a solvated electron. Quenching

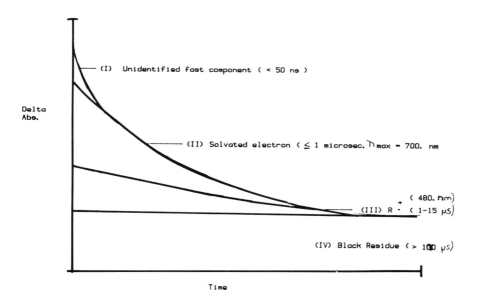

FIGURE 1.   Schematic summary of lifetime components
observed for the photolysis of Armadale fulvic acid in
the nanosecond time domain.   Excitation at 355 nm.

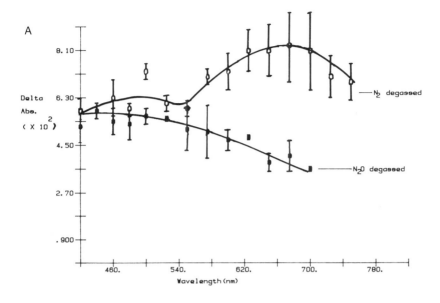

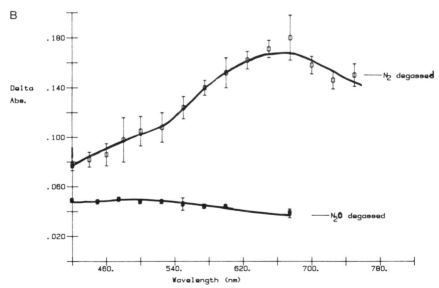

FIGURE 2.   Nanosecond   transient absorption spectrum of
FA at 200 ns after excitation by a   300 ps   pulse in the
presence of N_2O: (A) pH = 4.0, (B) pH = 7.0.   Spectra are
corrected for ground state absorption.   Pulse energy is
30 mj.

results in the presence of Cu^{+2} and O_2 further confirm this assignment.

The 475 nm transient reported in the earlier work (6) appears in these spectra as well, and in all cases is superimposed on a "black", featureless background (component IV of our kinetic scheme). The 475 nm transient decays with a lifetime of approximately 1-10 microseconds.

Picosecond excited state absorption spectra have been recorded for samples at pH 2.0, 4.0 and 7.0, and in all cases, the presence of the 675 nm transient is established at a probe pulse delay of only 20 ps after excitation, which is as early as it is possible to measure with an excitation pulse of 20-30 ps half width (See FIGURE 3). Measurements made by Rentzepis (14) on the solvation time of electrons in aqueous media, indicate the emergence of the "normal" $e^-_{(aq)}$ absorption spectrum at 650-700 nm at times earlier than 5 ps. Thus, our result is consistent with prompt generation of the electron. The 475 nm absorbing species is also present at 20 ps, suggesting that it is formed concurrently with the solvated electron.

"Picosecond Domain" studies also show the growth of a broad featureless transient spectrum in the early nanosecond domain (See FIGURE 4A); this feature matches the characteristics of the "black" residue (component IV) of our "nanosecond" kinetic summary. This species is not seen until after approximately 2 ns. It is not a "primary" species like the other two. Its absorption spectrum grows in with a risetime of about 2 ns and achieves an approximate steady state at 6-8 ns following excitation (See FIGURE 4B).

The featureless "black" spectral signature is clearly seen when the initial spectrum (at 20 ps) of the promptly formed 475 and 675 nm transients is subtracted from spectra recorded at later times (See FIGURE 4). This result indicates complete formation of the 475 nm transient within the first 20 ps following excitation, and further suggests its formation concurrently with the appearance of the solvated electron, since it, too, remains unchanged, in spectrum past 20 ps. Therefore, it appears likely that the 475 nm transient is in fact, the radical cation, $R^{.+}$, associated with the site generating the solvated electron. Because photoionization of phenols is known to occur in water, highly substituted phenolic structures in the fulvic acid could be good candidates to account for the generating sites of the solvated electrons.

There is some complication of the sample behavior at pH 7.0 in the early time domain (See FIGURE 4B). An early component of decay is present centered at 475 nm with a decay time of about 100 ps. Results obtained in our laboratories on picosecond emission of the Armadale sample (15), using a streak camera, indicate a

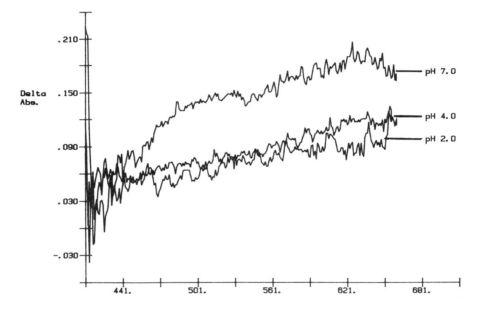

FIGURE 3.   Transient   absorption spectrum of FA at pH =
2.0, 4.0, and 7.0.   Spectra were recorded 20 ps   after a
20 ps   excitation pulse   are corrected   for ground state
absorption.   Pulse energy was 3 mj.

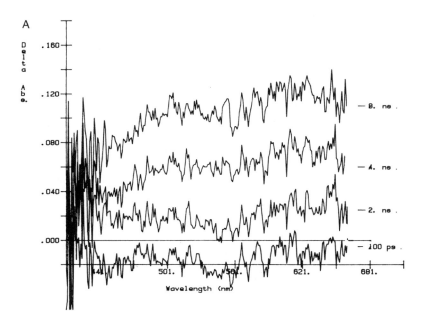

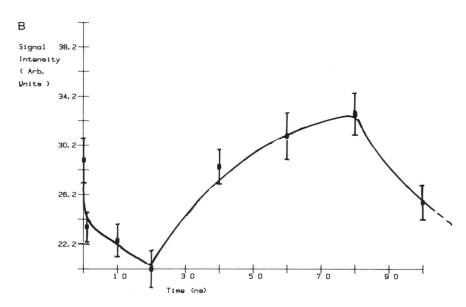

FIGURE 4. (A) Formation of the "black residue" component
on the early nanosecond time scale. Spectra recorded
are differential, the 20 ps Spectrum has been substrac-
ted.   Pulse energy was 3 mj; (B) Picosecond to early
nanosecond kinetic profile for FA at pH = 7.0. Absorption signal was integrated over the observation wavelength range of 475-520 nm. Pulse energy 3 mj.

significant component of emission, which decays with a time constant of 100 ps emission ($\lambda >$ 400 nm). The early decay in absorption at pH 7.0 seems to correspond to this emission component in duration.

Quenching Studies. The solvated electron component at 675 nm was studied under conditions of oxygen and copper quenching (FIGURE 5). It appears that in our (concentrated) solutions of fulvic acid (200 mg/l), and at elevated laser power (3-30 mj), it is formed by a one photon process. Conditions for observation of these spectra with excitation at 355 nm and on the nanosecond scale match those cited by previous authors (6). Moreover, we were able to observe the solvated electron formation at reduced power (2-3 mj) on the picosecond scale in (concentrated) solution (200 mg/l), suggesting, at least for our material, that there is no intensity threshold for formation of e⁻ solv.

While both the spectrum of this species and its sensitivity to N_2O strongly suggest its identity as a solvated electron, we are able to offer further confirmation. In the presence of dissolved O_2 the solvated electron is scavenged according to the equation:

$$O_2 + e^- = O_2^-$$

with an observed rate constant of 2×10^{10} M^{-1} s^{-1} according to pulse radiolysis studies (16). A Stern-Volmer plot for quenching by oxygen yielded a quenching rate constant of $1.2 \pm 0.1 \times 10^{10}$ M^{-1} s^{-1}, which is in reasonable agreement with the radiolytic measurements.

Measurements carried out for quenching of $e^-_{(aq)}$ by Cu^{+2} yielded a quenching rate constant, k_q, of $1.6 \pm 0.2 \times 10^{10}$ M^{-1} s^{-1}, which is in satisfactory agreement with the radiolytically measured rate constant (16):

$$Cu^{+2} + e^- = Cu^+ \qquad k_{obs} = 3.3 \times 10^{10} \ M^{-1} \ s^{-1}$$

Both sets of results clearly indicate that the solvated electron is quenched by free metal ion and uncomplexed oxygen.

We have also examined the static quenching behavior for Cu^{+2} and O_2 by comparing the values of $\triangle A_0$, the initial transient absorption at t = 0, at various concentrations of quencher. In both cases, we observed apparent static quenching effects, although the small O_2 effects should be regarded with some caution. Both sets of results suggest quenching by species bound to the fulvic acid close to the generating site of the solvated electron.

pH measurements have provided further confirmation of the solvated electron's identity. Reaction of H^+ with e⁻ solv. yields hydrogen according to the reaction:

$$H^+ + e^- = H\cdot \qquad k_{obs} = 2.1 \times 10^{10}\ M^{-1}\ s^{-1}$$
$$2H\cdot = H_2$$

The lifetime is 480 ns at pH 4.0, yielding a k_q value of $1.2 \pm 0.2 \times 10^{10}\ M^{-1}\ s^{-1}$, in approximate agreement with the radiolysis value quoted above (16). The value of k_q for H^+ quenching was estimated from the Stern–Volmer law and lifetimes of 480 ns (at pH 4.0) and 1130 ns (at pH 7.0). A comparison of values of $\triangle A_0$ from measurements made indicates static quenching on various time scales by a factor of 1.5 – 2 on going from pH 7.0 to pH 4.0. Inspection of the spectra at 20 ps directly show the static quenching effect (See FIGURE 3).

Consistently, we have found that the quenching rate constants evaluated for the solvated electron are approximately half the literature values observed for quenching by free H^+, Cu^{+2}, and O_2. In view of the aggregate nature of humic materials, it is probable that a significant fraction of the solvated electrons are generated in the interior of the humic particles. Diffusion of the quenchers into the interior is limited, reducing the overall effectiveness of the quenching processes, and hence, the observed k_q's.

Studies were carried out on the sample at specific long times after excitation in an attempt to study the 475 nm and "black residue" signal quenching. Quenching of the 475 nm signal has remained inaccessible to quantitative analysis due to its low intensity, and to the fact that it is superimposed on the more intense background level of "black residue" signal (See FIGURES 2A and 2B). The "black residue" signal persists for hundreds of microseconds while the very weak cation radical component decays with a lifetime of a few microseconds. The value is quite pH sensitive and generally matches the range of values reported in previous work (6). Accurate determination of T for either species was not feasible.

We have verified the linearity of formation of both signals vs energy. Linearity (except for saturation of the R^+ signal at the highest energies) suggests monophotonic formation processes, at energies up to 30 mj.

Quenching studies of the "black residue" were conducted by comparison of signal amplitudes at the single time of 100 microseconds after excitation. From this comparison, we compute the ratio Q:

$$Q = \frac{\triangle A[M]}{\triangle A_0} \times 100$$

where $\triangle A[M]$ is the transient absorption observed for concentration, $|M^{2+}|$, of quencher, while $\triangle A_0$ is the signal intensity observed in the absence of quencher (See FIGURE 6).

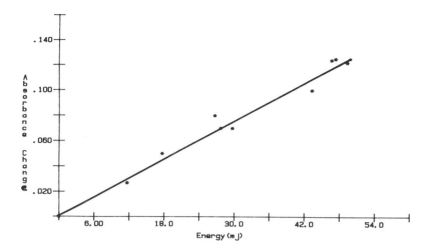

FIGURE 5. Plot of transient absorbance <u>vs</u> pulse energy for the solvated electron transient absorption on the nanosecond time scale at 675 nm.

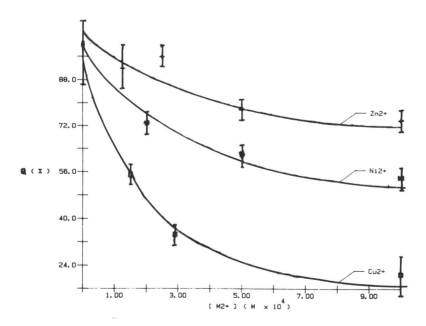

FIGURE 6. Plot of "black residue" signal intensity quenching <u>vs</u> concentration of metal ion quencher at a time of 100 microseconds. Sample pH = 6.0. All signals corrected for ground state absorption.

Quenching of this long transient was studied at pH
6.0 in the presence of millimolar quantities of Cu^{+2},
Zn^{+2}, and Ni^{+2}. Metal ion quenching was found to follow
the order $Cu^{+2} > Ni^{+2} > Zn^{+2}$. The maximum value of Q
was computed and plotted vs the two electron reduction
potential ([18]) for each metal ion species (I.U.P.A.C.
values ([18]):

$$M^{+2} + 2e^- = M+$$

Interestingly, this yields a linear relationship between
Q and E although the slope (value) is small. Moreover,
we have been able to add oxygen quenching results to
these lines. These results may suggest an electron
donating character to the fulvic acid interaction with
the quenchers, although the small slope of the curve
seems to eliminate the likelihood of assignment as
electron transfer (redox) quenching.

In view of recent work by Zepp et al ([19]) in
determining the energy of triplet states formed in the
irradiation of humic waters in sunlight, a set of
triplet states is implied in our photophysical scheme.
Triplet state energies were determined ([19]) by means of
the cis-trans isomerisation of 1,3-pentadiene, a process
which occurs via a triplet pathway. Approximately 40%
of the triplet states produced in the samples studied
were capable of sensitizing this isomerisation while the
remaining 60% were of lower energies and studied by
sensitized formation of singlet oxygen. The mean energy
of the higher energy triplet states was 250 kJ/mol
(corresponding to an absorption maximum of 465 nm).

The broad range of triplet state energies reported
is consistent with character of the "black residue"
signal we observed in our experiments. In considering
the superposition of the weak cation radical signal on
the underlying residue, our results predict a dual
character for the transient absorption observed at 475
nm. This proposal is consistent with the results of
Fischer et al ([6]) whose work demonstrated a composite
nature to the 475 nm transient that they observed
several microseconds after excitation. Their signal
intensity was partially quenched by triplet energy
acceptors and correlated directly with the photooxidation rate of the probe molecules para-isopropyl phenol
and para-methoxy phenol.

Conclusions Concerning Band Assignments. Two aspects of
the photophysics are clear: electrons and radical
cations are formed promptly. The third well defined
component, the "black residue", arises with a time
constant similar to the decay of the fluorescence of
fulvic acid and has a range of energies, plus lifetime
and quenching patterns, that suggest the triplets that
sensitization experiments show to be present. We can

add that the main transients for e $_{(aq)}$ and R$^+$ cannot be excited with the 530 nm green line of the Nd:YAG laser.

Discussion

A Proposal for a Model of FA Spectra and Photophysics.
In the study of humic substance photophysics the inherent complexity of the materials presents a considerable challenge to the interpretation of the results. The role of quinoid chromophores has frequently been invoked in explanations of the photochemical properties of humic waters (4, 5, 6). We feel, however, that since the dominant fraction of our sample functionality is phenol carboxylate, its contribution to the photochemical behaviour of humic substances should not be underemphasized. We wish to propose a model from a more general starting point.

A general problem must be evaluated before choosing a model. The main photoactive groups of fulvic acids be they phenolic, phenol carboxylate or quinoid, pose a difficulty for the explanation of humic substance spectra. In all cases, the dominant fraction of absorption of these species lies well into UV below 300 nm. One would therefore expect a maximum fluorescence emission for excitation in the 250-300 nm wavelength range since this corresponds to a pathway for maximum population of singlet fluorescing states of organic chromophores of these structures.

In fact, humic substance fluorescence is most efficiently excited at 350-400 nm rather than at the shorter wavelengths (13). The emission is broad band and extends from 400-500 nm. While the fluorescence properties of a number of phenol carboxylate model compounds have been reported and compared with those of fulvic acid, it has been pointed out by Buffle et al (13) that few of these compounds approach the excitation and emission wavelengths of fulvic acid. Furthermore, the ratio of fluorescence to concentration of dissolved organic carbon was much higher for these model compounds that for fulvic acids. At high DOC levels (> 100 mg/l), the wavelengths of fluorescence excitation and emission shifted significantly to the red as concentration increased. This indicated that the fluorescence properties of the dissolved humic materials were strongly affected by aggregation phenomena.

An explanation of the observed properties may perhaps be found in the literature on photophysics of synthetic polymers (23). A common process in the photophysics of synthetic polymers (in solution and in the solid phase) which contain aromatic substituents is the formation of excimers and exciplexes, achieved by the face to face alignment of aromatic ring structures, with a typical spacing of 4 Å. The fluorescence of excimers is typically broadband, featureless and

significantly red shifted from the unassociated (monome-
ric) fluorescence. Some typical examples from the
literature collected in TABLE I indicate excimer
emission from many common aromatic centers (See TABLE
I).

TABLE I

Compound	Absorption Maximum ex (nm)		Emission Maximum ex (nm)	
	Monomer	Dimer (Excimer)	Monomer	Dimer (Excimer)
—OOCH–CH–⟨O⟩–CH=COOC₂H₄ O–⟨O⟩–OC₂H₄ (Reference 21) (Solution)			383	470
HC=ØH CH–CHØ (Reference 25) (Solution)			280	340
Bisphenol A diglycidyl ether resin (Reference 26) (Solution)	275	330–350	405	460
CH₃ ⟨O⟩ OH (Reference 24) (Solution)	280	300	310	350

Where ground state alignment of aromatic chromophores is optimum for excimer (or exciplex) formation, the
excimer forms upon the absorption of light rather than
by energy transfer from an excited singlet state to a
ground state chromophore. The term "excimer" in these
cases is loosely applied, and has been referred to more
precisely as a "contact pair, preformed in the ground
state" or an "excited pair complex" (21).
     The case of excimer formation in a series of
phenols has been reported (24) and may be relevant to
fulvic acid photophysics. Excimer formation was
observed in concentrated solutions of p-cresol for
excitation at 280 nm, but not for o or m cresols.
However, the absorption spectra of concentrated solutions of the o and m isomers contained a long wavelength
tail owing to ground state associations, believed to
arise from hydrogen bonding. This is especially
suggestive since hydrogen bonding is thought to be

crucial to formation and aggregation of FA's (27). Fluorescence excited in this longer wavelength region of the absorption spectrum for o, m cresol, had the character of excimer fluorescence.

This particular case of the cresols illustrates the point that, in some cases, excimer fluorescence may not be excited at the shorter absorption wavelengths. Emission from the excimer states may require absorption by ground state conformations close to the excimer geometry; this is especially true where the lifetime of the monomer is short compared with the time required for diffusional encounter. It seems likely that the humic substances, because they are aggregates, provide many possibilities for achieving these conformations, since chromophore concentration is locally high within the aggregates.

In the case of exciplexes, where the aromatic chromophores are dissimilar, we might expect an increased red shift in the ground state absorption due to a greater charge transfer character to the transitions. It seems plausible then, that excimers and exciplexes account for the 350 nm excitation maximum for humic substance fluorescence, since they match the character of the fluorescence emission and may account for the observed excitation wavelengths.

The solution behavior of exciplexes is even more complex, and accounts for the formation of radicals, triplet exciplexes and ordinary triplet states (20, 22). The general kinetic scheme for the photophysics of exciplexes has been summarized by Mattes and Farid (20) and is diagrammed below. Some of our results may be reconciled with the processes summarized by this scheme:

$$A \xrightarrow{h\upsilon} A^* \xrightarrow{D} {}^1[A^{\bar{\cdot}}/D^{\pm}] \longleftrightarrow {}^3[A^{\bar{\cdot}}/D^{\pm}] \longrightarrow {}^3_D A$$

$$|A^{\prime\prime\prime}D| \xrightarrow{h\upsilon}$$

$$A^{\bar{\cdot}} + D^{\pm}$$

$$A, D^+ \ products \qquad\qquad products \qquad {}^3D, A$$

$$(A = acceptor \ ; \ D = donor)$$

The formation of the solvated electron and radical cation may result from the loss of an electron from an excited EDA complex to yield a radical cation and ground state acceptor molecule (20). This is a suitably low energy process to be monophotonic:

$$[A^{III}D/H_2O] \longrightarrow A^{\bar{\cdot}} + D^{\dot{+}} + H_2O$$

The results of Fischer _et al_ (6) indicate a connection between the 475 nm and 700 nm transients in samples with a high TOC content. This connection supports our hypothesis because of the increase in the number of aromatic centers and aggregation (27) of the sample that occurs at higher humic substance concentration.

References

1. W.M. Draper, D.G. Crosby, J. Agric. Food Chem., 1984, 32, 231-237.
2. R.G. Zepp, N.L. Wolfe, G.L. Baughmon, R.C. Hollis, Nature, 1977, 267, 421-423.
3. T. Mill, D.G. Hendry, H. Richardson, Science, 1980, 207, 886-887.
4. R.M. Baxter, J.H. Carey, Nature, 1983, 306, 575-576.
5. T.M. Waite, F.M.M. Morel, Environ. Sci. Technol., 1984, 18, 860-868.
6. A.M. Fischer, T. Mill, D.S. Kliger, D. Tse, IHSS Symposium Proceedings, Birmingham, UK, July 23-28, 1984.
7. E.H. Hansen, M. Schnitzer, Anal. Chim. Acta, 1969, 46, 247-254.
8. D.S. Gamble, Can. J. Chem., 1970, 48, 2662-2669.
9. D.S. Gamble, M. Schnitzer, In "Trace Metal and Metal Organic Interactions in Natural Water", P.S. Singer Editor, Ann Arbor MI, Ann Arbor Science Publishers Inc., pp. 265-302.
10. C.H. Langford, D.S. Gamble, A.W. Underdown, S. Lee, In "Aquatic and Terrestrial Humic Materials", R.F. Christman and E.T. Gjessing Editors, Ann Arbor MI, Ann Arbor Science Publishers Inc., Chapter 11, pp. 219-237.
11. N. Serpone, D.K. Sharma, To Be Published.
12. R. Bonneau, J. Photochem., 1979, 10, 439-449.
13. J. Buffle, P. Deladoey, J. Zumstein, W. Haerdi, Schweiz Z. Hydrol., 1982, 44, 326-361.
14. P. Rentzepis, R.P. Jones, J. Chem. Phys., 1973, 59, 766-773.
15. C.H. Langford, D.K. Sharma, R. Lesage, J.F. Power, Environ. Tech. Lett., In Press.
16. M.S. Matheson, In "The Solvated Electron", A.C.S. Symposium, E.J. Hart, Chairman, Advances in Chemistry Series, Washington, 1965, p. 51.
17. K. Kryszewski, B. Nadolski, In "Singlet Oxygen-Reactions with Organic Compounds and Polymers", B. Ranby and J.K. Rabek Editors, Wiley, New York, 1978, pp. 244-253.

18. C.R.C. Handbook of Chemistry and Physics. Two electron reduction potentials were examined so that a comparison could be made between the redox properties of Cu^{+2}, Zn^{+2}, O_2^{+2}, and Ni^{+2}, since Ni^+ does not exist as a stable species. See 63rd Edition, C.R.C. Press, Boca Raton, Florida, USA, 1983, pp. D162-167.

19. R.G. Zepp, P.T. Schlotzhauer, R.M. Sink, Environmental Sci. Tech., 1985, 19, 74-81.

20. S.L. Mattes, S. Farid, Science, 1984, 226, 917-921.

21. M. Graley, A. Reiser, A.J. Roberts, D. Phillips, In "Photophysics of Synthetic Polymers", Science Reviews, Middlesex, England, 1982, pp. 26-38.

22. J. Birks, In "Photophysics of Aromatic Molecules", Wiley Interscience, London, England, 1970, Chapter 9.

23. D. Phillips, A.J. Roberts, In "Photophysics of Synthetic Polymers", Science Reviews, Middlesex, England, 1982.

24. A. Harriman, B.W. Rockett, J. Photochem.,1974, 2, 405-408.

25. G. Rumbles, In "Photophysics of Synthetic Polymers", D. Phillips and A.J. Roberts Editors, Science Reviews, Middlesex, England, 1982, pp. 5-25.

26. N.S. Allen, J.P. Binkley, B.J. Parsons, G.D. Phillips, N.X. Tennent, In "Photophysics of Synthetic Polymers", D. Phillips and A.J. Roberts Editors, Science Reviews, Middlesex, England, 1982, pp. 128-135.

27. A. Underdown, C.H. Langford, D.S. Gamble, Environ. Sci. Tech., 1985, 19, 132-136.

RECEIVED June 24, 1986

Chapter 13

Natural Photosensitizers in Sea Water: Riboflavin and Its Breakdown Products

Kenneth Mopper and Rod G. Zika

Rosenstiel School of Marine and Atmospheric Sciences, Division of Marine and Atmospheric Chemistry, University of Miami, Miami, FL 33149

Photosensitized reactions in surface seawater are implicated in a number of redox processes ranging from the photogeneration of species such as hydrogen peroxide to the photo-oxygenation of natural and anthropogenic compounds. Previous work has concentrated on the excited state properties of humic substances, but our preliminary work has shown that dissolved flavins, although present at low concentrations (usually < 1 nM), are an important class of compounds contributing to marine photochemical processes, and, as a group, undergo dynamic photochemical transformations in the sea. In this paper we present evidence for and discuss the implications of photoreactions of flavins in seawater, including their photosensitizing capacity, their contribution to the photoproduction of hydrated electrons, superoxide anion and hydrogen peroxide, the role of the excited state reactions of flavins on the initiation of free radical reactions, and the role of flavins in photosensitized production of low molecular weight organics, such as carbonyl compounds. We also present the first detailed data on temporal and depth distribution of flavins in coastal and open ocean environments.

In environmental photochemistry, research on photosensitized initiated reactions in natural waters has focussed mainly on humic materials because they are one of the most abundant and also most strongly absorbing constituents in these waters. However, other potentially important biogenically produced and photoreactive compounds exist in seawater. One such class of compounds, which has received little attention either in terms of their concentration and distribution or their photochemical characterization in seawater, is the flavins (FL). Flavins are of special interest because they are among the few naturally occurring organic compounds in seawater with large cross sections at incident

0097-6156/87/0327-0174$06.00/0
© 1987 American Chemical Society

sunlight frequencies (1). In addition, efficiencies of intersystem crossing from singlet to triplet states are high (2). Figure 1 gives the structures and the systematic names of riboflavin and its dominant photochemical breakdown products.

Virtually nothing is known about the spatial or temporal distribution of flavins in the marine environment. In fact, only two analyses of flavins in seawater have been previously reported, one from the Mediterranean (3) and one from an Australian coral reef (4). Past studies have largely been biological in scope, concerned primarily with the release of vitamins by marine organisms (4-7) and with the ecological role that vitamins may have in the sea (8). A serious limitation to such studies has been the lack of sensitive (pg/L) and selective analytical methods to determine low natural levels of these compound. Traditionally this has been done by the use of bioassay techniques. Recently, the development of modern high performance liquid chromatographic (HPLC) techniques, coupled with fluorometric detection, has greatly facilitated the measurement of riboflavin and its decomposition products in marine waters (4).

In this paper we present the first detailed measurements of flavin concentrations in open ocean and coastal environments, and preliminary experiments dealing with the marine photochemistry and photosensitizing properties of riboflavin and its breakdown products.

Experimental

The diurnal and depth distributions of dissolved flavins were determined at two stations off Florida: Florida Bay (coastal; 25° 19.4'N, 81° 09.8'W) and Tongue of the Ocean (oceanic; 25° 24'N, 78° 7'W) during the SOLARS I cruise (April 1-7, 1985; R/V Calanus) and the SOLARS II cruise (June 12 - 18, 1985; R/V Cape Florida), respectively. Samples were taken with a glass bottle (opened below the surface) or with teflon-lined Go-Flo bottles (General Oceanics). Samples for dissolved flavins were extracted and analyzed onboard by HPLC, usually within 10 min of sampling. The reversed phase HPLC separations were done on a 5 um Hypersil C-18 column using a mobile phase of 30% methanol/70% 20 mM sodium acetate (pH 5.6) in water at a flow rate of 1.5 ml/min. The flavins were detected by fluorescence using an excitation band of 320-390 nm and an emission band of 440-520 nm. Details of the extraction and chromatography are given elsewhere (9); typical chromatograms of flavins in natural seawater samples are given in Figure 2.

In addition to field measurements, several preliminary laboratory experiments were run to delineate the photochemical decomposition pathways of flavins and to elucidate their role in initiating secondary photo-reactions in seawater. For clarity, details of these experiments are presented under the appropriate sections following.

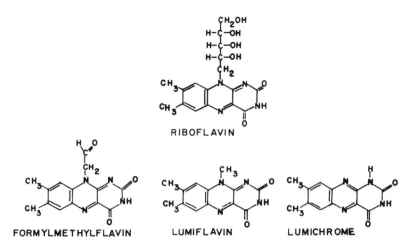

Figure 1.   Structures and names of flavins.

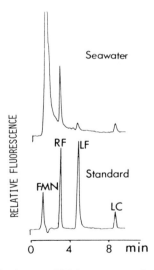

Figure 2. Reversed-phase HPLC separations of a 12.5 nM
standard mixture of flavins (0.25 pmol of each compound
injected) and a natural seawater sample from Biscayne Bay, FL.
- approximate concentrations are 190 pM riboflavin (RF), 22 pM
lumiflavin (LF) and 250 pM lumichrome (LC). The large initial
peak may be humic substances.

Results and Discussion

Photosensitization by Riboflavin and Lumichrome. The photosensitizing properties of riboflavin in seawater, specifically with
respect to singlet oxygen formation, have been investigated by
Momzikoff et al. (10). Their work demonstrated that riboflavin was
a particularly good producer of singlet oxygen and they suggested
that e^- or $H^{\cdot}$ transfer reactions would not be important, although
they did not experimentally demonstrate this. Their conclusion is
based on the fact that processes competing for the excited triplet
state of the flavin ($^3Fl^*$) are dominated by photophysical
deactivation processes (e.g. interaction with ground state oxygen,
fluorescence and vibrational relaxation). Given the high
concentration of dissolved oxygen relative to organic substrates in
seawater, the ratio of intermolecular e^- or $H^{\cdot}$ transfer to energy
transfer reactions in natural seawater would be expected to be
small.
    Nevertheless, this small fraction of e^- or $H^{\cdot}$ transfer
reactions could be a significant source of free radicals in the
environment. Futhermore, flavins, because of their biological
source and limited water solubility, could function more
efficiently via e^- or $H^{\cdot}$ transfer reactions in substrate enriched
micro-environments such as on particles, micro-organisms or in the
sea surface microlayer.
    In order to test whether environmentally significant levels of
naturally occurring flavins do indeed undergo e^- or $H^{\cdot}$ transfer
reactions, the photosensitized degradation of methionine by
riboflavin was examined. Methionine was chosen as a convenient
substrate to work with for analytical reasons and because different
products result from its reaction with $^1\Delta_gO_2$ or via oxidation by
triplet sensitizers (11). Figure 3 shows the effect of added
riboflavin upon the photoinduced degradation of methionine in
seawater. During the reaction, the fluorescence spectrum of the
solution rapidly changed. The change was interpreted as the
conversion of riboflavin to lumichrome (see below). Methionine was
measured by converting it to the dansyl derivative and then
quantifying it by HPLC against an internal standard (12). No
methionine sulfoxide, which is the product of the reaction of
methionine with singlet oxygen (11), was observed. The product of
the reaction of methionine with $^3FL^*$ should be methional, the
presence of which, although not analyzed for, was suggested by its
characteristic odor in the head space over the irradiated
solutions. In subsequent related experiments methional was indeed
identified as a major product using the HPLC method of Mopper and
Stahovec (13) which is based on reaction of carbonyls in seawater
with 2,4-dinitrophenylhydrazine. It is apparent from Figure 3 that
sub-nanomolar concentrations of flavins can function as efficient
photosensitizers in natural seawater.
    Figure 3 also shows a comparison between the relative
efficiency of riboflavin and two other natural aquatic
photosensitizers, namely a soil fulvic acid and phlorglucinol based
polymer which is believed to be an exudate of a benthic macrophyte
(14), to oxidize methionine. Based on the concentration of
sensitizer needed to decompose methionine at a rate of 0.05

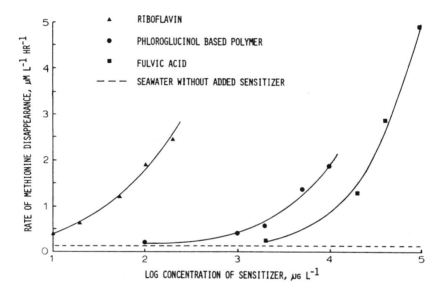

Figure 3. Comparison of the concentration dependence of added
photosensitizer on the photodegradation rate of methionine.
For each case the solutions were 5 μM in methionine and were
irradiated for 2 hours using only wavelengths > 300 nm isolated
from a mercury medium pressure lamp. All samples were prepared
in air saturated artificial seawater of ionic strength 0.7 and
with pH of 8.1.

umol/L/hr, the relative efficiencies are 280:100:1 for riboflavin, phlorglucinol polymer and fulvic acid, respectively. It is difficult to extrapolate this relative comparison to natural seawater because of the uncertainty involved in determining humic substance concentration and absorbance and quantum yield versus wavelength dependence. If it is assumed that marine humic substances have characteristics similar to the model fulvic acid used in this study, that their concentration is in the range of 150-800 ug/L (15), and that the flavin concentration is 1 nM (.376 ug/L), then the flavins potentially constitute a significant fraction (i.e. 13-70%) of the combined photosensitizer activity in seawater. Thus, even low concentrations of flavins in natural seawater could be competitive with much higher levels of other naturally occurring photosensitizers. If flavins are highly variable in their distribution, as might be anticipated given their biological origin, then a considerable range of photosensitizer activity from these compounds would be expected.

Role of Flavins in Hydrogen Peroxide Formation. Flavins may function as photosensitizers through photoelectron ejection (16). If this process is occurring in seawater, the only significant reaction of e^-(aq) would be with O_2 to produce O_2^-. Disproportionation of O_2^- would generate H_2O_2. The other reactive product would probably be the flavin radical cation.

Reducing agents such as EDTA, methionine and other amino acids have been shown to enhance the generation of O_2^- in aerobic solutions of photosensitizers including flavins (17-18). These results are consistent with a picture of a light driven system of flavin (LC,RF) acting as a photosensitizer, molecular oxygen as an electron acceptor and an unidentified substance (RH), possibly humic/fulvic acid or some component thereof, as an electron donor which in concert produce hydrogen peroxide in seawater. These reactions can proceed as shown in equations 1 through 4:

$$^3Fl^* + RH \xrightarrow{k_1} HFl. + R. \tag{1}$$

$$^3Fl^* + O_2 \xrightarrow{k_2} Fl^+ + O_2^-. \tag{2}$$

$$HFl. + O_2 \xrightarrow{k_2} Fl + HO_2. \tag{3}$$

$$Fl^+ + RH \longrightarrow Fl + RH^+ \tag{4}$$

by either reduction of the $^3FL^*$ by the donor or by oxidation of $^3FL^*$ by oxygen followed by subsequent regeneration of the sensitizer by the donor. Other interpretations can be made, such as direct photoionization to form hydrated electrons; however, information as to the photochemistry of flavins in seawater, their excited state reactions with molecular oxygen and plausible electron donors is needed in order to assess whether flavins play an appreciable role in the production of hydrogen peroxide in marine systems (19). A preliminary evaluation of flavins as a potential photochemical source of H_2O_2 and oxidant of e^- or $H^{\cdot}$ donor substrates was made by comparing rates of production of H_2O_2 during sunlight exposure of (1) Gulf Stream seawater (GSS), (2) GSS with 5×10^{-6} M methionine, (3) GSS with 1×10^{-9} M riboflavin and (4) GSS with 1×10^{-9} M riboflavin and 5×10^{-6} M methionine. It is evident from Figure 4 that riboflavin, even when added at only 1 nM, a concentration typical of total dissolved flavins in coastal waters (see below), is a significant source of H_2O_2 (and perhaps O_2^-). In addition, hydrogen peroxide production can be enhanced by the addition of an e^- or $H^{\cdot}$ donor such as methionine. That enhancement is also observed when only the donor is added indicates that reaction mechanisms similar to those functioning for flavins might be occurring for the natural photosensitizing consituents in seawater.

Production of Low Molecular Weight (LMW) Carbonyl Compounds from Flavin Induced Photochemical Reactions. Electron or $H^{\cdot}$ transfer reactions are important in that they can produce O_2^-, H_2O_2 and also initiate free radical reactions in seawater. In particular, the generation of flavin radicals from electron or $H^{\cdot}$ transfer reactions may play an important role in the oxidation of dissolved organic matter in seawater. At the low concentrations of flavins in seawater, $H^{\cdot}$ abstraction will probably be the major reaction pathway of the flavin radical provided sufficient concentrations of electrons or hydrogen atom donors are present. Other significant pathways are probably addition reactions of $HFl^{\cdot}$ to O_2 or to long lived radicals such as those found in humic materials. In seawater the radical, $R^{\cdot}$, generated in the above reaction, would react predominantly with ground state O_2 to form the organoperoxy radical (20) which can then undergo several reactions to yield LMW carbonyl compounds as well as other oxidized products (21-22) through pathways such as the following.

$$R\cdot \quad + \quad O_2 \quad \longrightarrow \quad RO_2\cdot \qquad (5)$$

$$RO_2\cdot \quad + \quad R'H \quad \longrightarrow \quad ROOH + R'\cdot \qquad (6)$$

$$RO_2\cdot \; + R'O_2\cdot \quad \longrightarrow \quad \text{Various products (i.e. } ROOR', \qquad (7)$$
$$R'CHO, RCHO, R'CH_2OH, R'O\cdot,$$
$$RO\cdot, O_2)$$

Low molecular weight organic fragments, such as simple organic acids and carbonyl compounds, are common products formed from photosensitized oxidation of more complex organic substrates by flavins (2, 23-24). Thus, by monitoring the photoproduction of these "fragments", one may be able to study various photooxidative processes even in complex media, such as seawater and other natural waters, where the nature of the organic substrates being oxidized is not known.

Experiments were performed to determine whether the production of carbonyl compounds could be used to study flavin-sensitized photooxidation of organic matter in seawater. Duplicate solutions (0.5 - 1 umol/L) of riboflavin, lumichrome + ribose, lumazine

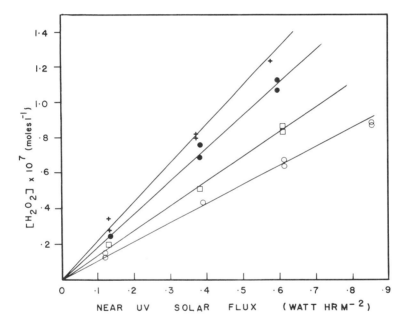

Figure 4. Photochemical production rates of H_2O_2 in midday sunlight: (O) in Gulf Stream seawater (GSSW), (□) in GSSW + 1 x 10^{-9} M riboflavin, (●) in GSSW + 5 x 10^{-6} M methionine, (+) in GSSW + 5 x 10^{-6} M methionine + 1 x 10^{-9} M riboflavin.

[2,4(1H, 3H)-pteridinedione], and marine humic acid (isolated by G.R. Harvey; 25) in filter-sterilized, aerated seawater (Biscayne Bay, FL) and organic-free distilled water were irradiated in sealed, sterile quartz glass vessels with a sunlamp (Westinghouse Model MH 400/E; lower cut-off   320 nm) for 4-6 h. Aliquots of irradiated samples and controls were removed for carbonyl analysis by HPLC of the 2,4 dinitrophenyl-hydrazones. Contamination from sample workup and preconcentration steps was avoided by injecting derivatized seawater samples directly into the liquid chromatograph (13). Peak identification was achieved by co-injection with authentic substances. Analysis of underivatized samples showed no peaks in the region of the chromatograms where carbonyl hydrazones elute.

The addition of photosensitizers to natural seawater significantly enhances carbonyl production rates, Table I and Figure 5, presumably as a result of enhanced photosensitized oxidation rates of dissolved organic substrates. However, this interpetation is not straightforward since riboflavin or humic acid are significant sources for LMW carbonyls as indicated by the production of these compounds in organic-free distilled water containing only these photosensitizers, Table I. In the case of riboflavin, the absorbed energy is transferred intramolecularly to the ribityl group followed by oxidative fragmentation (26-27). Irradiation of an equimolar solution of lumichrome and ribose gave a significantly lower carbonyl production rate then riboflavin alone, Table II, supporting the idea that intramolecular energy transfers are important in riboflavin decomposition and carbonyl production.

<u>Isoalloxazine-Containing Products from the Photodegradation of Riboflavin.</u> Irradiation of riboflavin in deoxygenated aqueous solution leads to a series of reactions whereby the ribityl side chain is cleaved and the isoalloxazine ring is reduced (28). Both triplet ($^3RF^*$) and singlet ($^1RF^*$) excited states are photoreactive. The three main isoalloxazine products of the reaction are lumichrome, lumiflavin and formylmethylflavin (see Figure 6a). Song and Metzler (28) suggested that lumichrome arises principally from photocleavage of the $^1RF^*$ excited state, whereas formylmethylflavin and lumiflavin arise from the cleavage of the $^3RF^*$ state.

The photodecomposition pathways and products of riboflavin in seawater have not been studied in detail, although some observations have been made. Zika (12) found lumichrome as the only major isoalloxazine product while Mopper and Zika (29) also detected minor amounts of lumiflavin in addition to lumichrome production, upon irradiation (sunlight or polychromatic artificial light) of seawater solutions of riboflavin. Dunlap and Susic (4) also observed the production of minor amounts of lumiflavin from the photodegradation of FMN (riboflavin-5'-phosphate) in seawater, the major product being lumichrome. The absence of the expected formylmethylflavin (itself quite photolabile) and the only minor production of lumiflavin are possibly due to efficient quenching of the triplet state. Dissolved oxygen is the most likely candidate as a quencher, due to its high concentration in seawater, although

Table I. Effect of Photosensitizers on the Photoproduction[1] of
LMW Aldehydes in Sterile Seawater and Distilled Water

Photosensitizer[2]	Seawater[3]			Distilled Water[3]			% Due to Photooxidation[4]		
	c_1	c_2	GXL	c_1	c_2	GXL	c_1	c_2	GXL
	(nmol/l/h)			(nmol/l/h)			(%)		
Riboflavin	193	17	7	107	25	0	55	100	0
Lumazin	20	2	5	0	0	0	0	0	0
Humic Acid	27	12	4	5	9	0	19	75	0

1 Photoproduction is taken as net production (production in
irradiated sample minus dark control and minus production in
irradiated seawater alone).

2 [Riboflavin] = 1 uM; [Lumazin] = 1 uM; [Humic Acid] = 10 mg 1^{-1}.

3 c_1 = Formaldehyde; c_2 = Acetaldehyde; GXL = Glyoxal.

4 Percent aldehyde production in seawater due to photochemical
degradation of the photosensitizer; i.e.: [(carbonyl production in
distilled H_2O)/(production in seawater)] X 100%.

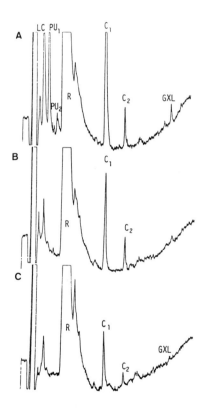

Figure 5. HPLC chromatograms of carbonyl compounds formed during the irradiation of filter-sterilized seawater containing added photosensitizers: A. 1 μM of riboflavin, B. 10 mg/L of humic acid and, C. no addition. C_1 - formaldehyde, C_2 - acetaldehyde, GXL - glyoxal, LC - lumichrome, R - excess DNPH reagent.

Table II. Production of Carbonyl Compounds from Irradiated
Solutions of Riboflavin, Lumichrome & Ribose, and Ribose

Sample	Rate of Carbonyl Photoproduction $(nmol/l/h)$ [1]				% Rib^2 C Oxidized to LMW Aldehydes
	Formaldehyde	Acetaldehyde	PU_1 [2]	PU_2 [2]	
Lumichrome & Ribose (1 uM each) in distilled H_2O	18	18	0	0	2.9%
Riboflavin (1 uM) in distilled H_2O	103	30	75	19	28%
Ribose (10 uM)	< 1	1	0	0	< 0.1%

[1] Corrected for dark controls and production in irradiated water alone.

[2] Rib: Ribose or Ribityl; PU_1 & PU_2: Unknown carbonyl compounds (see Figure 5); PU_2 may be glycolaldehyde.

low concentrations of both phenol, bromide and iodide ion have been shown to quench $^3RF^*$ (28, 30). Figure 6B outlines the de-activation pathways available for excited state flavins, including internal conversion (generation of heat), fluorescence, phosphorescence and reaction with quenchers and reactive substrates. Our preliminary studies indicate that RF and FMF have short half lives in sunlight irradiated seawater (on the order of a few minutes or less), whereas LC and LF are significantly more stable (with half lives on the order of hours for LF to days for LC).

Evidence for Photochemical Control Over the Distribution of Flavins in the Sea. Based on the relative photolability of flavins in seawater (see above), one would expect to find strong diurnal and depth variations in flavin concentrations in the sea, if photochemical processes are of first order importance. To examine this, we determined the diurnal variation of flavins at one coastal site off Florida and the depth distribution at one open ocean site (Tongue of the Ocean). The results for the diurnal study are shown in Figure 7. As predicted from the half lives, RF and FMF appear to be quite photolabile, being present at relatively high concentrations only at night. The stable photoproducts, LC and LF, on the other hand, are present throughout the entire diurnal cycle. Note that the concentration of lumichrome is more than an order of magnitude greater than the other flavins, suggesting that it turns over at a slower rate.

Results from oceanic depth profile measurements of flavins in the Tongue of Ocean, Figure 8, indicate that during the afternoon, RF is at relatively low concentrations in the upper 25 meters, which is in agreement with the diurnal study. In the deeper water (> 300 m), the only detectable flavin is RF suggesting that LC and LF are solely derived from photochemical processes, not microbial processes. In addition, the profiles also suggest that lumichrome is more stable than lumiflavin in the water column, as lumichrome is advected to greater depths, which supports our preliminary experimental results on flavin stabilities.

From these first field studies, we conclude that flavins as a group undergo dynamic photochemical transformations in the sea. In addition, as a result of the rapid breakdown of RF, most of the photosensitizing is actually done by LC, the major stable photoproduct and the flavin detected at the highest levels in seawater. Finally, the concentration of total dissolved flavins in natural seawater, 0.1 - 2 nM, is sufficiently high that flavins should be considered as potentially important photosensitizers in the sea.

Acknowledgments

This research was supported by the National Science Foundation on grant OCE-8517041. The opportunity to participate in cruises as part of the SOLARS program was provided in part by the Office of Naval Research on grant N00014-85C-0020. We also wish to thank Susan Vastano, William Stahovec, Peter Milne and Cindy Moore for their excellent assistance.

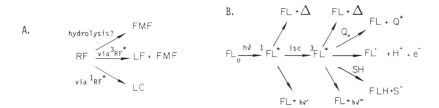

Figure 6.   A. Pathways for photodegradation of riboflavin.   B.
Pathways for de-activation of flavins (FL) in aqueous solution
including reaction with quenchers (Q) and substrates (SH) and
energy (Δ) losses through internal conversion and emission
steps.

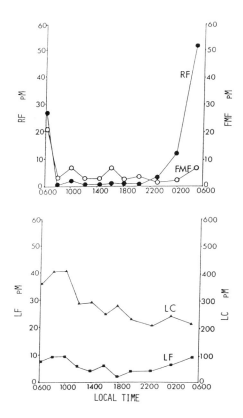

Figure 7.   Time of day variations in the concentrations of
various flavins.

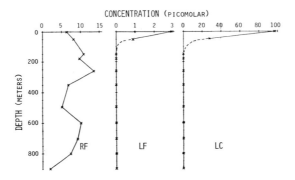

Figure 8. Depth profiles for LC, LF and RF in the Tongue of the Ocean.

Literature Cited

1. Zika, R.G. In "Marine Organic Chemistry"; Duursma, E.K.; Dawson, R., Eds.; Elsevier: Amsterdam, 1981; p. 299.

2. Heelis, P.F. Chem. Soc. Rev. 1982, 15-39.

3. Momzikoff, A. Cah. Biol. Mar. 1969, 10, 221-230.

4. Dunlap, W.C.; Susic, M. Mar. Chem. 1985, 17(3), 185-198.

5. Aaronson, S.; De Angelis, B.; Frank, O.; Baker, H. J. Phycol. 1971, 7, 15-218.

6. Momzikoff, A. Cah. Biol. Mar. 1973, 14, 323-328.

7. Gaill, F.; Momzikoff, A. Mar. Biol. 1975, 29, 315-319.

8. Provasoli, L.; Carlucci, A.F. In "Algal Physiology and Biochemistry"; Stewart, W.D.P., Ed.; University of California Press: Berkely, 1974; Chap. 27.

9. Vastano, S.; Mopper, K.; Zika, R.G. Mar. Chem. 1986, in preparation.

10. Momzikoff, A.; Santus, R.; Giraud, M. Mar. Chem. 1983, 12, 1-14.

11. Sysak, P.S.; Foote, C.S.; Ching, T. Photochem. Photobiol. 1977, 26, 19-27.

12. Zika, R.G. Ph.D. Dissertation, Dalhousie University, 1978.

13. Mopper, K.; Stahovec, W.L. Mar. Chem. 1986, in press.

14. Ragan, M.A.; Craigie, J.S. Can J. Biochem. 1976, 54, 66-73.

15. Harvey, G.R.; Boran, D.A. In "Humic Substances in Soil, Sediment, and Water: Geochemistry, Isolation, and Characterization"; Aiken, G.R.; McKnight, D.M.; Wershaw, R.L.; MacCarthy, P., Eds.; John Wiley and Sons: New York, N.Y., 1985; pp. 233-247.

16. Getoff, N.; Solar, S.; McCormick, D.B. Science 1978, 201, 616-618.

17. Frisell, W.R.; Chung, C.W.; MacKenzie, C.G. J. Biol. Chem. 1959, 24, 1297.

18. Massey, V.; Palmer, G.; Ballow, D. In "Flavins and Flavoproteins"; Kamin, H., Ed.; University Park Press, 1971; pp. 349-361.

19. Zika, R.G.; Moffett, J.W.; Petasne, R.G.; Cooper, W.J.; Saltzman, E.S. Geochim. Cosmochim. Acta 1985, 49, 1173-1184.

20. Mill, T. In "Handbook of Environmental Chemistry"; Hutzinger, O., Ed., Springer-Verlag: New York, 1980; Vol. 2A, pp. 77-105.

21. Graedel, T.; Weschler, C.J. Rev. Geophys. Space Phys. 1981, 19, 505-539.

22. Cox, R.A.; Patrick, K.F.; Chant, S.A. Environ. Sci. Techn. 1981, 15, 587-592.

23. Enns, K.; Burgess, W.H. J. Amer. Chem. Soc. 1965, 87(24), 5766-5770.

24. Armstrong, J.S.; Hemmerich, P.; Traber, R. Photochem. Photobiol. 1982, 35, 747-751.

25. Harvey, G.R.; Boran, D.A.; Chesal, L.A.; Toker, J.M. Mar. Chem. 1983, 12, 119-132.

26. Smith, E.C.; Metzler, D.E. J. Amer. Chem. Soc. 1963, 85, 3285-3288.

27. Song, P.S.; Smith, E.S.; Metzler, D.E. J. Amer. Chem. Soc. 1965, 87, 4181-4184.

28. Song, P.S.; Metzler, D.E. Photochem. Photobiol. 1967, 6, 691-701.

29. Mopper, K.; Zika, R.G., unpublished data.

30. Lasser, N.; Feitelson, J. Photochem. Photobiol. 1975, 25, 249-254.

RECEIVED July 1, 1986

Chapter 14

Do Polycyclic Aromatic Hydrocarbons, Acting as Photosensitizers, Participate in the Toxic Effects of Acid Rain?

Jacques Kagan, Edgard D. Kagan, Isabelle A. Kagan, and Peggy A. Kagan

Department of Chemistry, University of Illinois at Chicago, Chicago, IL 60680

The light-dependent toxicity of non-carcinogenic polycyclic aromatic hydrocarbons (PAH) such as naphthalene, fluorene, phenanthrene, chrysene, anthracene, 9-
methylanthracene, fluoranthene, and pyrene has been
examined in Daphnia magna, Artemia salina, immature
Aedes aegypti and Rana pipiens, and in fish
(Pimephales promelas). Data presented were obtained in
the laboratory, except for the tadpoles and fish,
which were exposed to sunlight. The light-dependent
toxicity of the carcinogenic benzo[a]pyrene in
mosquito larvae is shown for comparison. Although the
mechanism of light-dependent toxicity has not been
elucidated, the effects are probably too rapid to
involve modifications of the genetic material.
    PAH´s are generated in the combustion processes
held responsible for acid rain. Our results suggest
that one must now question whether the death of
aquatic organisms in natural environments should be
ascribed solely to an increase in acidity.

Polycyclic aromatic hydrocarbons (PAH´s) are found in the atmosphere, soil, and in the food chain (1); they have received considerable attention, particularly because of their mutagenic and/or
carcinogenic properties, which are thought to depend upon metabolic
activation of the hydrocarbons into oxygenated products (1).   A
relationship between the carcinogenicity of PAH´s and their high
photodynamic activity toward protozoa such as Coleps and Paramecium
species was first noted by Mottram and Doniach (2) and Doniach (3).
It was further investigated by Epstein et al. using P. caudatum (4),
and by Small et al. (5) and Bauer and Graef (6) using Tetrahymena
pyriformis. In the interval, Matoltsy and Fabian demonstrated a
photodynamic effect of carcinogenic PAH´s in third-instar larvae of
Drosophila melanogaster (7-8).
    Few papers have described photodynamic effects produced by
PAH´s in larger aquatic organisms. Morgan and Warshawsky compared
the rates of photosensitized immobilization of nauplii of the brine
shrimp Artemia salina induced by nineteen carcinogenic and twenty-

0097-6156/87/0327-0191$06.00/0
© 1987 American Chemical Society

two non-carcinogenic PAH´s (9). They reported a correlation between photodynamic activity and carcinogenicity, except for compounds having six or more rings, which showed no photosensitizing ability regardless of carcinogenicity. They even suggested that carcinogenesis by PAH´s might result from sub-lethal photodynamic effects. Interestingly, they found benz[a]acridine, a non-carcinogenic compound used as reference, to be almost twice as photoactive as benz[a]pyrene, a highly carcinogenic molecule.

As a consequence of the early research on the photobiology of PAH´s which correlated carcinogenicity and light-dependent toxicity, one would have expected non-carcinogenic PAH´s to be non-phototoxic. The results of Morgan and Warshawsky (9) already suggested that this premise was not firmly supported by experimental facts. Anthracene, a small non-carcinogenic PAH, provides another example invalidating the suggested general relationship. The acute toxicity of this compound to bluegill sunfish (Lepomis macrochirus) in the presence of sunlight was discovered and carefully studied by Bowling et al. (10). Oris et al. also observed a strong bioconcentration effect in fish treated with dilute solutions of anthracene (11). Spacie et al. analyzed the uptake, depuration, and biotransformation of anthracene and benzo[a]pyrene in bluegill sunfish (12). The light-dependent toxicity of anthracene to Daphnia pulex and third-instar larvae of A. aegypti was reported by Allred and Giesy (13), and that in immature Rana pipiens by Kagan et al. (14).

After investigating the toxicity of photosensitizing molecules to several organisms, particularly larvae and eggs of insects (15-19), we evaluated the light-dependent toxicity of representative non-carcinogenic PAH´s in aquatic organisms, such as the larvae of the mosquito Aedes aegypti, brine shrimps (A. salina), water fleas Daphnia magna, embryonic forms of Rana pipiens, and fish (fathead minnows, Pimephales promelas).

Materials and Methods

The light source was a bank of 8 tubes No. RPR-3500A from the Southern New England Ultraviolet Co, Hamden, CT, mounted 5 cm apart. They emit between 320 and 400 nm, with a maximum at 350 nm. The organisms were irradiated between 7 and 9 cm from the sources, where the light intensity, measured with a Yellow Springs Radiometer YSI 65A and probe YSI 6551, was 13 $W.m^{-2}$. The chemicals were sensitizers from Fisher Chemicals, used without further purification. Each stock solution contained 1 g/l in ethanol or dimethylsulfoxide. Serial dilutions were made by mixing 0.100 ml with 0.500 ml of solvent, repeating the process as often as needed. One complete series of experiments with all the organisms and all the sensitizers was conducted in a dark room, under a dim amber light. Dark controls tested the effect of the solvent alone, a previously irradiated sensitizer solution (at the highest concentration used), and the various sensitizer solutions. The LC_{50} values were obtained graphically, from the plots expressing the percent survival of the organisms as a function of the sensitizer concentrations (on a logarithmic scale). Brine shrimp eggs (0.5 g, from Patco, Fort Atkinson, Wisconsin) in 500 ml of salt solution (9) were kept overnight in a water bath with vigorously bubbling air at 28°C. A brine shrimp suspension (0.5 ml) was transferred into a 7 ml vial, and 2.5 ml of aged water and 20 μl of the desired sensitizer solution were added. All the organisms were still alive after 2 h of incubation in the dark. The irradiation was then conducted for 30 min, the results recorded, and the organisms irradiated for another 30 min. Typical experiments involved 150-200 organisms per vial. At least 6 series of determinations were performed with each sensitizer.

Daphnia magna obtained from the same supply house were maintained in the laboratory and fed commercial yeast. About 10 mature organisms were transferred into each glass vial, and the total volume of water was adjusted to 3 ml. The sensitizer (20 ul) was added, and the open vials were irradiated after 1 h of incubation. Sensitizer concentrations ranged from 6.7 to 0.0009 ppm. After 30 min of irradiation, the number of survivors in each vial was recorded and the irradiation resumed for another 30 min. The death of the immobilized organisms was determined by the absence of heart beats and movements of the thoracic appendages under a microscope. Occasionally, young organisms were born during the course of the experiments. Their fate was not included in the results.

The mosquito larvae came from a stock of Aedes aegypti (Rock) originally obtained from Prof. G. Craig, Jr., University of Notre Dame, and maintained in our laboratory. In the morning egg sheets were placed in a pan containing water and some liver powder and were incubated at 32 °C for about 6 h. The first-instar larvae were transferred into clean aged tap water, and 12-20 larvae were transferred into each vial. The volume was adjusted to 3 ml, and 20 ul of sensitizer solution was added. After overnight incubation in the dark, the vials were first examined for light-independent toxic effects and then irradiated by UV lamps for 30 min. The surviving larvae were counted under a microscope and then irradiated for another 30 min. The LC_{50} values were determined as above, using the results from 4 to 6 series of experiments. Dead larvae were found floating on top of the water or lying at the bottom; they did not respond to mechanical or light probing, and microscopic examination revealed that their mouthparts were immobile.

Tadpoles of Rana pipiens (embryonic stages, Schumway 24 to 28) were collected at the Fifty-fifth Street Pond in Downers Grove, Illinois on June 5, 1983 and on June 8-10, 1984, as well as in Devil's Lake State Park, Wisconsin, on June 15, 1984. In each experiment 10 to 20 tadpoles were placed in a 100 ml beaker containing 50 ml of aged tap water. After addition of sensitizer, the organisms were kept in the dark for 1 h, exposed to sunlight for 30 min, returned to the darkroom, and their survival determined after 24 h. The average from 4 experiments was used for determining the LC_{50} values.

The fathead minnows (Pimephales promelas), purchased from a local fishing supply house, were about 5 cm long and weighed about 0.8 g. They were kept for at least 24 h in aged tap water prior to irradiation. Five fish were placed In a beaker containing 400 ml of sensitizer solution for 30 min before exposure to natural sunlight for 1 h. Each series of experiments was conducted in duplicate.

Results and Discussion

The solubility properties of PAH's severely limit the amounts which can be utilized in experiments in aqueous media. The maximum nominal sensitizer concentration used was 6.67 ppm, which exceeds the published solubility values in pure water (20) for most of the compounds tested (Figure 1). The small amount of solvent used to introduce the sensitizers into water must slightly increase this solubility, but the new values were not measured.

Usually, the PAH's studied here caused little toxicity when animals were maintained in the dark. When the toxicity was enhanced by treatment with long wavelength ultraviolet light, solutions of sensitizers previously irradiated in the absence of organisms showed no enhanced toxicity in the dark. The toxic reactions therefore depended on the simultaneous presence of the organisms, the sensitizer, and the light. The magnitude of the effects depended upon the species used, their stage of development, and the experimental conditions selected for the tests. It is therefore difficult to establish absolute comparisons, and this report is meant only to demonstrate the effects which can be observed, rather than to produce detailed quantitative values. Although we originally intended to observe the sunlight-dependent properties of PAH's, the variability of climatic conditions made these studies irreproducible. Consequently, light sources emitting principally in the long-wavelength range of the ultraviolet spectrum were also utilized. The emission characteristics of the lamps used in this work, as provided by the manufacturer, are shown in Fig 2.

Naphthalene, anthracene, phenanthrene, 9-methylanthracene, fluorene, chrysene, fluoranthene, and pyrene were studied. In most cases, sunlight-dependent toxicity was demonstrated but, except for tadpoles and fish, only the results obtained indoors using the UV light sources are reported here.

Daphnia. The PAH's were not toxic to Daphnia in the dark. The presence of ultraviolet light dramatically affected the activity of some PAH's, killing the organisms with LC_{50}'s as low as a few parts per billions. The results, obtained by averaging the data obtained in four to six experiments, are recorded in Table I. The LC_{50} values, with standard deviations in parentheses, were obtained immediately after irradiation of organisms which had been in contact for 1 h with the sensitizers in the dark.

Neither naphthalene nor fluorene displayed any effects, and chrysene showed only minimal light-dependent toxicity, even at the highest concentration selected for this study, 6.7 ppm. The LC_{50} of 9-methylanthracene was one-fifth that of phenanthrene after 30 min treatment, about one tenth after 1 h. Anthracene, in turn, had an LC_{50} about 7 times smaller than 9-methylanthracene after 30 min, 3 times smaller after 1 h. Fluoranthene and pyrene were still more active than anthracene, by a factor of 5 after 1 h of irradiation. The experiments involving 30 min and 1 h of irradiation showed that light-dependent toxicity levels were not directly proportional to the exposure times. The largest change (a 5-fold increase in LC_{50} for a doubling of the irradiation time) was observed for 9-methylanthracene and for pyrene.

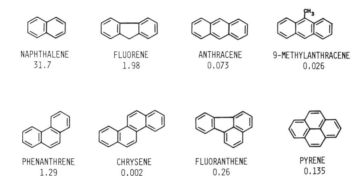

Figure 1. Structure and aqueous solubility of PAH's in mg/kg (Data taken from ref. 20)

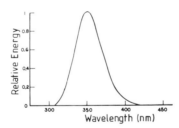

Figure 2. Emission characteristics for the ultraviolet lamps used in this work (RPR-3500A from the Southern New England Ultraviolet Co, Hamden, CT)

Table I. Survival of D. magna

SENSITIZER	LC_{50} after irradiation for	
	30 min	1 h
Naphthalene	N.R.	N.R.
Fluorene	N.R.	N.R.
Chrysene	N.R.	1.9 (0.85)
Phenanthrene	1.0 (1.2)	0.45 (0.3)
9-Methylanthracene	0.2 (0.2)	0.06 (0.03)
Anthracene	0.03 (0.04)	0.02 (0.03)
Fluoranthene	0.011 (0.004)	0.004 (0.005)
Pyrene	0.02 (0.02)	0.004 (0.004)

The effect of the incubation time on the level of light-dependent toxicity was tested more specifically with fluoranthene. The incubation time ranged from 5 min to 120 min, with a 30-min irradiation in all cases. The LC_{50} value was 0.032 after 5 min, 0.015 after 120 min, and 0.012 ppm after overnight incubation. Variations in irradiation time, therefore, produce a greater effect than variations in incubation time.

Oris et al. (11) and Allred and Giesy (13) described the light-dependent toxicity of anthracene against D. pulex. They utilized fixed concentrations of sensitizers, measuring the time required for immobilizing the organisms with sunlight. Therefore, their results are not directly comparable to ours, which were obtained by varying the concentrations and keeping the irradiation times fixed. However, their active concentrations were 0.03 to 0.003 ppm, within the range used in our work, where we recorded the death of the organisms rather than their immobilization.

Mosquito larvae. Three strains of the mosquito Aedes aegypti were used in our qualitative studies: the wild type (Rock), Trinidad (DDT resistant), and DLS$_1$ (Dieldrin resistant). Many of our early surveys, with these sensitizers as well as with others (17-18, and unpublished results), established that the three strains showed exactly the same response toward the photosensitized treatments. In other words, resistance toward DDT or Dieldrin gave A. aegypti no resistance toward photoactive insecticides. Consequently, the determinations summarized in Table II were made with the Rock strain only.

The results (with standard deviations in parentheses) are for the irradiation of larvae which had been in contact overnight with the sensitizer in the dark. No dark toxicity was observed, except with fluorene, 9-methylanthracene, and pyrene, which had LC_{50} values of 3.0, 2.8, and 3.0 ppm respectively. These are in excess of their aqueous solubility.   The results observed with mosquito larvae are generally similar to those obtained with D. magna. Here again naphthalene, fluorene and chrysene showed little or no light-dependent toxicity. Pyrene and fluoranthene were clearly the most active, the latter giving a LC_{50} value down to 0.012 ppm after 1 h of irradiation.

Table II. LC_{50} values for A. aegypti

SENSITIZER	LC_{50} after irradiation for	
	30 min	1 h
Naphthalene	N.R.	N.R.
Fluorene	2.7 (0)	2.7 (0)
Chrysene	2.7 (0)	1.7 (1.5)
Phenanthrene	0.5 (0.1)	0.5 (0.1)
9-Methylanthracene	1.5 (1.4)	0.4 (0.3)
Anthracene	0.15 (0.04)	0.15 (0.04)
Fluoranthene	0.05 (0.05)	0.012 (0.001)
Pyrene	0.02 (0.03)	0.02 (0.03)

Brine shrimps.   The brine shrimps (Artemia salina) used were one day old, younger than those used by Morgan and Warshawsky (9). For convenience we recorded the toxic effects in terms of short-term immobilization rather than death of the organisms.

Table III summarizes the light-dependent toxicity, following incubation of the organisms for 2 h in the dark. The relative activity of the sensitizers resembled that found above but the range of LC_{50} values was smaller. Our results cannot be directly compared to those of Morgan and Warshawsky (9), who studied three of our compounds in older organisms without systematically varying the concentration of the sensitizers. In that work, relative photodynamic activities (with Benz[c]acridine = 1) were 0.72 for pyrene, 0.20 for chrysene, and 0.15 for fluoranthene, a ranking similar to that found in Table 3, but at the concentrations used (between 2 and 40 ppm)

many compounds were certainly not totally dissolved. Also, it is not
clear from the article whether all the measurements were made at a
single concentration. The combination of the two changes, age of the
organisms and concentrations of sensitizers, could account for the
quantitative differences observed in the two studies.

Table III. LC_{50} values for A. salina

| SENSITIZER | LC_{50} after irradiation for | |
	30 min	1 h
Naphthalene	N.R.	N.R.
Fluorene	N.R.	3
Chrysene	N.R.	3
Phenanthrene	N.R.	N.R.
9-Methylanthracene	0.25	0.25
Anthracene	0.04	0.02
Fluoranthene	0.04	0.04
Pyrene	0.008	0.008

Tadpoles. Some of the PAH's were tested for sunlight-dependent
toxicity to tadpoles in order to compare them to anthracene (14).
After incubation with the test compounds for 1 h, the organisms were
exposed to sunlight for 30 min either in the morning or in late
afternoon. No toxicity was detected at that point; only the following day was any mortality apparent. Table IV summarizes the results
for the 24-h survival of the late embryonic stages of Rana pipiens
(Schumway 24 to 28) irradiated for 1 h after 30 min of incubation
in the dark. Dark controls displayed no evidence of toxicity. The
large number of tadpoles at the same developmental stage required to
repeat this study with ultraviolet light sources was no longer
available to us at the time.

Table IV. LC_{50} values for immature R. pipiens.

SENSITIZER	LC_{50}
Naphthalene	N.R.
Chrysene	N.R.
Phenanthrene	N.R.
9-Methylanthracene	N.R.
Anthracene	0.11
Fluoranthene	0.09 (0.02)
Pyrene	0.14 (0.08)

Minnows.   Only preliminary results were available with pyrene and fluoranthene. Pyrene induced no immediate acute toxicity, but a 24-h LC_{50} value of 0.2 ppm was observed after only 30 min of incubation and 1 h of irradiation with sunlight (Fig 3). In contrast, fluoranthene produced immediate light-dependent toxicity (Fig 4).

The LC_{50} values reported here are higher than those observed in bluegill sunfish exposed to anthracene for 48 h prior to irradiation, which took place over 3 days (10). It is likely that longer treatments of our fish with the other PAH's would also result in increased light-dependent toxicity .

Concluding Comments

Mechanism.   The high light-dependent toxicity observed in this work may be largely accounted for by a good match between the emission of the lamps, which peaked at 350 nm (Fig 2), and the main absorption bands of fluoranthene (357 nm, ϵ 8400), anthracene (355 nm, 7770) and, to a lesser extent, pyrene (334 nm, 29,400). Conversely, the inactivity of naphthalene (221 nm, 10,600), fluorene (301 nm, 10,000), or chrysene (319 nm, 12,200) is certainly due in large part to the very low emission of our light source into the absorption region of the molecules. Sunlight, which provides very little energy below 350 nm, also failed to induce any appreciable toxicity with the last group of sensitizers.

The light-dependent toxicity data reported in this paper result from the analysis of restricted interactions between selected organisms, PAH's, and light. An important limitation of this work concerns the relatively short exposure of the organisms to the chemicals (the longest incubation was overnight with the mosquito

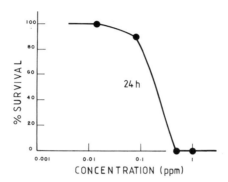

Figure 3. Fate of P. promelas treated with pyrene for 30 min and exposed to sunlight for 1 h. The survival of the organisms was recorded 24 h after the irradiations. The LC_{50} is 0.2 ppm.

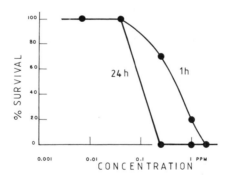

Figure 4. Fate of P. promelas treated with fluoranthene for 30 min and exposed to sunlight for 1 h. The survival of the organisms was recorded 1 h ($LC_{50} = 0.5$ ppm) and 24 h ($LC_{50} = 0.1$ ppm) after the irradiations.

larvae), and to the light (no more than 1 h). Also, the lamps did
not provide any emission in the UVB region, and therefore did nopt
fully simulate solar radiation. We intend to perform a more compre-
hensive study later and, particularly, to determine the light-
dependent toxicity of PAH's singly and in combinations, when the
sensitizers are already present in the water surrounding the organisms at birth as well as when they are introduced at different
developmental stages.

Another limitation of this work concerns the toxic effects
observed. Only acute toxicity data were reported, and more subtle
effects at sub-lethal concentrations were neglected. More recently,
however, we also observed the delayed light-dependent toxicity of
pyrene toward first-instar mosquito larvae. Figure 5 describes the
survival of A. aegypti larvae in the presence of 0.005 ppm of
pyrene, in the dark (solid) and treated with UV light(open). One day
later, 58% of the larvae were alive (compared to 98% of the controls), and 38% survived on day 5 (compared to 80% of the controls).
The survival curve for the pupae phase peaked at 28% instead of 68%
in the controls, and practically all of these pupae successfully
produced adults. At the next higher concentration, 0.03 ppm, all
the larvae died upon irradiation. At the next lower concentration,
0.0009 ppm, there was no significant difference between the fate of
the organisms which had been irradiated and that of the dark controls (Fig 6). The LC_{50} value for pyrene based on the delayed
effects was 0.0045 ppm, compared to the acute toxicity value of
about 0.01 ppm obtained in these particular series of experiments.

The mechanism of light-dependent toxicity for the PAH's at the
cellular level is unknown. The rapid death of the organisms suggests
that modifications of their genetic material are probably not of
primary importance. Indeed, experiments with benzo[a]pyrene dramatically illustrate that for mosquito larvae carcinogenicity is a very
minor risk compared to light-dependent toxicity (Figure 7). Damage
of cellular membranes, perhaps through singlet oxygen-mediated lipid
peroxidation, would be a reasonable path. Oris et al. (11) reported
that bluegill sunfish treated with anthracene and ultraviolet light
displayed damage to their gill epithelium, as well as increased
respiration rate. They suggested that the respiration apparatus was
one potential site of toxic action. Our fish appeared to respond
similarly, but no detailed morphological examinations have yet been
conducted on any of the organisms treated in this study.

There has also been much interest in the effects of PAH's on
human skin, particularly concerning the treatment of psoriasis (21-
22). Whether or not a single mechanistic scheme will account for all
the photobiological properties of these molecules remains to be
established.

The acid-rain connection. This report demonstrates the light-
dependent toxicity of representative PAH's in common aquatic organisms. Naphthalene and fluorene were essentially inactive under our
experimental conditions. Others were extremely toxic, particularly
fluoranthene and pyrene, but only in the presence of ultraviolet
light. Typically, PAH's are present in coal and petroleum products,
and they are also produced by incomplete combustion of organic
matter (23). More than 200 PAH's have been found in the environment. Their production in combustion processes is favored by an
oxygen-deficient flame, temperatures in the range 650-900 °C, and
fuels which are not highly oxidized (24). PAH's and oxides of

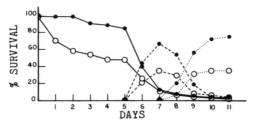

Figure 5. Fate of 1st-instar A. aegypti larvae treated with 0.005 ppm of pyrene in the dark (solid circles), and irradiated (open circles) for 30 min . The survival of the larvae, pupae, and adults is shown with solid lines, broken lines, and dotted lines respectively. Reproduced with permission from Ref. 30. Copyright 1986, Pergamon Press.

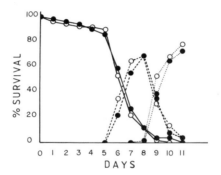

Figure 6. Fate of 1st-instar A. aegypti larvae treated with 0.0009 ppm of pyrene in the dark (solid circles), and irradiated (open circles) for 30 min. The survival of the larvae, pupae, and adults is shown with solid lines, broken lines, and dotted lines respectively.

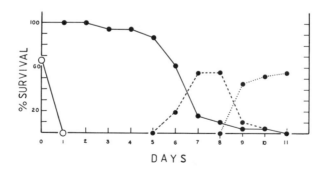

Figure 7. Fate of first-instar larvae of A. aegypti treated with 0.005 ppm of benzo[a]pyrene in the dark (solid circles) and irradiated for 30 min (open circles). The survival of the larvae, pupae, and adults is shown with solid lines, broken lines, and dotted lines respectively. Reproduced with permission from Ref. 30. Copyright 1986, Pergamon Press.

sulfur and nitrogen are generated simultaneously during the combustion of organic fuels. Both types of pollutants can be transported far from their points of formation, and while the inorganic components' role in the generation of acid rain is well recognized, it is conceivable that some of the ecological damage usually assigned to acid rain might instead be due to photodynamic reactions, particularly in aquatic environments.

It has been estimated that nearly 230,000 metric tons enter the world's oceans and surface waters every year (25). The ecological consequences of these findings deserve scrutiny. Oris et al. observed that current environmental concentrations of anthracene were less than the measured acute toxicity threshholds for the aquatic organisms which they studied (11). However, they warned that small increases of PAH concentrations in surface waters could cause dramatic impact on aquatic ecosystems. Pyrene and fluoranthene, which are more phototoxic than anthracene, may be among the most abundant PAH's found in air samples. In Norwegian air surveys, for example, these two together made up roughly one-third of all the hydrocarbons (26). Though the concentration of PAH's in natural waters varies, it can be very high (27). Of course, the presence of sensitizers in aquatic environments does not necessarily induce light-dependent toxicity toward all the organisms, since light attenuation through natural waters takes place rather rapidly, depending upon the nature of the impurities (28-29). The intensity, fluence, and spectral distribution of the light to which a given organism is exposed, as well as the rate of photodegradation of the sensitizers, will ultimately determine the photobiological response. Sensitized organisms which remain near the surface during the daytime should be the most severely affected.

Acknowledgments. We are indebted to Prof. G. Craig, Jr, Notre Dame University, for the original mosquitoes, to Prof. R. L. Willey, University of Illinois at Chicago, for the identification of the Daphnia magna, and to Prof. H. E. Buhse, Jr., who assisted with the collection of tadpoles and their identification. We are also grateful for the generous advice which they provided. Initial funding for this research was received from the National Institutes of Health (GM 24144). J. K. was later indebted to many review panels, particularly at the National Institutes of Health, the National Science Foundation, and the Environmental Protection Agency, for generous comments, and to the Research Board of the University of Illinois for financial support.

Literature cited

1. Yang, S. K.; Deutsch, J.; Gelboin, H. V. In "Polycyclic Hydrocarbons and Cancer", Gelboin, H. V.; Ts'O, P. O. P. Eds.; Academic: New York, 1978; Vol. 1, pp. 205-231.
2. Mottram, J. C.; Doniach, I. Nature 1938, 140, 933-4.
3. Doniach, I. Brit. J. Exp. Pathol. 1939, 20, 227-35.
4. Epstein, S. S.; Small, M..; Falk, H. L.; Mantel, N. Cancer Res. 1964, 24, 855-62.
5. Small, M.; Mantel, N.; Epstein, S. S. Exp. Cell Res. 1967, 45, 206-17.

6. Bauer, L.; Graef, W. Zentralbl. Bakteriol. Parasitendkd.
    Infektionskr. Hyg. Erste Abt. Orig. Reihe B Hyg. Praev. Med.
    1976, 161, 304-16.
7. Matoltsy, A. G.; Fabian, G. Nature 1946, 149, 877.
8. Matoltsy A. G.; Fabian G. Arch. Biol. Hungarica 1947, 17, 165-
    70.
9. Morgan, D. D.; Warshawsky, D. Photochem. Photobiol 1977, 25,
    39-46.
10. Bowling, J. W.; Laversee, G. J.; Landrum, P. F.; Giesy, J. P.
    Aquatic Toxicol. 1983, 3, 79-90.
11. Oris, J. T.; Giesy, J. P.; Allred, P. M.; Grant, D. F.;
    Landrum, P. F. in The Biosphere: Problems and Solutions, T. N.
    Veziroglu Ed.; Elsevier: Amsterdam, 1984; pp 636-658.
12. Spacie, A.; Landrum, P. F.; Leversee, G. J. Ecotoxicol.
    Environ. Saf. 1983, 7, 330-41.
13. Allred, P. M.; Giesy, J. P. Environ. Toxicol. Chem. 1985, 4,
    219-26.
14. Kagan, J.; Kagan, P. A.; Buhse, Jr., H. E. J. Chem. Ecol.
    1984, 10, 1115-22.
15. Kagan, J.; Chan, G. Experientia 1983, 39, 402-3.
16. Kagan, J.; Beny, J.-P.; Chan, G.; Dhawan, S. N.; Arora, S. K.;
    Prakash, I. J. Nat. Prod. 1983, 46, 646-50.
17. Kagan, J.; Beny, J.-P.; Chan, G.; Dhawan, S. N.; Jaworski, J.
    A.; Kagan, E. D.; Kassner, P. D.; Murphy, M.; Rogers, J. A.
    Insect Sci. Application 1983, 4, 377-81.
18. Kagan, J.; Kolyvas, C. P.; Jaworski, J. A.; Kagan, E. D.;
    Kagan, I. A.; L.-H. Zang, L.-H. Photochem. Photobiol. 1984, 40,
    479-84.
19. Kagan, J.; Kolyvas, C. P.; Lam, J. Experientia 1984, 40, 1396-
    7.
20. Mackay, D.; Shiu, W. Y. J. Chem. Eng. Data 1977, 22, 399-402.
21. Kochevar, I. E.; Armstrong, R. B.; Einbinder, J.; Walther, R.
    R.; Harber, L. C. Photochem. Photobiol. 1982, 36, 65-9.
22. Kaidbey, K. H.; S. Nonaka, S. Photochem. Photobiol. 1984, 39,
    375-8.
23. Guerin, M. R. in "Polycyclic Hydrocarbons and Cancer"; H. V.
    Gelboin; P. O. P. Ts'O, Eds.; Academic: New York, 1978; Vol. 1,
    pp. 3-42.
24. Baum, E. J. in "Polycyclic Hydrocarbons and Cancers"; H. V.
    Gelboin; P. O. P. Ts'O, Eds.; Academic: New York, 1978; Vol 1,
    pp. 45-70.
25. Neff, J. M. "Polycyclic Aromatic Hydrocarbons in the Aquatic
    Environment"; Applied Science Publishers, Barking, U.K., 1979;
    266 pp.
26. Bjørseth, A.; Sortland Olufsen, B. in "Handbook of Polycyclic
    Aromatic Hydrocarbons"; A. Bjørseth, Ed.; Marcel Dekker: New
    York, 1983; pp. 507-24.
27. Borneff, J. ; Kunte, H. in "Handbook of Polycyclic Aromatic
    Hydrocarbons"; A. Bjørseth, Ed.; Marcel Dekker: New York, 1983;
    pp. 629-652.
28. Smith, R.; Baker, K. S. Photochem. Photobiol. 1979, 29, 311-23.
29. Calkins, J. 1982. in "The Role of Solar Ultraviolet Radiation
    in Marine Ecosystem"; J. Calkins, Ed.; Plenum: New York; pp.
    247-262.
30. Kagan, J. ; Kagan, E. D. Chemosphere 1986, 15, 243-51.

RECEIVED May 27, 1986

HETEROGENEOUS REACTIONS

Chapter 15

Photochemistry in Aqueous Surface Layers: 1-Naphthol

Richard A. Larson[1,2] and Stewart A. Rounds[1]

[1]Institute for Environmental Studies, University of Illinois, Urbana, IL 61801
[2]Environmental Research Laboratory, U.S. Environmental Protection Agency, Athens, GA 30613

1-Naphthol was reactive toward direct photolysis in buffered aqueous solutions (at pH 7, half-life in sunlight was about 90 min) and in cyclohexane (half-life about 15 min). The reaction rate in water increased with pH. The mechanisms of the principal photolysis pathways in both solvents did not involve singlet oxygen. In aqueous solution, the major ether-extractable product, lawsone, may have been formed by a radical process involving 1,2-naphthoquinone and superoxide as intermediates. In cyclohexane, most of the photolysis products observed were very polar. Several oxygen-containing compounds derived from the solvent were also observed. In a two-phase system including cyclohexane and pH 7 buffer, the photolysis appeared to proceed by independent mechanisms in both phases, but intermediate polar products formed in the organic layer diffused into the aqueous layer. In a system containing a surface-active material, SDS, the rate of photolysis decreased; the photoproducts were typical of those observed in cyclohexane rather than water.

The fact that the air-water interface is an area of unusual properties relative to the underlying water column has been recognized for many years. The surface tension of pure water, for example, is much greater than that of natural waters containing organic matter, even though the bulk concentration of such materials may be very low (1-10 mg/l). In fact the surface tension of many natural waters is very close to that of weakly associated liquids such as benzene. This suggests that much of the organic matter nominally dissolved in water must have considerable surface-active properties. Molecules showing such activity are those where there is a strong separation between polar and nonpolar regions within the molecular structure; a

0097-6156/87/0327-0206$06.00/0
© 1987 American Chemical Society

simple example would be a long-chain fatty acid or a detergent sulfonate. Two types of surface-active molecules, wet and dry surfactants, have been distinguished (1). Wet surfactants are those in which a large portion of the molecule is physically located in the subsurface layer and only a small fraction of the surfactant projects above the surface into the air. Such molecules are normally of quite large size and include proteins, which typically have a few hydrophobic chains and a large regions of hydrophilic structure. Dry surfactants are those such as detergents, in which most of the molecule projects out of the water and only a small portion is associated with it. Although in early studies of surface microlayers, most attention was given to the determination of dry surfactants, recent work has confirmed that most of the material consists of polymeric, wet surfactants. For example, recent work on surface-active materials in freshwaters indicates that humic substances were the predominant surface-active materials in nearly all samples. Only in a few exceptional cases was the surface activity due partly to the presence of detergents (2).

Another event which will lead to a surface film on water is a spill of a hydrophobic material such as petroleum. In this case, it is likely, at least in a fresh spill, that the surface layer will be dominated by insoluble material (aliphatic and aromatic hydrocarbons) rather than surface-active material.

Many hydrophobic pollutants may tend to become more concentrated in naturally occurring microlayers, but because they are typically thin (<100 angstroms) only a very small fraction of the total pollutant load is likely to occur there. The situation is likely to be different in an oil spill event, in which the material floating on the surface of the water body is likely to form a thicker layer and also to be somewhat more stable to being disrupted by wind or wave action.

If a coherent, largely hydrophobic film exists on the surface of a water body, it may promote environmental alteration reactions of chemicals in several ways. It may act as a hydrophobic phase into which nonpolar organic compounds may partition and increase their concentration relative to the subsurface water; this may allow concentration-dependent processes to occur at faster rates. These would include oxidation reactions which require atmospheric oxygen as a reactant, since oxygen is significantly more soluble in nonpolar environments than in water. Biotic reactions may also occur faster at the air-water interface, since many types of bacteria and other microorganisms tend to concentrate there.

In order to predict the fate of an anthropogenic pollutant in natural waters, it is necessary to know how it is transported and how it is transformed, either biologically or abiotically, in the environment. For many compounds, photochemical degradation reactions are important destruction pathways. The behavior of a photochemically active compound in a surface layer, either one made up of surface-active or water-insoluble compounds, is likely to be dissimilar to its behavior in aqueous solution. Only a few studies have examined the question of the photochemical fates of organic compounds in natural surface layers: in one recent example, Zadelis and Simmons reported that the photolysis of naphthalene in Lake Michigan microlayer material was slower by a factor of ca. 2 relative to lake water (3). As mentioned previously, the surface film formed during accidental discharges of organic liquids such as petroleum into a water body is a very different type of environment, being a mixture of compounds which are usually very insoluble. During the course of exposure of a petroleum distillate film to light and air, however, photochemical changes may take place which lead to the formation of more polar substances and thus change the nature of the "solvent." Thus, for example, when a #2 fuel oil was exposed to Pyrex filtered mercury arc light, hydroperoxides, phenols, carboxylic acids and carbonyl compounds were produced. In the absence of a water phase, the oil became cloudy due to the separation of these hydrocarbon-insoluble substances; in the presence of water, some of the reaction products were extracted into the water phase, but some remained (4). Similar observations have been noted in the field during actual oil spills; crude oil from the IXTOC blowout in the Gulf of Mexico in 1979 had both a surface crust and a brownish suspended material associated with it. The crust tended to slough off and sink (5).

Mechanistic and product distribution differences between organic solvents, organized systems such as micelles, and water may be due to many causes, such as proximity effects due to differences in solvation, retardation or promotion of photoionization and other electron-transfer processes, concentration effects caused by increased solubility in one phase of a two-phase system, selective quenching or promotion effects by codissolved solutes, or other factors.

In this paper we report some preliminary investigations of the photochemical reactions of 1-naphthol (1) in water, in organic solvents, and in two-phase systems simulating surface films. 1-Naphthol has several properties that make it a desirable probe

1

for natural photochemical processes. Although quite hydrophobic, with an octanol-water partition coefficient of about 200, it is relatively water soluble (7.7 x 10^{-3} $\underline{M}$) (6). In addition, it has UV absorption maxima at 292, 308, and 322 nm, making direct photolysis possible. Furthermore, it has a relatively low-lying triplet state which has been shown to transfer energy to ground-state (triplet) oxygen, converting it to singlet oxygen ($^1O_2$); thus it may also be capable of indirect photochemical reactions.

Previous photochemical studies of naphthols have shown that 1-naphthol reacted with externally generated (methylene blue) $^1O_2$ to form 1,4-naphthoquinone (7). On the other hand, it has been observed that 1-naphthol forms the 1,2-isomer of naphthoquinone by free radical oxidations (8). Other naphthols show similar reactions with $^1O_2$; for example, 1,5-naphthalenediol (2) forms juglone (3) with externally generated $^1O_2$, but no juglone is formed when it is treated with superoxide (O_2^-) (9).

Experimental

1-Naphthol (Aldrich) was recrystallized from water to a constant sharp melting point before use. Diethyl ether was tested for peroxides by shaking a portion with acidified KI solution and only peroxide-free ether was used for extraction. Other reagents were used as supplied. Buffers were prepared with phosphate salts, except for pHs 10.0 (bicarbonate) and 9.0 (borate). For most experiments, which were 10^{-4} M in 1-naphthol, the light source was a GE model RSM sun lamp; in use, the lamp was positioned 10 cm above the solution, which was contained in a beaker immersed in a continuous-flow water bath to maintain a constant temperature (27 ± 2^0) and covered with a Pyrex watch glass. This arrangement gave similar UV intensities to those observed for a typical cloudless midsummer day (midmorning or midafternoon) in the northern hemisphere at 40^0 latitude, as measured by a digital radiometer (Ultraviolet Products, Inc., San Gabriel, CA) having separate UV-A and UV-B probes. Some kinetic experiments were performed in natural sunlight; the 1-naphthol samples, dissolved at about 10^{-5} M in appropriate solvents, were exposed in test tubes between 10 AM and 2 PM on sunny days in Athens, GA (latitude 34^0 N). The first-order rate constant for disappearance of 1-naphthol was determined by following the decrease in its concentration by high-performance liquid chromatography; a variable-wavelength UV detector, set at 292 nm, was employed. This rate constant was divided by the rate constant for the p-nitroanisole actinometer, determined under identical conditions, to give a relative rate constant (K_{rel}) (10). First-order kinetics were observed in all experiments, and no loss of 1-naphthol was noted in dark controls. Deaerated samples were prepared by purging with argon.

In preparative-scale (10^{-3} M 1-naphthol) experiments, an Ace-Hanovia 450-W medium-pressure mercury arc was used with a Pyrex filter sleeve and a magnetically stirred Ace water-cooled reaction vessel. In experiments involving rose bengal as a sensitizer, tungsten lamp illumination was used. Ultraviolet spectral changes were measured with a Perkin-Elmer model 552A spectrophotometer. For GC-MS analysis, a Hewlett-Packard 5985A instrument was used with a fused silica capillary column coated with a bonded nonpolar polymethyl silane phase introduced directly into the electron impact ionization source. Compounds were tentatively identified by comparison to published spectra and confirmed where possible with authentic standard materials.

Results and Discussion

Aqueous solution. During the irradiation of 1-naphthol in water, its disappearance was noted by the loss of its strong ultraviolet absorption at 292 nm. The reaction could also be followed by the increased intensity of a new peak at 262 nm. A smaller peak at 440 nm was also observed. In runs done at alkaline pH (10) it was also possible to monitor the disappearance of the enolate of 1-naphthol at 331 nm (the pKa of 1-naphthol is 9.34).

The photoreaction showed a definite pH dependence, with the faster rates occurring at higher pH (Fig. 1), indicating that the naphtholate anion may be the principal species involved in the photolysis. The anion also absorbs sunlight more strongly. The rate constant relative to the p-nitroanisole actinometer for 1-naphthol photolysis at pH 7 was about 4, corresponding to an approximate half-life of 90 min in midday summer sunlight. Control experiments for all these reaction conditions demonstrated that light was required for the reactions to occur. In the absence of oxygen, destruction of 1-naphthol still occurred, but the rate fell to approximately one-eighth of that measured in air-saturated samples.

Although many of the products of the reaction were very polar, as shown by HPLC and thin-layer chromatography, we were able to determine some of the products by extracting the aqueous solution of a preparative-scale reaction done at pH 8 with diethyl ether and analyzing the extract by gas chromatography-mass spectroscopy (GC-MS). The principal ether-soluble product was 2-hydroxy-1,4-naphthoquinone (lawsone, $\underline{4}$). The mass spectrum of lawsone was sufficiently characteristic to distinguish it clearly from other hydroxynaphthoquinone isomers such as juglone (11). Lawsone has also been reported previously as a product of photolysis of 1-naphthol in alkaline solution (12).

Minor products included 1,4-naphthoquinone and a possible nonoxidative dimer with an apparent molecular weight of 288 (1-naphthol mw = 144).

It is likely that lawsone is a "second-generation" photoproduct. One mechanism by which it could be formed is the decomposition of 1,2-naphthoquinone with water. The source of the 1,2-quinone is presumed to be the reaction of 1-naphthol and superoxide radical, produced from dissolved oxygen by electron transfer from an excited state of 1-naphthol (9):

$$\xrightarrow[-H_2O]{H^+} \quad \xrightarrow[[O]]{H_2O}$$

In a separate reaction using rose bengal in water as a sensitizer, we confirmed that 1-naphthol exposed to externally generated $^1O_2$ gave 1,4-naphthoquinone as the sole ether-extractable product.

Cyclohexane solution. The photooxidation reactions of 1-naphthol in a hydrocarbon solvent, cyclohexane, were much different from those in water. This was demonstrated clearly by UV spectral changes during the reaction which showed only the loss of the principal 292-nm absorbance maximum of 1-naphthol; no new maxima, only increasing end absorption, were observed. Kinetic studies showed clearly that the rate of 1-naphthol photolysis in cyclohexane was far faster than in water; K_{rel} in cyclohexane was 22 (half-life about 15 min in summer midday sunlight). A preparative-scale reaction in cyclohexane confirmed that the product distribution in the hydrocarbon solvent was different. During the photolysis, an insoluble yellow residue formed. When this residue was taken up in methanol and examined by GC-MS, most of the identifiable products appeared to be derived from the solvent; such compounds as cyclohexanol and possibly 1,2-dimethoxy-cyclohexane were present. The principal cyclohexane-soluble product of the reaction, dicyclohexyl ether, also appeared to be derived from the solvent by a free-radical process. Another important product of this reaction, whose structure has not yet been determined, is apparently a compound retaining a monosubstituted benzene ring and having two (possibly adjacent) carbonyl groups, as shown by its mass spectrum (Fig. 2) which has major ions at m/z 77 (relative intensity 13), 105 (19), and 133 (base peak).

Two-phase experiments. We conducted a photolysis experiment in which 1-naphthol was dissolved in a small amount of cyclohexane and layered over a pH 7 buffer. The partition coefficient for 1-naphthol between these two solvents favored cyclohexane by about 5:1. In this experiment, UV spectral data indicated that to some extent the photoreactions developed product distributions that would have occurred if the other phase had been absent. Thus, in the water layer, which did not contain much 1-naphthol to begin with because of the unfavorable partition coefficient, the usual maximum at 264 nm appeared and increased in intensity as it did in the single-phase aqueous experiments. In the cyclohexane layer, the loss of the 292-nm maximum for 1-naphthol was observed as before, but a minor peak at 270 nm could also be observed. Also, the end absorption intensity decreased with time, probably because nonpolar photooxidation products were

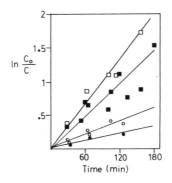

Figure 1. Sunlight photolysis of 1-naphthol in aqueous buffers.
Closed circles, pH 5; open circles, pH 6; closed squares, pH 7;
open squares, pH 8.   Rate constants relative to p-nitroanisole
actinometer: pH 5, 0.9; pH 6, 1.9; pH 7, 4.1; pH 8, 6.0.

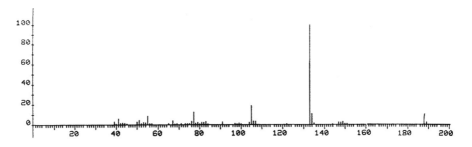

Figure 2. Mass spectrum of major product of 1-naphthol photolysis in cyclohexane or in aqueous SDS.

diffusing into the aqueous phase. Several such products which were not identified in the cyclohexane-only system were observed in the two-phase experiment, including a dihydroxynaphthalene, phthalic anhydride, phthalide (5), and an oxidative dimer of 1-naphthol having an apparent molecular weight of 286. The latter dimer had an intense fragment ion at m/z 143, and is likely to be a one-electron ("phenol-coupling") oxidation product.

5

The degradation of 1-naphthol was also investigated in the presence of a dry surfactant, sodium dodecyl sulfonate (SDS). A quantity of SDS calculated to give a surface layer of 0.1 mm thickness was used with an aqueous buffer at pH 7. The rate of this reaction was very much slower than the corresponding reaction in the absence of SDS; similar results were reported for the photodestruction of naphthalene in the presence of actual lake water surface layer material (3). The mechanistic reasons for the rate inhibitions observed in systems containing surface-active materials are uncertain. After exposure to the lamp, the reaction mixture was passed through a Dowex-2 anion exchange resin to remove the SDS, and the aqueous eluate was extracted with dichloromethane and analyzed by GC-MS. The products were the apparent benzenedicarbonyl compound with the ions at m/z 77, 105, and 133; a possible nonoxidative dimer (the same one observed in the pH 8 buffer preparative photolysis experiment) with a molecular weight of 288; and a small amount of 1,4-naphthoquinone.

Acknowledgments

We thank the National Research Council for a senior associateship at the U. S. EPA Environmental Research Laboratory (Athens, GA) to one of us (R. A. L.), and Dr. Richard Zepp of that laboratory for helpful discussions. The contents of this paper do not necessarily reflect the views of the U. S. Government, nor does the mention of trade names or commercial products constitute their endorsement by the U. S. Government.

Literature Cited

1. MacIntyre, F. *J*. *Rech*. *Atmos*. 1974, 8, 561.

2. Cosovic, B.; Vojvodic, V; Plese, T. *Water* *Res*. 1985, 19, 175.

3. Zadelis, D.; Simmons, M. S. In "Polynuclear Aromatic Hydrocarbons: Formation, Metabolism, and Measurement," Cooke, M.; Dennis, A. J., Eds., Battelle Press, Columbus, OH, 1983, p. 1279.

4. Larson, R. A.; Bott, T. L.; Hunt, L. L.; Rogenmuser, K. Environ. Sci. Technol. 1979, 13, 965.

5. Patton, J. S.; Rigter, U. W.; Boehm D.; Fiest, D. L. Nature 1981, 290, 135.

6. Korenman, Y. I.; Polumestnaya, E. I.; Lyapina, N. K. Izv. Vyssh. Uchebn. Zaved., Khim. Khim. Tekhnol. 1978, 21, 953; Chem. Abstr. 89:169867m (1978).

7. Griffiths, J.; Chu, K.-Y.; Hawkins, C. Chem. Commun. 1976, 676.

8. Teuber H. J.; Gotz, N. Chem. Ber. 1954, 87, 1276.

9. Duchstein H.; Wurm, G. Arch. Pharm. 1984, 317, 809.

10. Dulin D.; Mill, T. Environ. Sci. Technol., 1983, 16, 815.

11. Khariton, K. S.; Sandigurskaya, M. E.; Bordakh, O. D. Izv. Akad. Nauk Mold. SSSR, Ser. Biol. Khim. Nauk 1976, 2, 68: Chem. Abstr. 86:15939n (1977).

12. Aly O. M.; El-Dib, M. A. Water Res. 1971, 5, 1191.

RECEIVED May 27, 1986

Chapter 16

Algal-Induced Decay and Formation of Hydrogen Peroxide in Water: Its Possible Role in Oxidation of Anilines by Algae

Richard G. Zepp, Y. I. Skurlatov[1], and J. T. Pierce

Environmental Research Laboratory, U.S. Environmental Protection Agency, Athens, GA 30613

Studies of the rates of decomposition and photo-production of hydrogen peroxide (H_2O_2) by several green and blue-green algae in water are reported. Results suggest that algae have an important influence on the environmental concentration of H_2O_2, a widely distributed oxidant in natural waters. The algal-catalyzed decomposition of H_2O_2 in the dark was found to be second-order overall, first-order with respect to H_2O_2, and first-order with respect to algal biomass. Exposure of algal suspensions to sunlight resulted in a buildup of H_2O_2, indicating that algae can photoproduce as well as decompose this oxidant. Kinetic results for the algal-induced photooxidation of substituted anilines are presented and a mechanism involving the intermediacy of H_2O_2 is discussed.

Recent investigations have shown that hydrogen peroxide (H_2O_2) is a common constituent of the hydrosphere, including clouds, rainwater, freshwater, and seawater (1-3). In Figure 1, we have summarized several of the processes likely to be important in the formation and decay of H_2O_2 in natural water bodies.

Both field and laboratory studies indicate that the major pathway for production of H_2O_2 in natural waters is photochemical (2-3), although it also is introduced to water bodies through rain and biological processes. The photochemical formation is most likely mediated by electron transfer to dioxygen to form superoxide ion, an oxidant that dismutes to form H_2O_2. The conjugate acid of super-oxide ion, the hydroperoxyl radical, also rapidly disproportionates to form hydrogen peroxide (4).

[1]Current address: Institute of Chemical Physics, Academy of Sciences of the Union of Soviet Socialist Republics, Moscow, USSR

Several pathways can account for the decomposition of hydrogen peroxide in natural waters. Some of these decay processes not only remove H_2O_2, but also result in the oxidation of chemicals, possibly including various pollutants, that are present in natural waters. These processes include direct oxidation (5), peroxidase-catalyzed oxidation (6), and free radical oxidation initiated by photochemical or metal-catalyzed decomposition (7). Little is known about the significance and rates of these various processes under environmental conditions, but they have all been shown to occur rapidly with certain organic substrates in the laboratory.

Many previous studies have shown that the light-induced transformation of certain pollutants is greatly accelerated in natural waters compared to distilled water. Oxidations via photoproduced H_2O_2 may account for the results of some of these investigations. In this paper, we report results that quantify the rates of photoproduction and decomposition of H_2O_2 by several pure cultures of algae in water. Results also are presented which indicate that H_2O_2 or a precursor thereof may be involved in the algal-induced photooxidation of anilines.

Experimental

Materials. Analytical grade m-toluidine and p-butylaniline were obtained commercially from ChemService and used as received. Aniline (Aldrich) was purified by treating an aqueous solution with activated charcoal (0.1% by weight). The charcoal was removed by filtration through a 0.2 μm Millipore filter. The filtrate was extracted by ether and, after drying over anhydrous sodium sulfate, the layer was evaporated under vacuum. The aniline finally was distilled under vacuum. Horseradish peroxidase (HRP) (activity 152 purpurogallin units/mg), catalase (from bovine liver, activity 17,600 units/mg protein) and leuco malachite green (LMG) [4,4'benzylidene-bis (N,N-dimethylaniline] were obtained from Sigma Chemicals. The LMG was purified by first washing a benzene solution (0.1 g/ml) with 5% aqueous sodium hydroxide. The benzene layer was separated, dried over anhydrous sodium sulfate, then evaporated to dryness. The resulting residue was recrystallized twice from hexane.

The algae used in the studies were either obtained on slants from the Starr collection (8) at the University of Texas, Austin, Texas, or from a collection of Dr. Gary Kochert, Botany Department, University of Georgia, Athens, Georgia. The bacteria-free algae from the Starr collection were handled and grown under aseptic conditions. UTEX 76, UTEX 26, UTEX 89, Chlamydomonas sp., Chlorococcum hypnosporum, Anabaena variabilis, and Chlorogonium sp. were grown in medium and under conditions specified by Zepp and Schlotzhauer (9). UTEX 625 and UTEX 1444 were grown at 39°C in the media that is described by Kratz and Myers (10) as modified by Van Baalen (11) using an 8:16 hr light-dark cycle.

Equipment. The algae were grown in a New Brunswick Scientific Co. controlled environment incubator shaker. Kinetic studies were conducted using algae suspensions that were agitated on a New Brunswick G-10 gyrotary shaker.

A Perkin Elmer Lambda 3 uv-visible spectrophotometer was used in the peroxide assays. The algae suspensions were filtered using Micromate 5-cm^3 glass syringes equipped with Millipore filter holders containing Whatman GF/C filter pads.

Aniline solutions were analyzed using a Micromeritics Model 7170 high pressure liquid chromatograph equipped with a column packed with ODS-3; mixtures of acetonitrile and water were used as mobile phase.

Kinetic Procedures. The algae culture suspension (100ml) was placed in a sterile 200-ml Erlenmeyer flask. The flask was covered with aluminum foil to block out light. The temperature of the reaction was kept at 18°C throughout the experiment. The kinetic run was started by adding sufficient H_2O_2 to result in an initial concentration of 5.0 μM.

The reaction mixture was then placed on the shaker at a shaker speed of 100 rpm. After one minute of shaking, a 4.5-ml aliquot of the solution was filtered and mixed with 0.5 ml of a peroxidase/LMG assay solution (12 μM LMG, 40 mg/L peroxidase in pH 4.0 acetate buffer). A blue color formed immediately when the H_2O_2 and the assay solution were mixed. The sample was then allowed at least 20 minutes to develop completely. More samples were taken at intervals throughout the run until about two halflives were complete.

Using the spectrophotometer, the absorbance of the samples at 617 nm was determined versus distilled water. The absorbance at 750 nm also was determined and subtracted from the 617 nm absorbance to yield a corrected absorbance. A first-order rate constant for the corrected absorbance versus time then was calculated using an HP41C calculator programmed to fit the data by least squares analysis.

After completion of the kinetic run, 30 ml of the remaining algae suspension then was analyzed for its chlorophyll $\underline{a}$ content, C_a (12). Experiments on the photoproduction of H_2O_2 and the algal-induced oxidation of anilines were conducted in full sunlight as described by Zepp and Schlotzhauer (9) using a $\underline{p}$-nitroanisole actinometer (13) to measure light intensity.

Effects of H_2O_2 upon the oxidation of aniline in dark algal cultures were studied. To a suspension (100 ml) of the algae (C_a, 2000-5000 mg chl $\underline{a}/m^3$) in phosphate buffer containing 5.0 μM aniline was added sufficient H_2O_2 to make the initial concentration 20 μM. The resulting mixture was incubated on the shaker for three half-lives of the H_2O_2, then a portion (2.0 ml) was removed, filtered and analyzed for aniline and H_2O_2. This procedure was repeated five times. No reaction (<10%) of the aniline was observed after five cycles, indicating that less than 0.005 moles of aniline reacted per mole of decomposed H_2O_2. In a control experiment with

HRP (1 mg/L) substituted for the algae, the aniline was completely oxidized with one cycle of the H_2O_2 decomposition.

Results and Discussion

Kinetic Studies of H_2O_2 Decay. In the presence of all the types of algae studied, the decomposition of hydrogen peroxide was first-order with respect to peroxide. As the typical results in Figure 2 illustrate, the catalysis was heterogeneous; catalysts released by the algae into bulk solution were not involved.

Other studies involving variation in algal concentration indicated that the decay rate of H_2O_2 also was first-order with respect to chlorophyll a content, C_a. The complete rate expression was second-order overall:

$$\text{Rate} = k_1 \ [H_2O_2] = k_{bio} \ C_a \ [H_2O_2] \qquad (1)$$

Plots of pseudo-first-order rate constants, k_1, versus algal biomass expressed as micrograms chlorophyll a/L were linear (Figure 3).

Second-order rate constants for catalysis of H_2O_2 decay by five freshwater green algae and four cyanobacteria are reported in Table I. Most of the microorganisms examined were quite efficient at removing H_2O_2, indicating that algal-induced decomposition is likely a major pathway for its decay in freshwaters. For example, using the median value of 0.0044 m^3 (mg chl a)$^{-1}$h^{-1}, the half-life for H_2O_2 in the euphotic zone of a eutrophic lake ($C_a = 100$ mg/m^3) is estimated to be about 1.5 hours.

Table I. Kinetic Data for Algal-catalyzed Decay of Hydrogen Peroxide -- 18°C in Dark

Algae	$10^3 \ k_{bio}$ m^3(mg chl a)$^{-1}$h^{-1} [a]
Cyanobacteria	
Nostoc muscorum	8.8 $\pm$ 2.0
UTEX 625 (Synechococcus leopoliensis)	4.3 $\pm$ 1.1
UTEX 625 - after 4 hours of sunlight exposure	3.2 $\pm$ 0.8
UTEX 1444 (Anaebaena flos-aquae)	2.2 $\pm$ 0.5
Anabaena variabilis	7.7 $\pm$ 1.2
Green algae	
UTEX 76 (Scenedesmus quadricauda)	4.4 $\pm$ 1.1
UTEX 89 (Chlamydomonas reinhardtii)	0.18 $\pm$ 0.04
Chlorococcum hypnosporum	6.3 $\pm$ 0.9
Chlamydomonas sp.	1.2 $\pm$ 0.2
Chlamydomonas sp. - after 5 hours of sunlight exposure	0.1 $\pm$ 0.02
Chlorogonium sp.	5.5 $\pm$ 1.3

[a] Mean ($\pm$ s.d. for three kinetic runs)

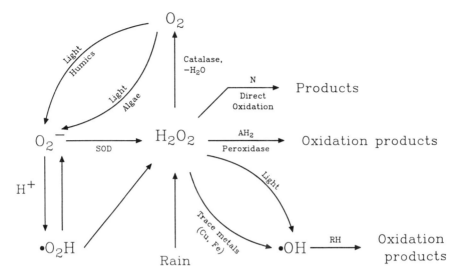

Definitions: SOD — Superoxide dismutase in biota
N — Nucleophile that reacts with H_2O_2
AH_2 — Substrate capable of oxidation by peroxidases, H_2O_2 (e.g. phenols, anilines)
RH — Organic chemical

Figure 1. Processes that contribute to the formation and decay of hydrogen peroxide in aquatic environments.

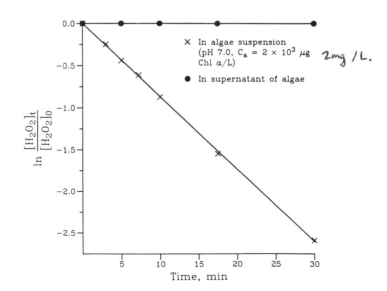

Figure 2. Kinetic data for the decay of hydrogen peroxide in suspension of UTEX 1444.

Rates of H_2O_2 Photoproduction. Exposure of the Chlamydomonas sp.
cultures to solar radiation resulted in a buildup of H_2O_2 (Figure 4).
The rate of formation increased with increasing light exposure and
with increasing algae concentration. Moreover, the ability of the
Chlamydomonas to catalyze the decay of H_2O_2 decreased sharply with
increasing irradiation (Table I). Sunlight exposure also reduced
the H_2O_2-decomposing ability of the cyanobacteria, UTEX 625, but
the effect was not nearly as pronounced as with Chlamydomonas (Table
I). These results indicate that the degree of H_2O_2 buildup may be
related in part to photodegradation of peroxide-decomposing enzymes.

Rates of photoproduction of H_2O_2 by several algae are compared
in Table II. The tabulated values correspond to averages observed
during a 5-hour exposure to midday sunlight at Athens, Georgia. For
unknown reasons, the Nostoc muscorum produced H_2O_2 much less efficiently. The lower efficiency may in part be ascribed to the much
larger size (and lower surface area per biomass) of the Nostoc cells
(about 50 μm in diameter) compared to the other algae
studied (<10 μm).

Table II. Kinetic Data for Photoproduction of Hydrogen Peroxide by
          Various Algae in Sunlight

Algal Type	$10^{-3} C_a$,mg chl a/m^3	Average Rate of Peroxide Production (M h^{-1} x 10^6)[a,b]
Chlamydomonas sp.	0.9	0.8
Chlamydomonas sp.	0.097	0.15
Chlorogonium sp.	1.0	0.6
Anaebaena variabilis	0.9	1.7
Nostoc muscorum	1.0	0.04

[a]Peroxide completely decomposed by brief treatment (1 minute) with
catalase. [b]Midday, near-surface sunlight intensity, spring, latitude 34°N.

Algal-induced Oxidation of Anilines. Kinetic studies indicated
that several anilines were oxidized when exposed to sunlight in
suspensions of Chlamydomonas sp., a green algae (Figure 5). In
previous studies, we have presented evidence that this oxidation
is not metabolic (9). Aniline and its alkyl-substituted derivatives
were found to be unreactive in the supernatant from centrifuged
algal suspensions, indicating that the photocatalysis was heterogeneous. Variation of the alkyl substituent on the aromatic ring
of aniline had a pronounced effect on the rate of the reaction
(Figure 5). Relative rate constants for the reaction correlated
with octanol-water partition coefficients for the anilines (Table
III). This hydrophobic effect supports a reaction mechanism
involving partitioning of the substrate on the algal cells, as
previously postulated by Zepp and Schlotzhauer (9) (Figure 6).

The above discussed results suggested a possible role of
hydrogen peroxide in the aniline photooxidations. In support of

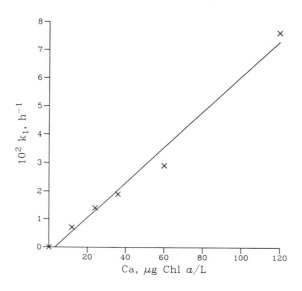

Figure 3. Dependence of first-order rate constant for decay of hydrogen peroxide on concentration of Chlamydomonas sp.

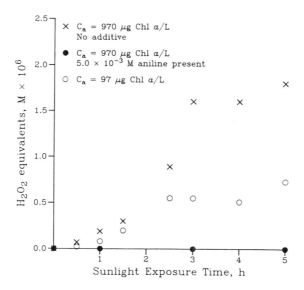

Figure 4. Photoproduction of hydrogen peroxide in suspensions of Chlamydomonas sp. exposed to sunlight.

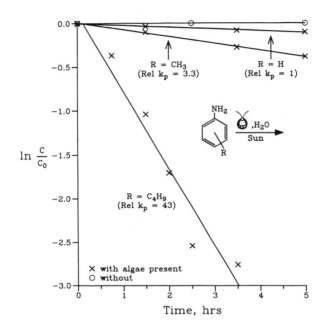

Figure 5.   Kinetic plots for oxidation of anilines in suspension of
Chlamydomonas sp. exposed to sunlight.

I.   P $\rightleftarrows$ P–Algae $\xrightarrow{\text{Light}}$ Products

II.   Algae + Light $\xrightarrow[\text{O}_2]{\text{H}_2\text{O}}$ H$_2$O$_2$

        H$_2$O$_2$ + P–Algae $\xrightarrow{\text{Light?}}$ Products

Figure 6.   Possible pathways for the algal–induced oxidation of
anilines.

Table III. Comparison of Rate Constants and K_{ow}'s for Alkyl-Substituted Anilines

Compound	log K_{ow} [a]	In Algae Suspension log k_{rel} [b]
Aniline	0.98	-0.73
m-Toluidine	1.40	-0.21
p-n-Butylaniline	2.6 [c]	0.91

[a]Ref. 15; [b]Ratio of rate constant in sunlight to rate constant for p-nitroanisole actinometer (conditions 1 M aniline; 240 mg chl a/m³ Chlamydomonas sp.; pH 7.0 in phosphate buffer; [c]computed value.

this concept, aniline strongly quenched the photoproduction of H_2O_2 by Chlamydomonas sp. (Figure 4), possibly indicating that the peroxide or a precursor thereof was diverted by reaction with the substrate on the cell. The idea was supported further by earlier studies (14) that showed that anilines are particularly susceptible to oxidations catalyzed by peroxidases. When H_2O_2 was added repetitively to dark algal suspensions (Chlamydomonas, Nostoc, Anabaena) containing anilines, however, no aniline oxidation occurred when the peroxide decomposed. Aniline was rapidly oxidized under the same conditions with added peroxidase. These results indicate that other substances, probably catalase enzymes (16), were responsible for the decomposition of H_2O_2 by the algae included in the present study. The inhibition of photoproduction of H_2O_2 by aniline must be attributed to physical or chemical quenching of a precursor to the H_2O_2 or possibly to a light-induced reaction between H_2O_2 and aniline on the surface of the algal cell (Figure 6). A detailed examination of the nature of this oxidation was beyond the scope of this study.

Conclusions

(1) Green and blue-green algae are capable of efficiently catalyzing the removal of trace hydrogen peroxide from water. A second-order rate expression describes the removal. The median second-order rate constant for nine algae was about $4 \times 10^{-3} m^3$ (mg/chl a)$^{-1}h^{-1}$.

(2) Exposure of algae to sunlight results in photogeneration of hydrogen peroxide. This finding indicates that the microbiota contribute to the photoproduction of peroxide in natural waters, although further research is required to establish the generality of this photoprocess.

(3) A green algae photocatalyzed the oxidation of anilines in a reaction that exhibited a pronounced hydrophobic effect. Anilines also inhibited the photoproduction of H_2O_2 by Chlamydomonas indicating that photochemically produced peroxide or a precursor thereof plays a key role in the oxidation.

Acknowledgments

A portion of this work was performed under the Bilateral Agreement of Environmental Protection, Project 02.03-31 "Forms and Mechanisms by Which Pesticides and Chemicals are Transported", between the United States and the Union of Soviet Socialist Republics. The technical assistance of J. Mims and C. Bakke is acknowledged as is the preparation of the figures by B. Bartell, R. Moon and P. Winter.

Literature Cited

1. Penkett, S.A.; Jones, B.M.R.; Brice, K.A.; Eggleton, A.E.J. Atmos. Environ. 1979, 13, 123.
2. Cooper, W.J.; Zika, R.G. Science 1983, 220, 711.
3. Draper, W.; Crosby, D.G. Arch. Environ. Cont. Toxicol. 1983, 12, 121.
4. Bielski, B.H.J.; Cabelli, D.E.; Arudi, R.L.; Ross, A.B. J. Phys. Chem. Ref. Data 1985, 14, 1041-1100.
5. Leung, P-S.K.; Hoffmann, M.R. J. Phys. Chem. 1985, 89, 5267.
6. Dunford, H.B.; Stillman, J.S. Coord. Chem. Rev. 1976, 19, 187-251.
7. Draper, W.M.; Crosby, D.G. J. Agr. Food Chem. 1984, 32, 231.
8. Starr, R.C. J. Phycol. 1978, 14, 47-100.
9. Zepp, R.G.; Schlotzhauer, P.F. Environ. Sci. Technol. 1983, 17, 462-468.
10. Kratz, W.A.; Myers, J. Am. J. Bot. 1955, 42, 282-287.
11. van Baalen, C.; Marler, J.E. Nature 1966, 211, 951.
12. "Standard Methods for the Examination of Water and Wastewater"; 13th Ed.; American Public Health Association: New York, 1971; pp. 746-747.
13. Dulin, D.; Mill, T. Environ. Sci. Technol. 1982, 16, 815.
14. Job, D.; Dunford, H.B. Eur. J. Photochem. 1976, 66, 607.
15. Leo, A.; Hansch, C.; Elkins, D. Chem. Rev. 1971, 71, 525.
16. Saunders, B.C.; Holmes-Seidle, A.G.; Stark, B.P. "Peroxidase"; Butterworths: London, 1964.

RECEIVED July 8, 1986

Chapter 17

Photocatalysis by Inorganic Components of Natural Water Systems

Cooper H. Langford and John H. Carey

Department of Chemistry, Concordia University, Montreal, Quebec, Canada, and National Water Research Laboratory, Canada Center for Inland Waters, Burlington, Ontario, Canada

A brief inventory of aquatic components potentially active as photocatalysts includes colloidal and sedimentary oxides and sulfides, metal complexes of organic ligands, and certain metal ions in clays. The reactions are to be understood in terms of the redox reactions following ligand to metal charge transfer and its extension to solid lattices, reactions of photogenerated electron hole pairs according to the "microcorrosion cell" model. Studies, many of which were directed to development of waste treatment techniques, have suggested probable pathways.

Inventory of Chromophores

The first inorganic species to be considered as candidates for photoreactions important in natural waters were carboxylic acid complexes of Fe^{+3} and Cu^{+2} [e.g. the NTA complexes] (1, 2). In these complexes, photooxidation of the organic ligand is initiated by an excitation process in which a ligand localized electron is promoted into the partly filled $\underline{d}$ shell of the metal ion. This results in reduction of the metal ion. Since the reduced metal ion is often readily reoxidized by oxygen, the reactions can be rendered catalytic. The implications of the model studies have been validated by results obtained for both marine (3) and fresh (4) waters. In considering the extensions of these precedents, we must consider the range of possible metal organic complexes satisfying the conditions for charge transfer within the wavelength range available in illuminated waters, reducibility of the metal ion, and an irreversible first step for the oxidation of the

0097-6156/87/0327-0225$06.00/0

organic ligand that can effectively block back reaction.
The metal ions are few [notably Fe(III), Mn(III, IV),
perhaps UO^{+2}, and Cu(II) in the uv limit]. The organic
ligands that give irreversible oxidation are predomina-
tely those which contain a carboxylate and can decompose
rapidly after one electron oxidation to release CO_2 and
escape back reaction or those containing functionality
like phenol where the result of one electron oxidation
is a relatively stable radical which may survive. The
overall impression is that the range of reactions will
be limited and that the evidence to date is consistent
with such a notion. Indeed, since a major source of
organic ligands in fresh waters is humic material which
has stronger light absorption at long wavelength than
most metal complexes and has photoinitiation pathways of
its own (5, 6) which may be metal ion quenched, the
interaction of metal ions with organic ligands may do as
much to quench photochemistry in natural waters as to
initiate it!

A more promising possibility for reactions of general significance began to emerge with the recognition
of the implications for natural water photochemistry of
the developing subject of initiation of photoreaction
following band gap irradiation of semiconductors. It is
interesting to reflect, in the face of current torrent
of papers on this subject (7), that the idea has been
around for a rather long time (8) and that some of the
earliest thoughts on its utilization for solution
reactions were connected to waste water treatment. A
report from the Robert A. Taft Center appeared in 1969
(9) and CCIW workers reported the dechlorination of PCBs
using anatase in 1975 (10).

There are important parallels between the way that
illumination of a semiconductor can produce reactive
species in solution and the reduction of the metal ion
and oxidation of the ligand characterizing the ligand to
metal charge transfer photochemistry described above.
But, aspects of the behaviour of the semiconductor-
solution interface can overcome several of the limitations mentioned for the homogeneous complexes. When a
semiconductor is illuminated with light of energy
greater than its optical band gap, an electron is
transferred to the conduction band leaving a hole in the
valence band. At the interface, electron transfer can
occur either from the conduction band to an acceptor, A,
in solution or from a donor, D, in solution to the
valence band. These processes are shown in FIGURE 1.
They compete with the fruitless recombination of
electron and hole to produce thermal energy. In the
case of the metal complexes above, the recombination
could only be avoided by production of "stable" chemical
intermediates. In this case, there are two other
possibilities for resistance to the back reaction. The

first is essentially thermodynamic and the second is essentially kinetic.

When a particle of sufficient size electrochemically equilibrates with the E_h of the surrounding solution, the Fermi level in the semiconductor bulk comes to the potential of the environmental E_h. This usually results in band bending at the interface and a depletion layer at the surface of the semiconductor with a potential gradient (<u>11</u>) favouring the separation of the photogenerated charge carriers as is shown in FIGURE 2. This means that the band bending can promote charge separation in a way unavailable to a molecular system. The exact energetics will depend on the relation between the valence and conduction band energies and the E_h of the solution. One of the electron transfer processes, the one resulting from the transfer of the carrier toward the particle solution interface, is sometimes characterized as a photoreaction. The other, the one resulting from the transfer of the carrier transferred by the band bending toward the interior of the particle, is thought of correspondingly as a thermal reaction. But, the rate of each reaction will normally be governed by the rules of interfacial electron transfer. The two most important factors are the degree of exergonicity of the interfacial electron transfer and the extent of overlap of the distribution of energy levels of solute species and the band edges (<u>11</u>).

In natural waters, many interesting semiconducting particles, especially those of the well hydrated hydrous oxides which have large "interior" surface, will have particle sizes much smaller that the typical thickness of the depletion layer at the solution semiconductor interface. It might be assumed that such small particles would carry no advantage over molecular excited states in the competition of separation of charge carriers <u>vs</u> back reaction. This is not entirely the case. Even a small particle may have many atoms and the mobility of a carrier, once generated, is sufficiently large to carry it away from the site of generation. Moreover, a typical semiconductor will be capable of being "doped" with localized sites of one type or the other. These localized sites are traps that can capture photogenerated carriers in times of the order of a nanosecond or two. Evidence for this trapping mechanism has recently been developed in a study of the picosecond transfer from an excited dye to TiO_2 where the trapping process can be resolved and the back reaction is slow (<u>12</u>).

The picosecond spectra show that the time constants for trapping of an excess carrier from a semiconductor band to the localized sites which correspond to doping is a process in the nanosecond time domain. However, the trapped site spectra did not appear under all circumstances when light was absorbed at the

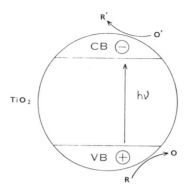

FIGURE 1. The Photocatalytic Semiconductor Particle "Corrosion" Cell Illustrated by TiO₂. Note that the Redox Couples may need to be Adsorbed if Reaction is to Compete with Recombination.

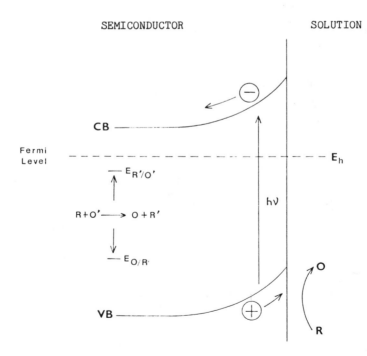

FIGURE 2. Energetics of Oxidation at the Semiconductor Electrolyte Interface.

semiconductor surface. Analysis of the circumstances indicated that the crucial factor was the competition between recombination of holes and electrons at the surface and the escape of carriers into the interior. A key factor for the efficient escape of a carrier from the surface to the interior was the presence of a reactant on the surface that could react with either electrons or holes. At high light intensity, these initial steps must be in the picosecond time domain. Therefore, efficient photochemistry will depend very strongly on the presence of adsorbed reactants at the surface. With adsorbed reactants, even the small particle can considerably favour charge separation by an essentially kinetic mechanism.

We should add parenthetically that the observations just described may provide the resolution of a minor controversy. There has been some dispute over the role of light absorption by the semiconductor and by surface complexes. The greater absorptivity of the semiconductor suggests that light is absorbed by the solid. However, the requirement of a surface scavenger to prevent rapid recombination will give the overall kinetics the characteristics indicating a surface complex.

Colloidal photocatalysts can form in natural waters in a variety of ways. In general, precipitation of a solution species initiates. The processes include at least the following possibilities:

i. Iron and manganese oxides are precipitated by oxidation of low Eh solutions in environments such as those which occur when ground water emerges at the surface or reducing water flows from a wetland.

ii. U, V, Cu, Se, and Ag are precipitated as low valency oxides (or metals) when waters at high Eh mix with reducing waters or encounter organic reducing matter.

iii. Fe, Cu, Ag, Zn, Pb, Hg, Ni, Co, As, and Mo are precipitated as sulfides by reduction of sulfate waters, usually by sulfate reducing bacteria.

The final category of chromophore that we will consider here is the coloured inorganic ion adsorbed (or ion exchanged into) a site on a clay particle. In such cases, the light absorption is localized and charge separation does not occur because of migration of carriers in the solid. Rather, moderately efficient reaction can arise when target molecules can be coadsorbed and the initiating chromophore reacts efficiently with the coadsorbed molecule. An appropriate example is the uranyl exchanged clay photocatalyst which accomplishes the oxidation of alcohols to ketones (13).

Photocatalysts in the Natural Setting

Especially in the case of the particulate semiconductors, there is now an extensive laboratory chemistry of
the catalytic reactions which may be accomplished.
However, the situation in a natural setting is much more
complex than is characteristic of model studies. Before
we begin a review of important reactions now known, it
is useful to set out some comments on the factors, which
differentiate the laboratory study from the natural
system.

First, we must remain aware that natural waters do
not receive extensive illumination at wavelengths
shorter than about 350 nm. Thus, some of the processes
involving high band gap oxide photocatalysts which
attract a great deal of laboratory attention do not
figure importantly in natural systems. Much of our
attention should be directed toward processes utilizing
longer wavelengths. It is true that, at least for
shallow waters, models of the illumination available
have proved adequate to account for the overall rates of
photoreaction (14) so that this factor is well understood. On the other hand, we do not require large
quantum yields to produce significant effects. Half
lives of direct photolysis of organic chromophores have
been estimated between a few hours and thirty days (14).
If the shortest reflect quantum yields near one, then
values near 0.001 are still interesting on the time
scale of one month.

With colloidal photocatalysts, increased diffusive-
ness of light caused by scattering in turbid waters can
lead to enhanced photolysis rates. For example, a study
of the effects of clays on the rate of a uv photolysis
showed an initial increase in the photolysis rate on
addition of clay followed by a decrease when the clay
concentration finally produced offsetting light attenuation (15). The light available for photochemistry
should be measured by thermal lensing and photoacoustic
measurements. This has been demonstrated to be effective
for waters containing humic colloids and suspended fine
sands (16).

A very important difference between laboratory
photocatalysts and corresponding materials in the
natural setting is relative purity. In the laboratory,
most work has been conducted using pure mineral phases.
In natural waters, many minerals have colours characteristic of excitation of electrons from impurity levels
within the bandgap. In this case, the hole energies
will be less favorable for oxidative processes than in
the case of excitation at wavelength short enough to
promote electrons from the deeper lying conduction band.
This has been well documented by laboratory studies
directed toward the shifting of the water oxidation
reaction catalyzed by anatase toward the visible by

doping the titanium dioxide lattice with metal ions with
partly filled $\underline{d}$ shells. The case of doping with Cr(III)
is an especially interesting example ($\underline{17}$). Hydrogen
evolution from water was observed at Cr(III) doped TiO_2
irradiated with light passed through a 415 nm cutoff
filter. The electron promoted to the conduction band
has the reducing power of the conduction band edge. In
this case, the Cr(IV) produced has the oxidizing power
(locally) necessary to oxidize water. It appeared that
the Cr is located in the surface region of the particle
which was probably necessary to the oxidation of a
solution species. A typical coloured internal ion in a
mineral might not be as strongly oxidizing as Cr(IV) but
if it were, there would be a difficulty in its migration
to the surface to oxidize a solute.

    An additional relevant problem was identified in
this study of Cr doping of anatase. The photoreactivity
cut off at a doping level above 0.4% which corresponds
to the solubility limit in anatase. The authors believe
that a chromic oxide surface layer forms which blocks
reaction. This calls attention to a common stage in the
aqueous oxidative weathering of mineral particles, the
formation on the surface of a film of an oxide in the
higher oxidation state of the ion. This is seen,
especially, in the increase of Fe_2O_3 in the oxide
analysis of the products of weathering. Such surface
films may interdict the expected photoreactivity of the
underlying pure mineral at, as the example suggests, low
total levels. On the other hand, such films can produce
oxide semiconductors on underlying minerals that might
otherwise seem unpromising.

    Another aspect of the impurity doping which will be
common in mineral particles is illustrated by the effect
of Nb(V) on anatase. This ion substitutes isomorphical-
ly for Ti(IV) and as an n dopant creates a Shottky
barrier at the interface. This assists injection of an
electron from a reducing solute into the conduction band
($\underline{18}$). The flat band is also shifted cathodically. It
has recently been claimed that the relative inefficiency
of haematite as a photoanode is a function of low
mobility of carriers and that this problem may be
overcome by doping with Si(IV) ($\underline{19}$). In this we see the
last effect of doping, the modification of carrier
mobility.

    Having raised the question of surface films on
mineral particles, it is tempting to also comment here
on the tendency of particles to acquire organic coa-
tings. Again, the photochemical consequences are
complex. The organic matter may absorb light. These
excited states may "sensitize" the underlying minerals
by electron or hole injection. Some evidence for such a
process has been obtained in studies of fulvic acid
adsorbed on anatase ($\underline{20}$). On the other hand, hydrous
ferric oxides have recently been observed to quench the

photochemistry initiated by the fulvic acid. As a third effect, the organic film may be the redox species which reacts with the photogenerated carriers from the mineral particle.

Pathways of reaction - reduction

As mentioned above, both electrons and holes must be efficiently separated and both must reach the particle surface. Even when both reach the surface, recombination may still predominate if both are not consumed in appropriate fast reactions. It is worth reiterating that the requirements for fast reactions are twofold. The first is favorable energetics. The redox couples must be included within the band gap as shown in FIGURE 2. But, it is also necessary to maximize the rate of interfacial electron transfer. This is essentially a standard problem of electrochemical kinetics and, as such, one for which there are extensive precedents. Above, we mentioned the general theoretical rules. Here, we will give more attention to specific examples. In most cases, experimental results can provide precedents.

Since the main point will be to compare the rates of competing processes, it is useful to divide the discussion into reduction and oxidation reactions.

In order for an oxidant to react rapidly, it will be most advantageous for it to be present adsorbed on the surface so that mass transport will not limit the rate. This means that we should first consider the solvent which is always at the interface. The possibility of water acting as an acceptor to produce hydrogen has attracted a great deal of attention because of the possibility of storing solar energy in a chemical fuel by this process. Unfortunately, water is not that easy to reduce. In every case where there has been success, a known catalyst for hydrogen evolution has been required. Naturally occurring materials do not offer many of the known catalysts. The only example using a material which might occur in natural waters is the use of ZnS as a catalyst for H_2 evolution (21). Here the special property of ZnS to photodegrade partially leaving a deposit of Zn metal on the surface links the example to other cases. Hydrogen evolution most often is achieved by the mediation of a metal catalyst-commonly the noble metals known for their lower overvoltages for hydrogen. This "unreactivity" can prove beneficial in some environmental contexts. If water is not rapidly reduced there is a better opportunity for direct reaction with a solute (including xenobiotics).

The next most likely acceptor to occur at the surface of a mineral particle is the oxygen molecule which will generally be present at reasonable levels throughout the photic zone. Oxygen is strongly adsorbed on a number of surfaces and especially on oxide surfaces. The generation of the superoxide ion, O_2^-, from one electron reduction of the oxygen molecule is a well known reaction that has recently been shown to occur in humic waters (22). Many studies of photocatalysis at semiconductor surfaces including early work in one of our laboratories on the photolysis of PCBs in anatase slurries (9) have noted that no reaction occurs in the absence of oxygen. Superoxide is a good nucleophile. Also, a reaction of the following type is known:

$$O_2^- + \underset{}{\bigcirc}^{Cl} \longrightarrow O_2 + \underset{}{\circledast}^{Cl}$$

,which leads to loss of Cl^- and abstraction by the aryl radical. Some results on the model system of a dispersion of anatase in a solution containing chlorobenzoic acid as a water soluble chloroaromatic are shown in TABLE I. Fe(III) was the ultimate electron acceptor. Benzoic acid is produced. (It is interesting that we did not succeed in catalyzing the same reaction on irradiation of haematite.) Pathways based on superoxide deserve attention in a variety of situations.

TABLE I

Acid	Fe(II) Yield	Cl^- Yield	Salicylate Yield
Benzoic	0.121	–	0.017
o-Chloro-	0.139	0.041	<0.001
m-Chloro-	–	0.026	–
p-Chloro-	–	0.037	–

Superoxide is unstable in aqueous solution. Disproportionation occurs according to equation (2) and is a source of hydrogen peroxide which functions along with uv irradiation in a standard analytical method for the destruction of organic matter in natural water samples.

$$2O_2^- + 2H^+ = H_2O_2 + O_2 \qquad (2)$$

Hydrogen peroxide is also destructive to living systems.

Other electron acceptors present at the surface of excited particles may also be subject to photoreduction. For example, the reduction of surface Fe(III) to Fe(II) should be commonly possible. Cu(II) and Mn(IV) are other obvious candidates as inorganic species which may undergo reduction by conduction band electrons. The most sensitive organic groups may well be oxidized components of humic substances such as quinone structures.

Pathways of Reaction – Oxidation

The fate of the valence band holes is more complex. Again we begin with solvent. Its oxidation can occur via a number of pathways, some involving reactive intermediates such as hydroxyl radical. In the solution phase photolysis of various Fe complexes, we found that alcohols were useful diagnostic scavengers of reactive species (23). It was possible to differentiate between oxidation with hydroxyl radicals and direct oxidation by the charge transfer excited state by monitoring the reactivity patterns as a function of alcohol structure. t-Butanol was observed not to undergo direct reaction with the excited state, but to react only with OH radicals. All alcohols studied underwent hydroxyl radical abstraction but 1° and 2° alcohols have an additional pathway. In these latter cases, the intercept at zero ROH concentration of the higher part of yield vs ROH concentration curve defined yields for reaction with OH radical. The system holds promise for analysis of semiconductor oxidation pathways.

Experiments were conducted using 0.5% (wt) slurries of anatase in 0.1M HClO$_4$. In order to prevent complications due to the formation of hydrogen peroxide (vide supra), the solutions were deoxygenated with nitrogen prior to irradiation. Ferric perchlorate, which was shown in our previous work to be an effective final electron acceptor for the alcohol radicals, was added to the solution (0.010M) as the scavenger for alcohol radicals. After photolysis, solutions were filtered and the yield of Fe(II) was measured. The results are summarized in FIGURES 3 and 4. In both cases, the results were similar to the earlier solution phase studies in important respects. The products were Fe(II) and formaldehyde in the case of methanol, or isobutylene glycol in the case of t-butanol.

The results were different in one important respect from the earlier ones for photolysis of Fe(III) complexes in solution. The Fe(II) yield here showed very little dependence on t-butanol concentration and indicated a primary quantum yield of 0.170, approximately half the extrapolated intercept for methanol of 0.330. In ferric perchlorate photolysis studied earlier, both alcohols gave a common extrapolated yield equal to the independently determined primary yield for hydroxyl radical production. In other words, at the TiO$_2$ surface we appear to generate more "OH radical" for reaction with CH$_3$OH than "OH radical" to react with t-butanol. From these results, we infer that a hole reaching the anatase surface may produce one of two distinct oxidants in approximately equal quantity. These are a species capable of abstracting hydrogen (e.g. the OH radical) and a second less reactive oxidant. Preliminary results from parallel experiments

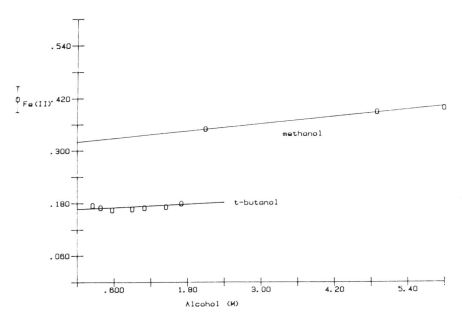

FIGURE 3.   Alcohol   Oxidation   at   the   TiO₂   Surface
Monitored by Fe(II) Production.

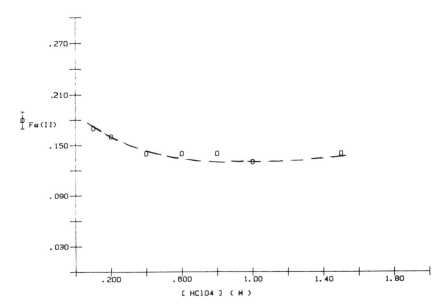

FIGURE 4.   Acid Dependency of t-Butanol   Oxidation at
TiO₂.

using ethylene glycol as an oxidant support these conclusions. At an ethylene glycol concentration of < 0.15M where direct electron transfer to the alcohol was unimportant in the reference solution phase study, both acetaldehyde (the H abstraction product) and formaldehyde (the direct OH radical reaction product) were produced in quantum yields > 0.1.

In the solution phase photolysis of ferric perchlorate in the presence of tertiary alcohols with more carbons than t-butanol, we observed that H abstraction by OH radicals produced some radicals that did not reduce Fe(III) to Fe(II). The addition of Cu(II) ions caused these radicals to be oxidized and resulted in additional ferrous ion production. For example, the ratio of Fe(II) quantum yields for 3-ethyl-3-pentanol without and with 0.0050M added Cu(II) was 0.844. When the anatase dispersion was irradiated under similar conditions, the ratio was 0.861. These results indicate fairly directly that the more reactive oxidant at the anatase surface is kinetically equivalent to OH radical.

Several studies of the hydroxylated anatase surface are available in the literature. Two types of surface OH groups have been distinguished, those bound to one Ti and those which bridge two. The singly bound hydroxyls are thought to be readily exchangeable, the bridging ones not. For most crystal faces, these two types occur in alternate rows and are thus available in approximately equal numbers. A plausible explanation for the above results is that either type of surface hydroxyl can function as a hole trap. If the hole is trapped at a singly bound hydroxyl, a species similar to the OH radical is produced. But, if the hole is trapped at a bridging group, a weaker oxidant capable only of the direct oxidation reaction pathway, is produced. This model has precedent in the homogeneous solution chemistry of Fe(III) where the bridged dimer is inactive toward photoproduction of OH radical.

FIGURE 4 shows that there is a drop in the Fe(II) yield as acid concentration is increased. This probably reflects the increase of positive charge at the surface and an electrostatic barrier to hole transfer across the surface. The surface also will change its proclivity to adsorb various potential reactants as a function of surface charge. This will be a general problem. It is important to keep track of the relation between the point of zero charge of the particles and the pH of the solution in considering any specific reactant.

Anatase is not a unique system. Many of the features of anatase were, after all, "anticipated" by the homogeneous chemistry of Fe(III). This leads to the suggestion that the mechanistic studies of anatase should provide considerable guidance to the behaviour of other oxide systems. For this reason, it is interesting to record here a number of reactions that have been reported using light absorption by anatase as initiating step. Many of these were explored for their possible utility in photochemical waste water treatment.

Donors of appropriate redox potential to react with holes at the anatase surface include organic acids, carbohydrates, fats, CN^-, and halides (24). (The cyanide reaction has been studied for its utility in treatment of the waste streams from gold mining operations in the Canadian Northwest Territories.) More immediately relevant to natural water is the observation that an anatase slurry could effect the decoloration of a chlorinated bleach plant effluent. A sample of amber colour, pH = 1.8, and low residual chlorine was irradiated in the presence of 0.5% (wt) anatase with light of 350 nm for periods up to 18 hr. The optical absorbance decreased by half in 1080 min. Small amounts of chloride and formaldehyde were detected (25). This reaction may provide a precedent for observation of a relation between photobleaching of humics in water and metal ions. If so, we are brought to the question of the reactivity of colloidal iron oxides.

As mentioned above, some laboratory studies have indicated that anatase is superior to all other oxides tested with reference reactions such as the alcohol oxidations (25) |and hydrogen evolution as well (24)|. However, recent work has also suggested that all that is required to increase the efficiency of ferric oxide photoanodes is suitable doping which may occur readily in nature. Recently two important studies have given specific evidence for the photooxidative activity of ferric oxides. The first is the report of Faust and Hoffman (26) that haematite can catalyze the photooxidation of SO_2 to sulfate. The scavenging compound was present in large concentration in these experiments so that there were no serious mass transport limitations on the delivery of the substrate directly to the surface. The second is the report of the oxidation of oxalate at a hydrous ferric oxide surface (27). There has been some concern that this last reaction is the reaction of a specific molecular species since the homogeneous ferric oxalate complex does undergo photooxidation at wavelengths below 520 nm. The distinction is not too important. If the iron ligand centered hole reaches the surface from the interior it must be transferred to the ligand. If it is generated by light absorption at the surface, the same local structure will result. The difference will be that the second case will show a small quantum yield which we will characterize by attributing it to the consequences of low hole mobility in the interior. If that problem can be overcome, the mechanisms merge. The preliminary indication is that the reaction is efficient enough to suggest the semiconductor mechanism. Thus, we see that some evidence for ferric oxides reacting with organic acids is in.

Relationships to Biological Activity

One last point is important. The pathways initiated by
inorganic photocatalysts may not terminate with the
immediate reactions themselves. The effect of photode-
chlorination of PCBs renders the organic products
accessible to biodegradation. A similar result was
obtained in a study of a lignin model compound, veratryl
alcohol (25). Irradiation of an anatase dispersion of a
solution gave vanillyl alcohol which is biodegraded by a
colony of organisms capable of degrading aromatics more
than three times faster. It is quite possible that one
of the most important areas for future investigation
will be the relation of inorganic photochemistry to the
increase of biodegradability of refractory organic
matter.

References

1. T. Trott, R.W. Henwood, C.H. Langford, 1972, Envir.
    Sci. Technol., 6, 367.
2. C.H. Langford, M. Wingham, V.S. Sastri, 1973,
    Envir. Sci. Technol., 7, 820.
3. R.H. Collienne, 1983, Limnol. Oceanog., 28, 83.
4. C.T. Miles, P.L. Brezonik, 1981, Envir. Sci.
    Technol., 15, 1089.
5. R.G. Zepp, P.F. Scholtzauer, R.M. Sink, 1985,
    Envir. Sci. Technol., 19, 74.
6. J.F. Power, C.H. Langford, D.K. Sharma, R. Bonneau,
    J. Joussot-Dubien, 1985, this symposium.
7. M. Graetzel, ed., 1983, "Energy Resources Through
    Photochemistry and Catalysis", Academic Press, New
    York.
8. For a Review of Earlier Work See: 1974, "Photo-
    effects in Adsorbed Species", Discuss. Faraday
    Soc., 58.
9. L.C. Kinney, V.R. Ivanuski, 1969, Robert A. Taft
    Research Center Report Number TWRC-13 Cincinnati,
    Ohio.
10. J.H. Carey, J. Lawrence, H.M. Tosine, 1976, Bull.
    Envir. Contam. Toxicol., 16, 697.
11. H. Gerischer, 1979, Topics Appl. Phys., 31, 115.
12. A.D. Kirk, C.H. Langford, C. St-Joly, D.K. Sharma,
    R. Lesage, 1984, JCS Chem. Communs.
13. S.L. Suib, K.A. Carrado, 1985, Inorg. Chem., 24,
    863.
14. T. Mill, et al, 1981, Chemosphere, 10, 1281.
15. G.C. Miller, R.G. Zepp, 1979, Envir. Sci.Technol., 13, 453.
16. J.F. Power, C.H. Langford, Unpublished.
17. E. Borgarello, J. Kiwi, M. Graetzel, E. Pellizetti,
    M. Visca, 1982, J. Am. Chem. Soc., 104, 2996.
18. P. Salvador, 1980, Solar Energy Material's, 2, 413.
19. C. Leygraf, M. Hendewerk, G.H. Somorjai, 1982, J.
    Catal., 78, 341.

20. C.H. Langford, 1982, Proc. ENERGEX, 1982, Solar Energy Society of Canada, Regina, Saskatchewan, August 1982, p. 928.

21. N. Zeug, J. Buchler, H. Kisch, 1985, J. Am. Chem. Soc., 107, 1459.

22. R.M. Baxter, J.H. Carey, 1984, Nature, 206, 575.

23. C.H. Langford, J.H. Carey, 1973, Can. J. Chem., 51.

24. T. Sakata, T. Kawai, 1983, Reference 7, Chapter 10.

25. J.H. Carey, B.G. Oliver, 1980, Water Poll. Res. J. of Canada, 15, 157.

26. B.C. Faust, M.R. Hoffman, Abstracts Environmental Division, 186th ACS National Meeting, Washington, DC, August 28th, 1983 – September 2nd, 1983.

27. M.C. Goldberg, K.M. Cunningham, Abstracts Environmental Division, 185th ACS National Meeting, Seattle, Washington, March 27th, 1983 – April 1st, 1983.

RECEIVED July 15, 1986

Chapter 18

Catalyzed Photodegradation of the Herbicides Molinate and Thiobencarb

R. Barton Draper[1] and Donald G. Crosby[2]

Department of Environmental Toxicology, University of California, Davis, CA 95616

A survey of oxidizing agents capable of supplementing
the natural oxidants of field water showed that the
rice herbicides molinate (I) and thiobencarb (VIII)
were degraded rapidly in sunlight-irradiated
suspensions of TiO_2 and ZnO. ZnO served both as a
semiconductor photooxidant and as the Zn(II) fertilizer
normally applied for plant nutrition. In a flooded
rice field, isolated basins were treated with Ordram
10G (molinate); after 3 days, an aqueous ZnO
suspension, stable in field water at pH 8 to 9, was
applied. The resulting immediate decrease in molinate
half-life from 60 h to 1.5 h indicates that applying
ZnO before releasing agricultural wastewater may
provide an economical means of intentionally degrading
persistent chemical residues.

Herbicides are applied extensively to protect California's valuable
rice crop. During 1983, for example, flooded rice fields in the
Sacramento Valley received aerial applications of 422 metric tons
of molinate (S-ethyl hexahydro-1H-azepine-1-carbothioate)(I) and
100 metric tons of thiobencarb [S-(4-chlorophenyl)methyl-N,N-
diethylcarbamothioate](VIII) as the 10% (a.i.) granular
formulations Ordram 10G and Bolero 10G, respectively. After
holding irrigation flood water for the four to eight days required
for residue dissipation and effective herbicidal activity, farmers
release it into agricultural drains which empty into the Sacramento
River.

Seasonal fish kills in these agricultural drains are attributed
to the rice herbicides. The molinate concentration in the Colusa
Basin Drain has approached 350 µg/L during early June when
herbicide use is heaviest. Farther downstream in the Sacramento
River, near Sacramento's drinking water treatment facility,
concentrations of molinate and thiobencarb have exceeded 20 ug/L

[1]Current address: Department of Chemistry, University of Texas, Austin, TX 78712
[2]Correspondence should be addressed to this author.

and 6 ug/L, respectively. Removal of these herbicides from irrigation waste-water by natural volatilization, hydrolysis, photolysis, and microbial breakdown proceeds so slowly that adequate dissipation does not occur before wildlife and human drinking water supplies are threatened. Our investigation evaluated the feasibility of enhancing the natural oxidizing activity of rice field water (1) in order to intentionally degrade rice herbicides.

Experiments

Herbicide solutions were prepared by dilution of a concentrated aqueous stock solution with distilled deionized water or rice field water. Solutions or suspensions in gas-tight Pyrex vessels were stirred and irradiated in a photoreactor (2), a 150 x 36 cm chrome-lined cylinder fitted with six F40BL fluorescent lamps. A 4-nitroanisole/pyridine actinometer (3) had a half-life of 50 min in the reactor, equivalent to spring sunlight in the Sacramento Valley.

Rate Measurements. Suspensions of titanium dioxide (TiO_2) or zinc oxide (ZnO) in distilled water or rice field water containing the herbicide were subjected to irradiation for 2 h in the photoreactor either (1) wrapped in foil to exclude light, (2) exposed to light with no semiconductor, or (3) exposed to light with semiconductor added. Samples were periodically withdrawn, extracted onto bonded-phase extraction cartridges, and analyzed by gas chromatography (glc).

TiO_2-Induced Photoproducts of Molinate. A 100 mg/L suspension of TiO_2 in 6.4×10^{-5} M aqueous molinate, irradiated 40 min in the photoreactor, provided a mixture of photoproducts. Molinate sulfoxide and hexamethyleneimine were extracted, derivatized, and detected according to a procedure described by Soderquist, et al. (4). A second irradiated suspension, extracted onto a C-8 bonded-phase cartridge and eluted with methanol, provided a concentrated solution of photoproducts suitable for analysis by high-performance liquid chromatography (HPLC), glc, and glc with a mass spectrometer detector (GC-MS).

ZnO-Induced Photoproducts of Thiobencarb. A 100 mg/L suspension of ZnO in 4.7×10^{-5} M aqueous thiobencarb, irradiated 15 min in the photoreactor, provided a mixture of photoproducts. After acidification, extraction with a bonded-phase cartridge, and elution, eluates were dried over anhyd sodium sulfate and concentrated under N_2. The C-8 cartridge eluate (methanol) was treated with diazomethane and the cyclohexyl cartridge eluate (ethyl acetate) was treated with N-methyl-N-(t-butyldimethylsilyl) trifluoroacetamide (MTBSTFA) for glc (FID detector) and GC-MS analysis.

Field Application of ZnO. Field plots consisted of four 2.4 m diameter aluminum rings placed in a flooded rice field at the UCD Rice Research Facility. In August, 1984, the rice plants were removed from these isolated basins, and granular molinate (Ordram

10G) was applied at an agricultural rate equivalent to 6.3
kg(a.i.)/ha. Water samples were collected from each basin at six to
nine h intervals and stored in glass at -4°C until analyzed. pH,
dissolved oxygen (DO), air temperature, and water temperature were
intensively monitored.

After 3 d, two basins were treated with an aqueous suspension of
ZnO (1 g/L) at an application rate equivalent to 14 kg(Zn)/ha,
giving a 8.3 mg(ZnO)/L suspension in the basins. Water samples from
both treated and control basins were taken at 0, 5, 15, 45, 120,
240, 411, and 1300 min after the ZnO application and analyzed for
molinate and 4-ketomolinate. In a similar experiment, performed
several days later, an application of 6.7 kg(Zn)/ha provided a 4
mg(ZnO)/L suspension in the basins.

Results and Discussion.

In our investigation of enhanced photodegradation, molinate and
thiobencarb proved to be particularly valuable probes. Neither
herbicide was degraded appreciably in sunlight by primary
photolysis, and both broke down only slowly when exposed to natural
photosensitizers (4, 5, 6, 7,). In addition to their satisfactory
physical-chemical properties, molinate and thiobencarb are key
pesticides for protection of a rice crop with a potential annual
market value over 500 million dollars. The herbicides, used on
500,000 acres of rice in California, control Echinochloa crus-galli
(barnyard grass) and Leptochloa fascicularis (sprangletop),
contributing to a rice yield that is three times the world average
(8). However, molinate and thiobencarb also contribute to serious
local water pollution problems.

For the intentional destruction of these herbicide residues, the
ideal agent would be inexpensive, rapid acting, dissipative or
controllable, non-polluting, and added directly to the rice field or
the adjacent drains. From a survey of a variety of reagents, the
semiconductor photocatalysts titanium dioxide and zinc oxide emerged
as attractive candidates.

Photooxidation by Titanium Dioxide and Zinc Oxide. Titanium dioxide
and zinc oxide have the ability to photo-induce the oxidation of
organic compounds (9, 10, 11,). The redox reaction involves the
absorption of light by the semiconductor solid which results in
promotion of an electron from the valence band to the conduction
band, leaving an electron-deficiency or "hole". In such n-type
semiconductors (those made electron-rich by doping with an electron
donor), the photogenerated hole migrates towards the solution
interface where oxidations occur. The electron moves away from the
interface into the bulk of the semiconductor particle. Ultimately,
a negatively charged aggregate is formed which can act as a reducing
center and effect solution-phase reductions, such as that of oxygen
to superoxide.

Surface-sensitized oxidations should occur with adsorbed organic
molecules having oxidation potentials less positive than that of the
semiconductor valence band. The valence band positions of TiO_2 and
ZnO, measured in water at pH 1, are reported to be +3.1 and +3.0 V

<u>vs</u>. SCE, respectively (<u>11</u>), making the photoexcited catalysts
potential oxidants of a wide variety of organic compounds (Table
I). In water, reactions may proceed by surface-sensitized
oxidation, initial oxidation of water to hydroxyl radical (<u>12</u>), or
possibly by reduction of oxygen with subsequent disproportionation
to hydrogen peroxide and subsequent photolysis to hydroxyl radicals.

Table I. Anodic oxidation potentials of some environmental
pollutants (<u>19</u>).

Compound	$E_{pk_{a/2}}$,V vs. SCE
2-Chlorophenol	+ 0.63
2,4-Dichlorophenol	+ 0.65
3-Chlorophenol	+ 0.73
4,4'-Dimethoxybiphenyl	+ 1.18
4-Hydroxybiphenyl	+ 1.24
2-Hydroxybiphenyl	+ 1.27
3-Chloro-4-hydroxybiphenyl	+ 1.30
3-Hydroxybiphenyl	+ 1.47
Biphenyl	+ 1.82
4,4'-Dichlorobiphenyl	+ 1.88
2,5,2',5'-Tetrachlorobiphenyl	+ 2.38
Decachlorobiphenyl	+ 2.63
Benzene	+ 2.32
Arochlor 1232	+ 2.23
Arochlor 1242	+ 2.39
Arochlor 1254	+ 2.42
Arochlor 1260	+ 2.43

In our experiments, TiO_2 and ZnO did not perform equivalently;
a 100 mg/L suspension of TiO_2 provided the same molinate degradation
rate as did a 5 mg/L suspension of ZnO. A further advantage of ZnO
as an intentional additive was its instability in light and water
(<u>13</u>, <u>14</u>); as it slowly dissolves, Zn(II) would become available for
rice plant nutrition. The pH dependence of ZnO stability could,
however, limit the utility of this catalyst; at pH $\leq$ 7, ZnO was not
an effective oxidant.

Products of Semiconductor-catalyzed Molinate and Thiobencarb
Oxidation. Examination of the photooxidation products of molinate
by GC-MS provided evidence of seven substances sufficiently stable
and concentrated to be chromatographed and detected by mass
spectrometry (molinate sulfoxide and sulfone decomposed).
Comparison of spectra and retention times with those of analytical
standards and literature reports (15, 16) confirmed the presence of
molinate (I), the oxidation products 4-hydroxymolinate (II) and 4-
ketomolinatee (III) (the most stable intermediate product), an
additional keto isomer, and a ring unsaturated isomer (IV) (Figure
1). Molinate sulfoxide (V) and sulfone (VI) were detected by
HPLC. The presence of hexamethyleneimine (VII) was verified by its
α,α,α-trifluoro-3,5-dinitrotoluene derivative (17).

Similarly, comparison of spectra and retention times with those
of MTBSTFA derivatized standards provided evidence for the presence
of 4-chlorobenzyl alcohol (X), 4-chlorobenzoic acid (XI), and 4-
chlorobenzyl mercaptan (IX) as ZnO-induced photoproducts of
thiobencarb (VIII) (Figure 2). The presence of a ring-hydroxylated
thiobencarb (XII), the major stable intermediate, was rationalized
from spectra of methylated and silylated derivatives.

None of the identified degradation products were persistent, and
none presently are recognized as toxic hazards.

Field Experiment. Measurement of pH (Figure 3) revealed a diurnal
variation between 8 and 9, the maximum occurring at mid-day due to
photosynthetic removal of HCO_3^- from the water (18). Dissolved
oxygen (DO) also varied diurnally between 8 and 17 mg/L, reaching a
maximum during mid-day. Basins treated with ZnO on Day 3 did not
exhibit as pronounced a rise in DO as did the controls, suggesting
that molecular oxygen may have been consumed in the ZnO
photooxidation consistent with a mechanism of surface-sensitized
reduction of oxygen to superoxide and formation of hydrogen
peroxide. Air and water temperatures (Figure 4) were normal but
reflected an unexpected rainfall on Day 3.

Figure 5 illustrates the dramatic reduction in molinate
concentration after application of 14 kg/ha of Zn as ZnO. The
molinate dissipation half-life decreased from 60 h in untreated
basins to 1.5 h in treated basins. Similar results were obtained
using 6 kg/ha of Zn as ZnO. During molinate oxidation, 4-keto
molinate reached a maximum concentration of 73 ug/L within 2 h and
then declined rapidly.

Thus, application of ZnO to a rice field after herbicide
treatment can be shown to provide an economical and agronomically-
feasible means of degrading persistent pesticide residues before
they reach public waterways. Intentional semiconductor-catalyzed
photodegradation may, in fact, have much more general utility and
might also be used to degrade many hazardous wastes under other
circumstances.

Acknowledgment

We are indebted to Richard M. Higashi and Rita Look for advice and
assistance. This work was supported in part by the California Rice
Research Foundation and U.S.D.A. Regional Research Project W-45.

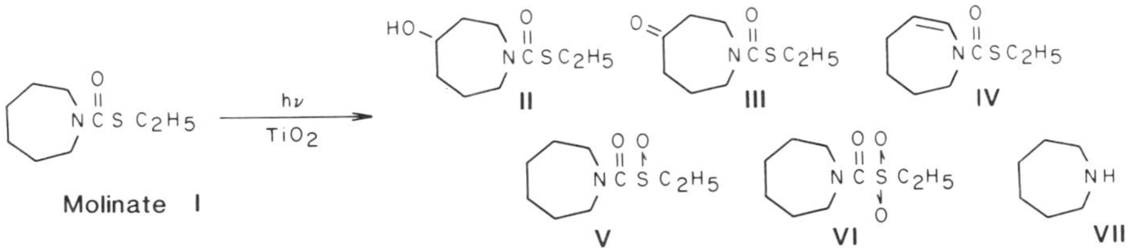

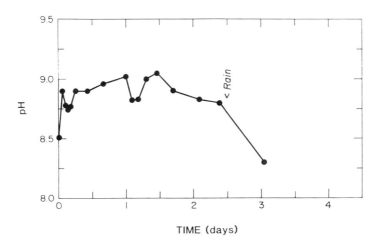

Figure 1. Major products of the TiO$_2$-catalyzed photooxidation of molinate.

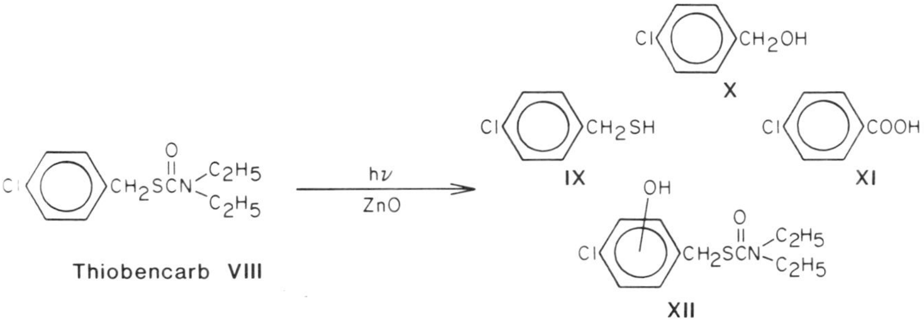

Figure 2. Major products of the ZnO-catalyzed photooxidation of thiobencarb.

Figure 3. Diurnal variation of pH in rice field basins.

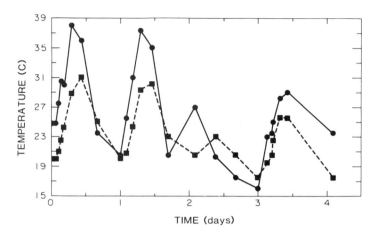

Figure 4. Diurnal variation of water (■) and air temperatures (●).

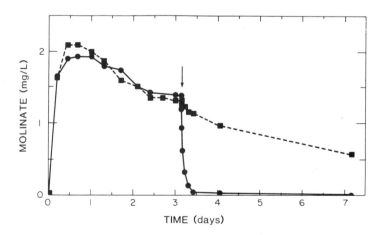

Figure 5. Effect of ZnO (14 kg/ha Zn) on molinate concentration in field water (■) when applied on Day 3 (↓) compared to an untreated control (●).

Literature Cited

1. Draper, W.M.; Crosby, D.G. Arch. Environ. Contam. Toxicol. 1983, **12**, 121–126.
2. Crosby, D.G.; Wong, A.S. J. Agr. Food Chem. 1973, **21**, 1052–1054.
3. Dulin, D.; Mill, T. Environ. Sci. Technol. 1982, **16**, 815–820.
4. Soderquist, C.J.; Bowers, J.B.; Crosby, D.G. J. Agric. Food Chem. 1977, **25**, 940–945.
5. Draper, W.M.; Crosby, D.G. J. Agr. Food Chem. 1981, **29**, 699–702.
6. Draper, W.M.; Crosby, D.G. J. Agric. Food Chem. 1984, **32**, 231–237.
7. Ross, R.D.; Crosby, D.G. Environ. Toxicol. Chem. 1985, **4**, 773–778.
8. Rutger, J.N.; Brandon, D.M. Sci. Am. 1981, **244**, 43–51.
9. Carey, J.H.; Lawrence, J.; Tosine, H.M. Bull. Environ. Contam. Toxicol. 1976, **16**, 697–701.
10. Fox, M.A. Acc. Chem. Res. 1983, **16**, 314–321.
11. Fox, M.A.; Chen, C.-C.; Younathan, J.N.N. J. Org. Chem. 1984, **49**, 1969–1974.
12. Jaeger, C.D.; Bard, A.J. J. Phys. Chem. 1979, **83**, 3146–3152.
13. Blok, L.; de Bruyn, P.L. J. Colloid Interface Sci. 1970, **32**, 518.
14. Gerischer, H. J. Electroanal. Chem. 1977, **82**, 133–143.
15. DeBaun, J.R.; Bova, D.L.; Tseng, C.K.; Menn, J.J. J. Agr. Food Chem 1978, **26**, 1098–1104.
16. Lay, M.-M.; Niland, A.M.; DeBaun, J.R.; Menn, J.J. In "Pesticide and Xenobiotic Metabolism in Aquatic Organisms"; Khan, M.A.Q.; Lech, J.J.; Menn, J.J., eds; ACS SYMPOSIUM SERIES No. 99, American Chemical Society: Washington, D.C.,1979; pp. 95–119.
17. Crosby, D.G.; Bowers, J.B. J. Agr. Food Chem. 1968, **16**, 839–843.
18. Mikkelson, D.S.; De Datta, S.K.; Obsemea, W.N. Soil Sci. Soc. Am. J. 1978, **42**, 775–730.
19. Fenn, R.J.; Krantz, K.W.; Stuart, J.D. J. Electrochem. Soc. 1976, **123**, 1643–1647.

RECEIVED June 27, 1986

MODELING AND ACTINOMETRY

Chapter 19

Photochemical Modeling Applied to Natural Waters

John M. C. Plane[1], **Rod G. Zika**[1], **Richard G. Zepp**[2], and **Lawrence A. Burns**[2]

[1]Rosenstiel School of Marine and Atmospheric Sciences, Division of Marine and Atmospheric Chemistry, University of Miami, Miami, FL 33149
[2]Environmental Research Laboratory, U.S. Environmental Protection Agency, Athens, GA 30613

In this presentation an attempt is made to examine the application of modeling photochemical processes in natural water systems. For many photochemical reactions occurring in natural waters a simple photochemical model describing reaction rate as a function of intensity, radiation attenuation, reactant absorptivity and quantum yield is insufficient. Other factors governing the species distribution must be considered. These factors are divided into processes that cause production, decay, and mixing and transport. Three different photochemically active compounds are used as examples to illustrate how these various factors affect their distribution. Hydrogen peroxide is used as an example of a compound which is produced in situ, while trifluralin and pentachloro-phenol are compounds that have very different absorption spectra and are introduced from external sources. The photochemically mediated distribution of these example compounds is evaluated by taking into consideration the effects of light attenuation, equilibrium partitioning of the compound into nonaqueous phases (e.g. sediments), and physical mixing in the water column.

Many chemicals found in natural waters are photosensitive to sunlight. For instance, some trace organic species, of either terrestrial or in situ biological origin, photoreact to form reactive transients such as hydroxyl radicals, H_2O_2, O_2^-, or singlet oxygen. These products in turn typically exhibit further chemistry (1). Moreover, some transition metal complexes and inorganic species such as NO_2^- and NO_3^- can be photolyzed directly

0097-6156/87/0327-0250$06.00/0
© 1987 American Chemical Society

by sunlight, changing their oxidation state and producing reactive products that are involved in further reactions (1).

The ability to model the chemistry of photoreactive species in natural waters is of great interest for four reasons. First, environmental photochemical modeling is necessary to extrapolate laboratory results to natural water systems. Modeling can be used to test hypotheses concerning the kinetics and mechanisms of photoreactions in the environment and to examine the contribution of competing processes that alter or form a chemical. Second, many photoreactive species are coupled to biological cycles; some are produced by organisms, while others may exert effects on them. In particular, knowledge of the effects of light on speciation of toxic organic chemicals or heavy metals can be of special importance. Third, recent research in the chemistry of the troposphere has shown that the oceans are probably an important source of several trace species found in the atmosphere. Because most biological and photochemical processes exhibit diel variations, there may be substantial corresponding variations in the air-sea exchange of photochemically and photobiologically supplied, and reactive gases. Current air-sea exchange rate calculations, however, generally do not take diel light variations into account. Gases for which natural waters are a source, such as COS, CH_3I, CH_3SCH_3, H_2S and CO, should vary dielly because their surface concentrations should be responsive to light intensity and to mixed turbulent dilution. Finally, photochemical modelling in conjunction with measurements of spatiotemporal distributions of transient photoproducts can be applied to estimate the age, origin, and mixing rates of water masses. This use of photochemically derived products to complement other tracer studies is a potentially powerful tool because the products of light-initiated reactions are often unique, are only generated in the illuminated upper layers of deep water bodies, and because the photoreaction rates can be described through standard chemical kinetic treatments.

In this chapter, we discuss some of the chemical, physical, and biological processes that are often significant in governing the distribution of photochemical reactants and transients in a water column. We are not concerned here with questions of horizontal transport, and our discussions are restricted to one-dimensional, mixed-layer, photochemical models. Examples of such models are presented where appropriate. Our discussion of the factors governing the distribution of chemical species in natural waters is divided into five parts--in situ photochemical formation, external sources, in situ photochemical decomposition, external loss, and turbulent mixing and transport. An attempt also will be made to indicate where laboratory measurements can be used as input into these models.

Factors Governing Species Distribution

In situ formation. The chemical and biological processes generating a chemical species (T) in natural surface waters may be symbolically expressed by the rate equation

$$d[T]/dt = Rf_l + Rf_d + Rf_b \qquad (1)$$

where Rf_l is the rate of photochemical reactions that form T, Rf_d is the rate of thermal reactions forming T, and Rf_b is the rate of biological reactions forming T. For some compounds, Rf_d or Rf_b are important terms and may dominate the formation of T. An example of this is CO_2, which has large biological sources and probably very small photochemical sources through reactions such as the decarboxylation of organic acids. For some cases such as H_2O_2, it is difficult to obtain any direct information about Rf_b and Rf_d. Generating a model in terms of exclusive photochemical formation of T, and comparing model predictions with observed profiles of T in a water column, can often point to the relative contribution of these different transient formation terms.

Rf_l is a function of the quantum yield for the photochemical formation process, as well as the rate of light absorption by the photoreactive species. The rate of light absorption depends upon a variety of factors including the absorptivities and concentrations of the photoreactive species, and light intensity. Light intensity in turn depends on latitude, season, time of day, and cloud cover (2). Also, light intensity decreases with increasing depth because of attenuation by scattering and absorption.

It is often possible to obtain some information from laboratory measurements on quantum yields for a particular process. An example is a recent study on the formation quantum yields of H_2O_2 in several different natural waters (3,4). These quantum yield versus wavelength plots for all of the waters studied are surprisingly similar with the rate of production of H_2O_2 being a linear function of sample absorbance at the irradiation wavelengths. Recent studies (5,6) indicate that photoreactions of organic precursors, which are largely responsible for light attenuation in natural waters, make an important contribution to the production of H_2O_2 in seawater. The organic precursors are mixtures with poorly characterized chromophores, so it is not possible to define primary quantum yields for H_2O_2 photoproduction from the individual reactive species. The approach followed by Zika et al. (4) involved defining an apparent monochromatic quantum yield, C_λ, for the overall production process as the number of moles of H_2O_2 produced per Einstein of photons absorbed at wavelength λ. The monochromatic accumulation rate is then the rate of photons absorbed per unit volume of water, multiplied by C_λ. The quantity C_λ can be measured over the range of solar wavelengths in samples of seawater in the laboratory.

A depth profile of the differential spectral intensity of sunlight can either be measured using a multiple bandwidth underwater light detector and input directly into a photochemical model, or be calculated using a suitable light attenuation model. For example, the model of Zepp and Cline (2) calculated the attenuation of light in the water column due to absorption and scattering. The absorbance of the particular body of water of interest must be specified from observation. The model then specifies solar fluxes at sea level as a function of time of day, total ozone column density, latitude, and season, partially based on analysis of climatological data. This type of model can then be adapted [e.g., see Zika et al., (4)] to calculate the rate of photons absorbed at a selected depth.

Finally, the monochromatic accumulation rate is integrated over the solar spectrum to obtain the total accumulation rate. The results of this procedure are illustrated in Figure 1, which shows the variation with depth of the photochemical rate of production of H_2O_2 at midday at $40°N$ for summer and winter in a freshwater sample. A rapid decrease of the rate with depth is apparent, particularly in this dark colored freshwater sample which attenuates most of the near-ultraviolet radiation in the upper 20 cm. Figure 2 shows how the calculated rate of photochemical production varies with time of day and extent of cloud cover at a chosen latitude and season.

External Addition of a Chemical Species

Two other source terms need to be considered. First, there is the possibility of dry or wet deposition of a chemical species to the water surface from the atmosphere. The rate of dry deposition depends on the concentration of the species in the gas phase, the concentration in surface water, the Henry's Law constant, and the reactivity of the species with seawater constituents, as well as the wind speed and the aerosol in the air adjacent to the water surface. The rate of wet deposition depends on the concentration of the species in the precipitation and the frequency and duration of precipitation events. Little information is currently available about these processes, although there is some evidence that a rainstorm can inject significant quantities of H_2O_2 into the upper meter of the water column. This effect is usually short-lived, however, due to rapid mixing (4).

Second, many natural and anthropogenic chemical species are injected into natural waters from terrestrial run-off or other environmental events.

In Situ Decomposition of a Chemical Species

The decomposition of a chemical species within the water column may be described by:

$$-d[T]/dt = Rd_d + Rd_{1i} + Rd_{1d} + Rd_b \qquad (2)$$

where Rd_d represents rates of thermal reactions removing T, Rd_{1i} and Rd_1 describe the rate of removal of T as a result of indirect and direct photochemical reactions and Rd_b represents the biological removal rate. Rd_d depends on factors such as the ionic strength, the composition and temperature of the water, and the concentrations of T and the materials with which it reacts.

Sufficient information for predictive estimates of rates of thermal and biological decay often are not available. Empirical rates determined by storing samples in the dark for periods of time can be used, but this procedure is prone to errors such as wall effects (7). The rate of indirect photochemical removal, Rd_{1i}, is expected to be dependent on the same factors as Rd_d as well as the intensity of solar radiation in the water column. This solar

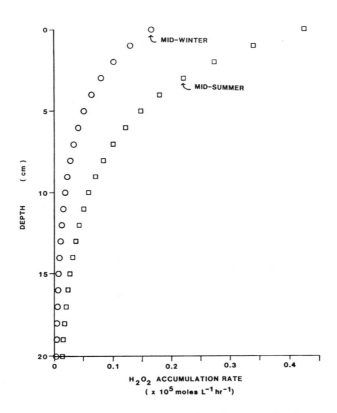

Figure 1. Photochemical model calculated accumulation rates of H_2O_2 versus depth for high organic material content freshwater sample from South Florida aquifer. Mid-day values at 40° latitude for two seasons are shown.

intensity determines the steady-state concentration of the species
with which T reacts.

The rate of direct photochemical removal is dependent on the
extinction coefficient and the quantum yield for the primary
process. As an example of this process, consider the case of two
compounds with very different absorption spectra illustrated in
Figure 3.   The effect of their rather different extinction
coefficients on the rate of direct photochemical decomposition is
demonstrated in Figure 4. These plots show the depth dependence of
the decay constants in two water bodies with different light
transmission characteristics.   In the more opaque, moderately
productive water, the rate coefficients decrease markedly with
depth. In general, R_{1d} depends on the same factors as the rate of
photochemical production, R_{f1}.

External Removal of a Chemical Species

Two types of physical loss processes should be considered in the
external removal of a chemical species.   First, the species of
interest may be lost to the atmosphere through water-air exchange.
This process depends on the Henry's Law constant for the chemical
species, as well as the atmospheric concentration and the structure
of the surface microlayers (8). Wind stress and turbulence of the
water body surface have a pronounced effect, especially for
surface-active materials for which bubble scavenging and surface
film ejection as aerosol takes place.   Transfer rates at the
air-water interface are complex problems in themselves and are not
dealt with in this Chapter.

The second important process to consider is physical loss of a
transient by partitioning into sediments on the bottom or suspended
particles in the water column. The potential significance of this
loss term is demonstrated in Figure 5, a plot of the log of the
partition coefficients between octanol and water (log P) for almost
20,000 industrial compounds.   The narrow distribution of these
coefficients is striking, the more so in the context of Figure 6.

Figure 6 illustrates pseudo-first-order system halflives,
estimated by the EXAMS model (9), for photolysis of a series of
generic organic substrates with differing K_{ow}'s ($P \equiv K_{ow}$) and
sediment/water partition coefficients, (K_p) but with the same
photolysis rate constants in the water column of a freshwater pond.
As the partition coefficients increase, the fraction of substrate
in the illuminated water column, and thus the system loss rate,
decreases due to increased sorption into bottom sediments. It is
noteworthy that this simulation, when compared with Figure 5,
indicates that sorption into bottom sediments has little or no
effect on the total rate of photochemical loss for a preponderance
of industrial chemicals.

Turbulent Mixing Within and Below the Photic Zone

Any model of photochemistry in natural waters must take into
account the effect of turbulent mixing on the concentrations of
transient species and their diel and seasonal variations. For the
oceans, the part of the water column of particular interest is the

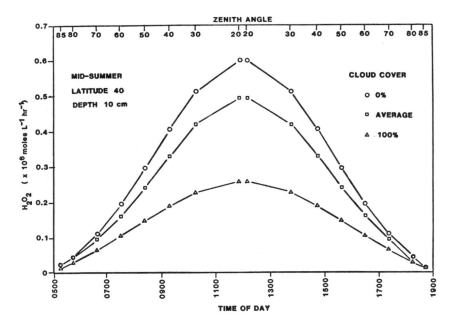

Figure 2. Photochemical model calculated H_2O_2 accumulation rates of H_2O_2 versus time of day in summer at 40^α latitude and 10 cm depth for different extents of cloud cover. The water used was from a South Florida aquifer and contained a high level of organic material.

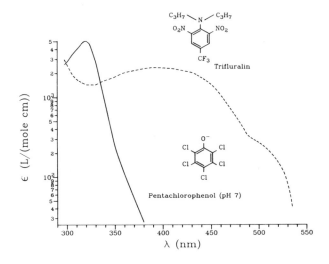

Figure 3. Electronic absorption spectra of pentachlorophenol and trifluralin in water.

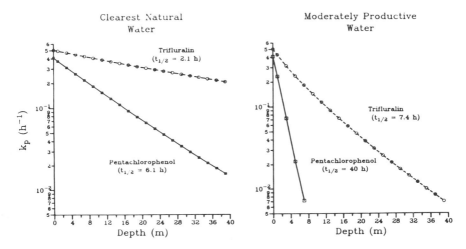

Figure 4. Computed depth dependence for the direct photolysis of trifluralin and pentachlorophenol in different water types (average rate constants parenthesized).

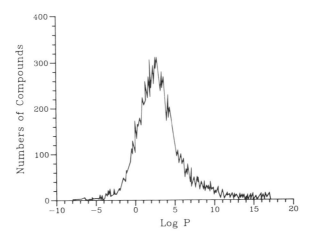

Figure 5. Distribution of octanol—water partition coefficients (P) computed for 19,965 industrial chemical (17).

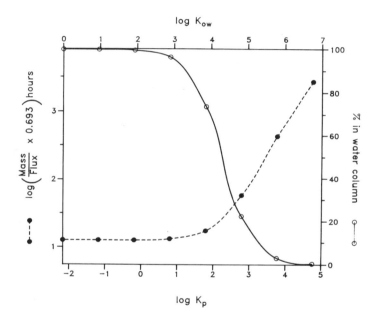

Figure 6. Computed effects of sorption to bottom sediments on the pseudo-first-order system halflives (log mass/flux) for a series of generic photoreactive substrates, each having the same photolysis rate but differing octanol-water partition coefficients (K_{ow}) and sorption partition coefficients (K_p).

upper 100 m. Photochemistry largely takes part in about the first 30 m (the photic zone), although this depth depends somewhat on the light transmission characteristics of the water.

Turbulent mixing near the surface is in many cases dominated by surface wind stress. Heat transport may also lead to vertical mixing. These mixing processes result in an homogeneous layer below the surface known as the mixed layer, the depth of which is largely a function of wind-stirring. This layer generally varies between 20 and 40 m over much of the ocean. The situation in lakes is similar except that the mixed layer is usually much shallower.

The aim of a turbulent mixing model is to assess the importance of mixing within the photic zone, and the way in which turbulence can mix water containing species that have either been photochemically produced or depleted, from the photic zone down to depths below the mixed layer. As indicated in the introduction, the aim of this Chapter is not to discuss the consequences of horizontal transport. For the oceans, such considerations are usually not necessary bearing in mind the homogeneity that is typically at a scale of several hundred kilometers, the velocity of horizontal transport, and the lifetimes of many photochemical species of a few hours to a few days (1).

When setting up a study, an investigator has several types of one-dimensional mixing layer models from which to choose. These models are distinguished by the ways in which they attempt to solve the one-dimensional conservation equations of momentum, heat, and salinity that describe the system. For instance, the turbulence closure model of Mellor and Durbin (10) has been used to model the photochemistry of H_2O_2 in the ocean (4). The results of this work will be used in the discussions below. This model uses second-order closure assumptions to reduce the conservation equations to two equations -- one for the mean specific turbulence kinetic energy and one for the vertical transport of specific horizontal momentum. This model has been criticized for its tendency to underpredict the depth of the mixed layer and the size of the step change in the temperature profile at the bottom of the layer, when compared with measurements.

Another approach involves the usage of eddy coefficients and mixing lengths. This method treats all transport by analogy to molecular diffusion, assuming that the turbulent fluxes can be expressed by the gradient of the transported quantity multiplied by an appropriate eddy diffusion coefficient. A recent example of this type of model is the work of Denman and Gargett (11) on phytoplankton in the upper ocean. This model is used for calculations presented later in this Chapter. Finally, bulk, mixed-layer models are available which assume that the top layer of the ocean is mixed thoroughly and that the vertical distribution of temperature, salinity, and horizontal velocity within this mixed layer is, if not uniform, then at least very much smaller than the variations across the layer boundaries or the variations within the thermocline.

The assumption of a uniform mixed layer permits vertical integration of the conservation equations and yields expressions for the turbulent transports in terms of the mean quantities and the external inputs. The turbulence energy equation is used to obtain an expression for the evolution of the layer depth which is needed for closure. Examples of models of this type are those of Niller (12) and Garwood (13). The predicted temperature profiles of these models have generally compared well with measurements (14). Detailed comparisons between these different types of one-dimensional models, however, are not the purpose of the present discussion, and the reader is referred to the referenced papers and the review by Niller and Kraus (15).

Once a model has been selected, an additional conservation or continuity equation is required to describe the transient species of interest. The eddy coefficients that govern the transport of the transient have been taken to be the same as those for heat transport [see e.g., (4)]. Thus, the temporal development of the transient can be modeled along with the development and diurnal variation of the stability of the water column. In this manner, the effects of wind-stirring and surface heat flux as well as of photochemical processes on the vertical profile of a transient can be investigated.

A recent example of such a model is that describing the distribution of H_2O_2 in the upper layer of the ocean (4), using the Mellor and Durbin model (10). Before considering the effect of turbulent mixing on transient distribution, refer to Figure 7, which shows the calculated time-depth profiles for H_2O_2 during winter in the Gulf of Mexico over a 2-day period beginning with sunrise, assuming the effects of photochemical processes alone and a complete absence of turbulent mixing.

The rates of photochemical production that were input into the model are taken from laboratory quantum yield measurements, discussed earlier (see section "In situ formation"). These are incorporated into a light attenuation model that employs the extinction coefficient of light in water with the clarity of the Gulf of Mexico. The dark decay lifetime of H_2O_2 was chosen to be 4 days, and constant with depth. The dark decay lifetime varies from hours in coastal environments to over a week in oligotrophic waters, but 4 days is commonly observed for offshore surface water (7). It is clear from Figure 7 that, in the absence of any mixing processes, H_2O_2 builds up to high concentrations with little diel variation because the dark decay life-time is much longer than one day. As expected, H_2O_2 is not produced at all below the photic zone. Measurements of H_2O_2 in the Gulf of Mexico (16), however, reveal much lower surface concentrations and significant concentrations down to about 70 m, and turbulent mixing has been invoked to account for these observations.

The turbulent mixing model was set up in this case with an initial temperature profile of neutral stratification between the surface and 80 m, and then allowed to vary according to surface wind stress and heat flux. The initial deviation of the currents from geostrophy was assumed to be zero. The surface heat flux was allowed to vary dielly in a sinusoidal manner with a small constant heat flux superimposed, simulating net heating in summer and cooling in winter.

Figure 8 shows the calculated time-depth section of H_2O_2 over a 2-day period. To emulate heat flux conditions typical of autumn/winter, a surface cooling was superimposed on the dielly

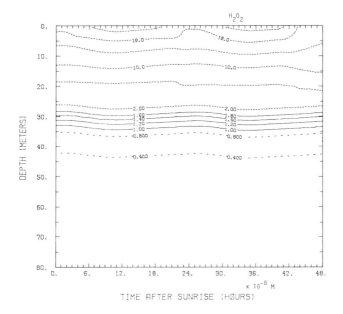

Figure 7. Calculated time-depth section of the H_2O_2 concentration due to photochemical production and destruction alone, over a two-day period beginning 0600 hrs local time. Conditions: mid-winter, latitude = 30°N, Gulf of Mexico.

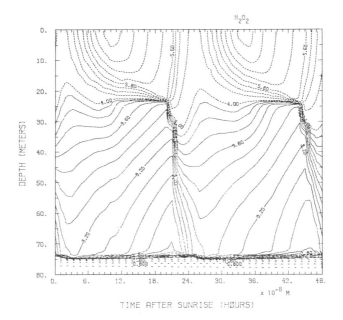

Figure 8. Calculated time-depth section of the H_2O_2 concentration, over a two-day period beginning 0600 hrs local time. Conditions: mid-winter, latitude = 30°N, Gulf of Mexico, wind stress = 1 dyne cm^{-2}, surface cooling = 10^{-5} Kms^{-1}.

varying heat flux, which has a noon-time maximum of 10^{-4} Km s^{-1}.
The model was integrated for 10 days prior to the 2 days that are
shown. The wind stress was set at a value of 1 dyne cm^{-2}, which
roughly corresponds to a 10-knot wind.

A comparison between Figures 7 and 8 shows the significant
effect that turbulent mixing can have on the vertical profile of
H_2O_2 in the water column. During the day, surface heating
establishes a stable layer in the upper 20 m that tends to trap
most of the H_2O_2 produced in the surface water. The peak surface
concentrations occur about 2 hours before sunset rather than at
noon, when the maximum solar flux occurs, because H_2O_2 continues to
accumulate during the afternoon, even though the light flux is
decreasing.

After sunset there is a gradual erosion of the surface
thermocline brought about both by nocturnal cooling and
wind-stirring, which continue throughout the night and establish a
deepening neutrally stratified layer approaching 20 m in depth
shortly before sunrise. Once there is continuity established
between the near surface neutrally stratified layer and the
preexisting neutrally stratified layer below 20 m, any additional
surface cooling will allow rapid mixing of the water down to the
next thermocline at 70 m.

The calculated time-depth section of the 1-hour changes in
H_2O_2 due to combined photochemical and transport processes is shown
in Figure 9. This illustrates more clearly that the intense mixing
is confined to relativley brief periods from shortly before sunrise
to midmorning at greater depth. The intense mixing to 70 m depth
is due to surface cooling superimposed on the diurnally varying
heat flux as the cool surface water breaks through the inversion
established during the previous day.

The increase in H_2O_2 is confined to the surface stable layer
during the day and becomes uniform within the upper 20 m during the
night. Once the 20 m thermocline is broken, this layer is rapidly
flushed. Essentially all of the H_2O_2 between 20 and 70 m is
rapidly injected within a few hours around sunrise. The size of
this effect, of course, depends upon the magnitude of surface
cooling during the course of the night. By contrast, in the summer
months when there is a net positive heating of the surface water, a
thermocline develops that traps the H_2O_2 at the depth where it is
produced in the photic zone, except for some wind-stirring near the
surface. This is shown in Figure 10. Wind-stirring produces a
mixed layer deeper than the photic zone (cf. Figures 7 and 10), and
the concentrations in the mixed layer are significantly higher than
in winter because of the increased rate of production during
summer.

The effects of varying the wind stress on the water surface
also should be considered. For the purpose of illustration, the
EXAMS II computer model (9) using eddy diffusion coefficients
provided by Denman and Gargett (11), is used to compare the
photochemical destruction of pentachlorophenol and trifluralin in
natural waters. As was described earlier in Figure 3, these
compounds have very different absorption spectra in the range of
solar wavelengths, and hence different rates of photochemical decay
(see Figures 5 and 6).

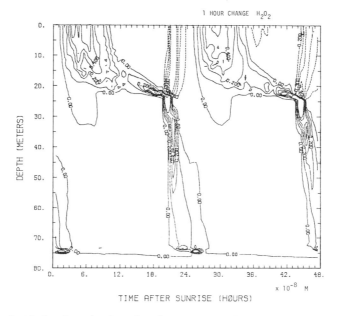

Figure 9. Calculated time-depth section of the one-hour changes in H_2O_2 over a two-day period beginning at 0600 hrs local time. Conditions: mid-winter, latitude = $30°N$, Gulf of Mexico, wind stress = 1 dyne cm^{-2}, surface cooling = 10^{-5} Kms^{-1}.

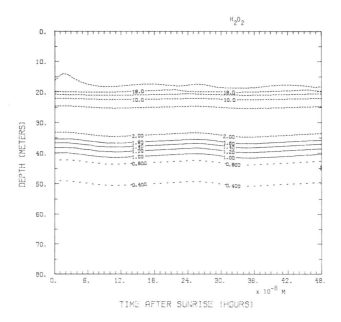

Figure 10. Calculated time-depth section of the H_2O_2 concentration, over a two-day period beginning 0600 hrs local time. Conditions: mid-summer, wind stress = 1 dyne cm^{-2}, surface heating = 10^{-5} Kms^{-1}.

The results of the model calculations are shown in Figure 11.
In all cases, the depth profiles that would have resulted with
complete rapid mixing of the entire water column is shown for
comparison. A uniform vertical distribution of substrate was
assumed as the initial condition. In Figure 11a, the vertical
profiles of the two compounds are compared over a 12-hour period,
under conditions of low wind stirring and in moderately productive
natural water. Trifluralin absorbs light up to about 540 nm and
shows significant photochemical removal down to depths of about 30
m. By contrast, pentachlorophenol is photolyzed rapidly only at
depths less than 10 m. In Figure 11b, the same comparison is made,
but under high wind conditions. For both compounds it is clear
that their concentration profiles follow the wind-stirred mixing
layer that develops after a few hours and produces a well-defined
base at about 25 m. This will be the case if the wind-stirring is
strong enough, when turbulent mixing will become faster than the
rate of photochemical destruction and a fairly homogeneous profile
will result within the mixed layer.

Figures 11c and 11d demonstrate the effect of increasing the
rate of photochemical decomposition by repeating the model
calculations in Figure 11a and 11b, but now for the case of the
clearest natural water. In Figure 11c, which illustrates the
results for low winds, trifluralin is almost completely removed
after 12 hours as solar wavelengths now penetrate down to 40 m.
Pentachlorophenol is now significantly removed near the surface,
but the rate of removal below 30 m is still slow (on the time-scale
of 12 hours). Figure 11d is the case of high wind stirring. The
profile of pentachlorophenol shows strong mixing and homogeneity
within the mixed layer and follows the base of the mixed layer at
25 m. By contrast, the profiles of trifluralin show only slight
discontinuities due to mixing, the result of the increased
photolysis rates in the clear water competing with the wind-driven
turbulent mixing.

Conclusions

In this Chapter, we have discussed in some detail the factors
affecting the concentration of a photochemical reactant or
transient product in the water column. These factors have been
divided into processes that cause production, decay, and mixing and
transport. In any model of photochemistry in natural water, all of
these processes may be coupled together and all must be considered.
It certainly should be clear from the examples in the last section
that turbulent mixing plays a substantial role in determining the
profile of the reactant or transient product in and below the
photic zone.

The coupling of photochemistry and physical mixing in a model
is a challenging task for three reasons. First, the photochemical
production and decomposition rates, as well as the dark decay rates
of interest, are often poor estimates. This is both because of the
lack of good laboratory kinetic measurements and because the light
attenuation models into which such measurements are incorporated
are subject to additional uncertainties. Second, the
one-dimensional mixing models make certain assumptions and

approximations in order to solve the momentum and heat continuity equations (15). The lack of precision of these mixing models must be borne in mind. Third, there is the question of obtaining suitable field measurements of reactant or transient product profiles in order to validate the prediction of a model. As analytical techniques improve, profiles can certainly be measured with higher accuracies.

When making a comparison with a model, however, there is the important question of the history of the water column in the few hours or days before a profile is measured. For example, if a profile of a transient was measured during a period of light winds, the model would predict a shallow mixing layer with the transient trapped near the surface, whereas a period of high winds shortly before might have mixed the transient well below the photic zone. Therefore, the model in this case would appear to have underestimated the depth of the mixing layer, depending of course on the lifetime of the transient. One way to get around this problem is to initiate the model with a measured transient profile and then have the model work forward in real time being continuously updated with relevant data such as the wind speed, cloud cover and surface heat flux, and periodically compared with measured profiles.

In spite of the difficulties that are present in developing models for aquatic photochemistry, much progress has already been made. Given the importance of being able to predict the distribution and lifetimes of many transients in the upper oceans and in freshwater, it is to be expected that a great deal of research will be done in this area in the future.

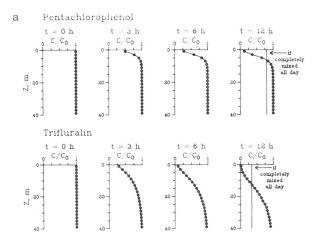

Figure 11. Vertical mixing effects on the computed concentration/depth profiles for pentachlorophenol and trifluralin (metalimnion at 25 meters): (a) moderately productive water, low winds (5 m/s). Continued on next page.

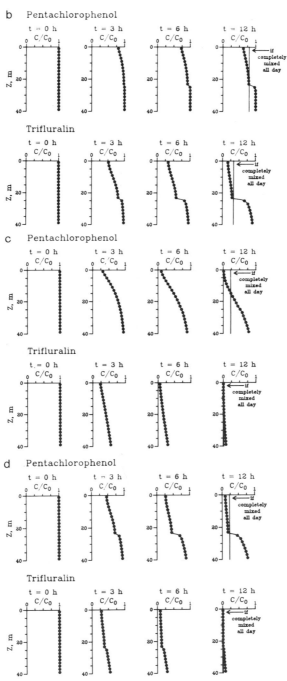

Figure 11.--<u>Continued.</u> Vertical mixing effects on the computed concentration/depth profiles for pentachlorophenol and trifluralin (metalimnion at 25 meters): (b) moderately productive water, high winds (15 m/s); (c) clearest natural water, low winds (5 m/s); and (d) clearest natural water, high winds (15 m/s).

Acknowledgments

This work was supported by the Office of Naval Research under contract N00014-85C-0020 and by the U.S. Environmental Protection Agency, Environmental Research Laboratory, Athens, GA.

Literature Cited

1. Zafiriou, O.C.; Joussot-Dubieu, J.; Zepp, R.G.; Zika, R.G. Environ. Sci. Technol. 1984, 18, 358A-371A.
2. Zepp, R.G.; Cline, D.M. Environ. Sci. Technol. 1977, 11, 359-366.
3. Cooper, W.J.; Zika, R.G.; Petasne, R.G.; Plane, J.M.C. Environ. Sci. Technol. 1986, submitted.
4. Zika, R.G.; Plane, J.M.C.; Gidel, L.T. J. Geophys. Res. 1986, submitted.
5. Cooper, W.J.; Zika, R.G. Science 1983, 220, 711-712.
6. Fischer, A.; Winterle, J.; Mill, T. This Volume 1986.
7. Zika, R.G., unpublished data.
8. Liss, P.S.; Proc. of Conf. on Gas-Liquid Chemistry of Natural Waters, 1984, p. 9.
9. Burns, L.A. In "Validation and Predictability of Laboratory Methods for Assessing the Fate and Transport of Contaminants in Aquatic Ecosystems" ASTM STP 865; Boyle, T.P., Ed.; Am. Soc. for Testing and Materials: Philadelphia, PA, 1985; pp. 176-190.
10. Mellor, G.L.; Durbin, P.A. J. Phys. Oceanogr. 1975, 5, 718-728.
11. Denman, K.L.; Gargett, A.E. Limnol. and Oceanogr. 1983, 28, 801-815.
12. Niiler, P.P. J. Marine Research 1975, 33, 405-422.
13. Garwood, R.W. Ph.D. Thesis, University of Washington, Seattle, 1976.
14. Martin, P.J.; Trans,. Am. Geophys. Un. 1985, 66, Paper No. 21F-06,
15. Niiler, P.P.; Kraus, E.B. In "Modelling and Prediction of the Upper Layers of the Ocean"; Kraus, E.B., Ed.; Pergamon Press, 1977; Chap. 10.
16. Zika, R.G.; Moffett, J.W.; Petasne, R.G.; Cooper W.J.; Saltzman, E.S. Geochim. Cosmochim. Acta 1985, 49, 1173-1184.
17. Veith, G.D., personal communication.

RECEIVED July 1, 1986

Chapter 20

Measurement of Quantum Yields in Polychromatic Light: Dinitroaniline Herbicides

William M. Draper[1]

Environmental Health Division, School of Public Health, University of Minnesota, Minneapolis, MN 55455

General procedures are described for determination of wavelength-averaged quantum yields in near UV light (310-410 nm). Calculations are discussed and a computer program in BASIC language is provided which allows rapid and accurate computation of Φ. In this work the widely available Rayonet photoreactor fitted with fluorescent black light lamps is used to measure Φ for fluchloralin, isopropalin, and profluralin, important dinitroaniline herbicides. Study of these pesticides demonstrates the utility of the procedure as well as the sensitivity of Φ to slight changes in molecular structure.

The burgeoning interest in mathematical modeling as a tool for predicting the fate of chemicals in the environment has emphasized the need for accurate measurement of rate constants for various chemical and photochemical processes. Models have been developed which allow accurate prediction of aquatic environmental photolysis rates for various seasons, latitudes and water depths (1,2). The predictive capability of such models is further enhanced by incorporating data on the attenuation of incident sunlight by endogenous substances in the water column, i.e., chlorophyll, organic carbon, and suspended material. The considerable success of these models is achieved by detailed estimation of the rate of sunlight absorption by the substrate under hypothetical environmental conditions.

The needed compound-specific inputs include molar extinction coefficients, indicating the efficiency with which incident light is absorbed, and a disappearance quantum yield (Φ) which gauges the efficiency for conversion of absorbed light energy to pho-

[1]Current address: California Public Health Foundation, Berkeley, CA 94704

tochemical reactions of the chromophore. ϕ and the absorption
spectrum, of course, are essential pieces of data for definition
of the fate of environmental chemicals. To date very few applicable environmental quantum yields have been published in the open
literature.

Unlike other physicochemical molecular properties affecting
environmental behavior, there are no useful guidelines or even
empirical relationships for prediction of ϕ. Subtle changes in
molecular structure, as will be demonstrated in this study, alter
the efficiency of competing photochemical and photophysical processes. For most molecules quantum yields are less than 0.01 (3)
indicating that the vast majority of electromagnetic energy
absorbed does not affect a chemical reaction of the substrate.
The variation of known quantum yields is remarkable, however,
ranging from greater than unity to less than 10^{-6}. Since there is
no alternative available to experimental measurement of ϕ, stan-
dardized and straightforward procedures and apparatus for ϕ
measurement are needed by environmental chemists.

The fundamentals of quantum yield measurement have been
described in various sources (2, 4, 5). For purposes of environmental modeling quantum efficiencies in solution are assumed to be
wavelength-independent. It is generally accepted, however, that
environmental ϕ measurements should be restricted to wavelengths
greater than 280 nm. Use of monochromatic light simplifies ϕ
determination since only a single extinction coefficient is
required and this approach has gained the widest acceptance. ϕ
measurement at 313 nm has been recommended (6) since most molecules absorbing sunlight are reactive at this wavelength.
Typically, medium pressure, high intensity mercury arc lamps are
utilized with the desired mercury line or band isolated by a
monochrometer or filter system. Characteristics of the available
lamps, preparation and use of chemical and glass filters and other
photochemical techniques are reviewed in Reference 4.

This chapter outlines a procedure for the determination of
wavelength-averaged quantum yields, that is, ϕ measured in
polychromatic light. In this case use of the Rayonet photoreactor
equipped with fluorescent blacklight lamps emitting over the range
of 310 to 410 nm was examined. The rationale for this approach
are the following: (1) such photoreactors are widely available in
chemical laboratories; (2) determination of ϕ in polychromatic
light is not difficult experimentally nor does it require additional effort when compared to single-wavelength ϕ; and (3) the
data obtained are in a form directly amenable to environmental
modeling. This procedure is applied here to selected dinitroanilines, widely used pre-emergence herbicides, as well as other
classes of commercial pesticides, some with known quantum yields.

Methods and Materials

Chemicals. Pesticides were analytical reference standards pro-
vided by the U.S. Environmental Protection Agency Pesticides and
Industrial Chemicals Repository (Research Triangle Park, NC).
Acetonitrile and toluene (pesticide grade) and other chemicals

(reagent grade) were obtained commercially and used as received. Water was 10 megaohm demineralized.

Solutions. Primary chemical standards (10 g/L) were prepared in acetonitrile with secondary standards (20 mg/L) obtained by serial dilution. For irradiation 25 ug/L (ppb) aqueous solutions were obtained by dissolving 0.125 mL of the respective secondary standard in 100 mL of demineralized water. UV absorption spectra were recorded (Beckman DU-7) for acetonitrile solutions often using the 20 part-per-million secondary standards, and 2.5- to 10-nm bandwidth average extinction coefficients were determined for wavelengths above 297.5 nm (1).

Irradiation. Samples (uniformly 5.0 mL) were irradiated in borosilicate glass test tubes (Pyrex #9820) sealed with foil-wrapped stoppers. Tubes were held in a merry-go-round apparatus and irradiated in a Rayonet RPR-100 photo-reactor (Southern New England Ultraviolet Company, Hamden, CT) equipped with 16 RPR-3500 lamps.

Actinometry. The dinitroaniline herbicide trifluralin was used as a chemical actinometer (7). The disappearance quantum yield of trifluralin varies with solvent as follows: water, 0.002 (1); acetonitrile-water (1:1, v/v), 0.0035; acetonitrile, 0.0052; isooctane, 0.018; petroleum ether, 0.017; toluene, 0.0091. Toluene was used in the present study since in this solvent trifluralin exhibited a convenient half-life (~10 min), the solvent was low in volatility, and could be analyzed directly by gas-liquid chromatography (GLC). Non aqueous actinometer solvents are generally to be avoided when measuring quantum yields for pollutants in water (8) due to differences in refractive index. This is not a concern here, however, since the cell geometry and sample volume are constant, and the light field is uniform for samples in a merry-go-round device (5). Typically, the eight positions of the merry-go-round apparatus were occupied by seven tubes containing the experimental substrate and one of the actinometer. Sample tubes were withdrawn periodically to generate a time series for the semi-logarithmic dissipation curve while the actinometer tubes were irradiated for a duration of about one half-life allowing multiple measurements of the light intensity.

Analysis. Aqueous solutions were extracted with 2 mL of toluene in tubes used for irradiation. Pesticide concentrations in the toluene extracts were determined directly by GLC using a ^{63}Ni electron capture detector and a 15 meter X 0.53 mm (ID) bonded silicone phase (1.5 micron film thickness, 95% dimethyl-5% diphenylpolysiloxane, "DB-5", equivalent to SE-52) fused silica capillary column mounted in a conventional packed port. The instrument operating conditions were: inlet, 250 °C; detector, 300 °C; helium carrier gas flow rate, 7 mL/min. With a column temperature of 180 °C the dinitroanilines were completely resolved and exhibited the following retention times: fluchloralin (4.71 min); profluralin (4.29 min); isopropalin (11.27 min); trifluralin (185 °C, 2.4 min). Details of the analysis of DDE, methoxychlor, methyl parathion and p-nitroanisole are provided elsewhere (7).

Results and Discussion

Lamp Emission Characteristics. Detailed knowledge of both the
light intensity and wavelength distribution are required for quantum yield measurements in polychromatic light. Accordingly, the
availability of accurate emission spectra or the capability for
their measurement will determine the utility of a given lamp in
such studies. Another factor which must be considered is light
transmission by the photolysis cell. Soft glass is opaque below
about 310 nm whereas borosilicate (Pyrex) glass transmits a
greater portion of UV-B radiation with a cutoff of about 280 nm
(4). Thin-walled borosilicate glass will transmit some UV light,
however, and the envelopes of some germicidal lamps are
constructed of this material. Cells of quartz or silica glass
(Vycor), although costly, are transparent over the
entire UV-visible range.

The mercury-excited phosphor lamps chosen for study here emit
about 90 percent of their energy as long wavelength UV or "black"
light according to manufacturer's specifications. The thick Pyrex
walls of the sample tubes block any energetic UV light which might
escape the lamp envelope without significant absorption of the
long wavelength UV radiation. The photoreactor chamber is a
cylindrical array (21.5 cm diameter) of 16 lamps and under typical
operating conditions the long wavelength UV light flux in the
center of the reactor is 9,200 microwatts/cm^2. Since the samples
are held at a distance of 6.6 cm from the lamp surface in the
merry-go-round apparatus, it is estimated that the samples are
subjected to an intensity of 10,280 microwatts/cm^2. This correction was estimated from an intensity-distance plot provided by the
manufacturer. Light energy over a series of 2.5-, 5- and 10-nm
bandwidths, those corresponding to the GCSolar model (1), were
converted from units of energy/time to light quanta/time for purposes of calculating the rate of light absorption.

An impression of the rates of photoprocesses in the photoreactor in relation to natural sunlight is gained on examining
Figure 1. The intensity of UV-A radiation (320-400 nm) is about
1.7 times the intensity of midday summer sunlight (latitude 40° N)
(1) and about 3.7 times that of midday winter sunlight. Thus,
molecules with principal absorption in the UV-A range are predicted to photodegrade at greater rates in the laboratory photoreactor. In the UV-B range, that below 320 nm, the photoreactor
has between 1.5 and 5.7 times the intensity of midday sunlight
depending on the season. Light of wavelengths below 320 nm is
most likely to overlap the absorption spectrum of organic molecules. Some environmental chemicals, i.e., polycyclic aromatic
hydrocarbons, which absorb longer wavelength radiation may photodegrade more rapidly in sunlight.

Calculations. The calculation of quantum yields is accomplished
with the following formula (2) which relates Φ to the direct
photolysis half-life and the rate of light absorption.

$$\Phi = \frac{(0.693)(6.02 \times 10^{20})}{2.303 \, t_{\frac{1}{2}} \, \Sigma \, \varepsilon_\lambda \, Z_\lambda} \qquad (1)$$

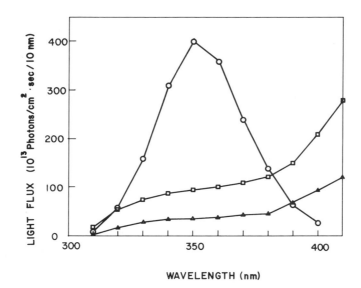

Figure 1. Spectra for fluorescent lamps (O), midday summer sunlight (□) and winter sunlight (Δ) for latitude 40 °N (1). Reproduced from Ref. 7. Copyright 1985, Pergamon Press Ltd.

In this expression $\bar{\phi}$ is dimensionless, the half-life has units of seconds and the twentieth-power term in the numerator is a conversion factor with units of moles/photon. The integral overlap of the lamp emission and the chromophore electronic spectrum, $\Sigma\varepsilon_\lambda Z_\lambda$, defines light absorption in photons mole^{-1} sec^{-1}. ε_λ is the average extinction coefficient for a given wavelength interval with Z_λ equaling the lamp output over this same band.

The first-order disappearance of the substrate yields a linear semilogarithmic plot with slope equal to k^{-1} and $t_{\frac{1}{2}}$ equal to $0.693/k$. Linear regression is used to obtain the best estimate of the substrate half-life. At the high chemical dilutions used in this procedure (ppb levels) conversion of the substrate is not critical since only a minute fraction of the incident radiation is absorbed and competition for light or quenching of excited states by photoproducts is not significant.

As outlined above the near UV irradiance experienced by samples in the photoreactor is typically 10,280 microwatts/cm^2. The actual intensity of light emitted, however, varies with the temperature of the arc wall, current, age of the lamps and other factors (4) necessitating the use of chemical actinometers. For measurement of wavelength-averaged quantum yields it is necessary to assume that the wavelength distribution of the light source is invariant. Thus, Z_λ values given in Table I are each corrected by the same factor as follows:

$$Z_\lambda \text{ (actual)} = Z_\lambda \text{ (10,280)} \times \frac{t_{\frac{1}{2}}, \text{trifluralin (10,280)}}{t_{\frac{1}{2}}, \text{trifluralin (actual)}} \qquad (2)$$

The numerator is the expected actinometer half-life for an irradiance of 10,280 microwatts/cm^2 while the denominator is the observed actinometer half-life. Expected trifluralin half-lives calculated according to Equation 1 with quantum yields stated above and spectral data compiled in Table I, are 44 and 9.7 minutes for aqueous and toluene solutions, respectively.

Rapid and Accurate Calculation of $\bar{\phi}$. For speed and accuracy in calculation of wavelength-averaged quantum yields a short computer program in BASIC language has proven useful (Figure 2). This program utilizes several simple arrays for storing variables and for inputting experimental data. In the array named LAMP (statement #70) values of Z_λ are assigned for the 15 wavelength intervals between 310 and 410 nanometers. The WAVE array declared in statement #230 prompts the operator to input ε_λ values for the reactant which are assigned to memory locations in EXTINCT. A fourth and final array, OVLAP, performs an arithmetic operation yielding the spectral overlap. Up to this point the program assumes the radiant energy to be 10,280 microwatts/cm^2, so-called "standard" conditions. As described above the actual rate of light absorption is obtained by a correction factor (statement #580) using experimental and standard half-lives for the trifluralin actinometer. The program outputs the following information: photon irradiance (ΣZ_λ); $\Sigma\varepsilon_\lambda Z_\lambda$; and $\bar{\phi}$. The use of a microcomputer allows calculation of $\bar{\phi}$ and confirmatory calculations in a short period of time.

Table I. Typical Spectral Irradiance Values and Dinitroaniline Herbicide Absorption Spectra

Wavelength (nm)	Photon Irradiance (Photons cm^{-2} sec^{-1})	Extinction Coefficients[b] (L $mole^{-1}$ cm^{-1})			
		Fluchloralin	Isopropalin	Profluralin	Trifluralin
297.5	–	1,920	1,400	3,480	3,820
300	–	1,790	1,280	2,980	3,340
302.5	–	1,660	1,210	2,500	2,920
305	–	1,570	1,150	2,290	2,590
307.5	–	1,480	1,090	2,140	2,190
310	3.9 E + 13	1,410	1,040	2,010	1,960
312.5	7.5 E + 13	1,370	1,020	1,850	1,840
315	1.2 E + 14	1,350	985	1,750	1,730
317.5	1.9 E + 14	1,330	997	1,650	1,630
320	2.6 E + 14	1,310	1,000	1,580	1,580
323.1	6.3 E + 14	1,360	997	1,540	1,530
330	1.6 E + 15	1,450	1,000	1,540	1,460
340	3.1 E + 15	1,580	997	1,650	1,580
350	4.0 E + 15	1,720	985	1,820	1,740
360	3.6 E + 15	1,910	991	2,020	1,960
370	2.4 E + 15	1,980	967	2,200	2,140
380	1.4 E + 15	2,030	1,030	2,350	2,290
390	6.3 E + 14	1,960	1,050	2,400	2,340
400	2.8 E + 14	1,840	1,060	2,350	2,340
410	9.6 E + 13	1,690	1,050	2,280	2,310
420	–	1,450	1,030	2,210	2,230
430	–	1,230	995	2,070	2,080
440	–	859	915	1,810	1,860
450	–	577	811	1,490	1,460
460	–	366	663	1,070	1,100
470	–	211	510	725	680
480	–	–	375	466	450
490	–	–	282	328	270
500	–	–	196	207	150

a   Total near UV intensity of 10,280 microwatts/cm^2

b   UV-visible spectra recorded in acetonitrile

```
10    PRINT "WHAT IS THE NAME OF THE COMPOUND?"
20    INPUT COMPOUND$
30    PRINT "WHAT IS THE HALF-LIFE FOR",COMPOUND$,"IN SECONDS?"
40    INPUT THALF
50    PRINT "WHAT IS THE HALF-LIFE FOR THE TRIFLURALIN ACTINOMETER WITH TO
      LUENE AS SOLVENT?"
60    INPUT EXHALF
70    DIM LAMP(16)
80 LAMP(1) = 3.9E + 13
90 LAMP(2) = 7.5E + 13
100 LAMP(3) = 1.2E + 14
110 LAMP(4) = 1.9E + 14
120 LAMP(5) = 2.6E + 14
130 LAMP(6) = 6.3E + 14
140 LAMP(7) = 1.6E + 15
150 LAMP(8) = 3.1E + 15
160 LAMP(9) = 4.0E + 15
170 LAMP(10) = 3.6E + 15
180 LAMP(11) = 2.4E + 15
190 LAMP(12) = 1.4E + 15
200 LAMP(13) = 6.3E + 14
210 LAMP(14) = 2.8E + 14
220 LAMP(15) = 9.6E + 13
230    DIM WAVE(16)
240 WAVE(1) = 310
250 WAVE(2) = 312.5
260 WAVE(3) = 315
270 WAVE(4) = 317.5
280 WAVE(5) = 320
290 WAVE(6) = 323.1
300 WAVE(7) = 330
310 WAVE(8) = 340
320 WAVE(9) = 350
330 WAVE(10) = 360
340 WAVE(11) = 370
350 WAVE(12) = 380
360 WAVE(13) = 390
370 WAVE(14) = 400
380 WAVE(15) = 410
390    DIM EXTINCT(16)
400 I = 1
410    IF I > 15 THEN   GOTO 470
420    PRINT "ENTER THE",COMPOUND$,"EXTINCTION COEFFICIENT FOR WAVELENGTH"

430    PRINT WAVE(I),"NANOMETERS."
440    INPUT EXTINCT(I)
450 I = I + 1
460    GOTO 410
470 SUM = 0
480 I = 1
490    DIM OVLAP(16)
500    IF I > 15 THEN   GOTO 550
510 OVLAP(I) = LAMP(I) * EXTINCT(I)
520 SUM = SUM + OVLAP(I)
530 I = I + 1
540    GOTO 500
550 KA = (2.303 * SUM) / 6.02E + 20
560 PHI = 0.693 / (THALF * KA)
570 STDHALF = 584.6
580 CFAC = EXHALF / STDHALF
590 TRUFLUX = 10280 / CFAC
600 CSUM = SUM / CFAC
610 CPHI = PHI * CFAC
620    PRINT "THE LIGHT INTENSITY IN THE PHOTOREACTOR IS",TRUFLUX,"MICROWA
      TTS PER SQUARE CENTIMETER."
630    PRINT "THE RATE OF LIGHT ABSORPTION BY",COMPOUND$,"IS",CSUM,"PHOTON
      S PER MOLE PER SECOND."
640    PRINT "THE QUANTUM YIELD FOR",COMPOUND$,"IS",CPHI"."
650    END
```

Figure 2. Microcomputer program in BASIC language for
rapid and accurate calculation of wavelength-
averaged quantum yields.

Method Validation. In studies reported elsewhere (7) satisfactory measurements of Φ have been obtained by this procedure when results were compared to published single-wavelength quantum yields determined at 313 or 366 nm or those measured in sunlight. This is the case even without the use of a chemical actinometer, e.g., assuming a constant light intensity of 10,280 microwatts/cm^2 in the operating photoreactor. Φ values for substrates which absorb the emitted radiation poorly (i.e., DDE and methoxychlor) as well as molecules with efficient long-wavelength UV chromophores (trifluralin) were determined with equal accuracy demonstrating the utility of the procedure and the accuracy of the available emission spectrum.

Dinitroaniline Quantum Yields. The dinitroanilines are a structurally diverse group of pesticides used in large volume for selective pre-emergence weed control in cotton, soybeans and corn. Electron-withdrawing substituents (e.g., nitro groups) in the 2- and 6- position are required for high herbicidal activity while functionality at other positions seems less critical (9). For this study dinitroanilines with minor modifications in the N-alkyl and para-ring substituents were examined (Figure 3).

The photochemical reactivity of this herbicide class is well known and has been studied in aqueous media (1), vapor phase (10), organic solvents (11) and on soil surfaces (12, 13). Photoreduced (e.g., amines and azobenzene and azoxybenzene dimers), N-dealkylated and cyclized derivatives appear to be the predominant photochemical transformation products. In practical application these pesticides must be soil incorporated due in large part to their photochemical instability. Interestingly, the dinitroanilines are potent photostabilizers capable of protecting photolabile insecticides on surfaces (14).

The substituted dinitroaniline herbicides absorb well into the visible region due to extended pi-electron systems. The λ_{max} for each (Table I.) is in the 380-400 nm range where extinction coefficients (log$_{10}$) are 3.0-3.4 for the pi to pi* electronic transition. These electronic spectra afforded excellent chromophores for absorption of the emitted black-light radiation.

Fluchloralin, isopropalin and profluralin each photodegraded rapidly in the laboratory photoreactor (Figure 4). The disappearance of both isopropalin and fluchloralin showed little deviation from an exponential curve, while photolysis of the least photolabile herbicide, profluralin, unexplicably showed greater experimental error. The data depicted in Figure 4 represent photolysis of a single substrate in solution. The low analytical concentrations of the chromophores (25 ppb) and the ability to resolve the reactants and photoproducts chromatographically, however, allowed simultaneous measurement of quantum yields for mixtures. Under similar experimental conditions trifluralin exhibited a half-life of 52-68 minutes (7). Over the period of the photolysis experiment no change in concentration was observed for solutions held in the dark.

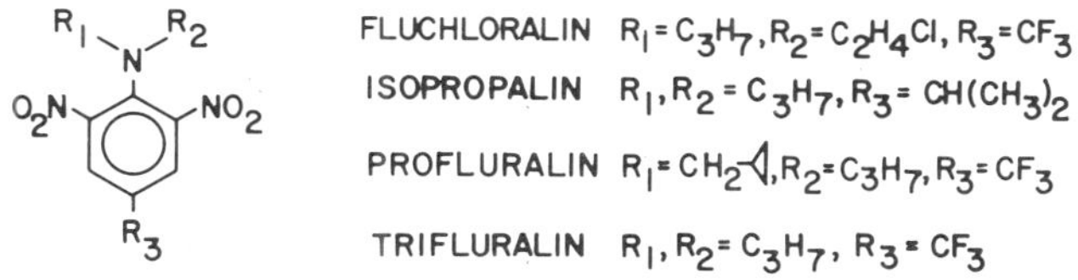

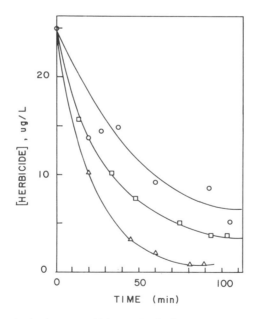

FLUCHLORALIN $R_1 = C_3H_7, R_2 = C_2H_4Cl, R_3 = CF_3$

ISOPROPALIN $R_1, R_2 = C_3H_7, R_3 = CH(CH_3)_2$

PROFLURALIN $R_1 = CH_2 \triangleleft, R_2 = C_3H_7, R_3 = CF_3$

TRIFLURALIN $R_1, R_2 = C_3H_7, R_3 = CF_3$

Figure 3. Chemical structures for substituted dinitroaniline herbicides.

Figure 4. Photodecomposition of dinitroaniline herbicides
in water: isopropalin (Δ), fluchloralin (□)
and profluralin (O).

Replotting the photodecomposition data on semilogarithmic scale revealed first-order reaction kinetics (Figure 5.) with no evidence of departure from linearity over several half-lives. Correlation coefficients for these lines varied between -0.95 and -1.0.

Photochemical kinetic data and outputs from the microcomputer program are summarized in Table II. As can be seen, the near UV radiant energy in the photoreactor varied little from experiment to experiment, but usually was substantially lower than the standard 10,280 microwatts/cm². These irradiance values are based on 5 or 6 consecutive ~one-actinometer-half-life measurements with the chemical actinometer during the photolysis experiments.

The importance of the para-CF₃ group to the dinitroaniline chromophore is evident from these data (and Table I) -- $\Sigma \epsilon_\lambda \ Z_\lambda$ for both fluchloralin and profluralin greatly exceed that of isopropalin with a para-CH(CH₃)₂ substituent. An interesting and not easily predicted result is that isopropalin is the most photochemically reactive of the analogs. Isopropalin utilizes absorbed radiant energy 4 to 6 times more efficiently than its para-CF₃ analogs. It appears from this limited survey of dinitroaniline structure-photoreactivity that the electron-donating para-substituent, while limiting light absorption, greatly enhances the chemical reactivity of the resulting electronically-excited state.

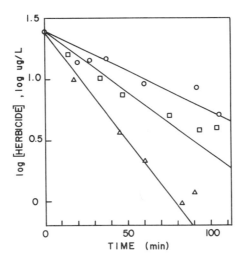

Figure 5. Semilogarithmic plots for photodecomposition of dinitroaniline herbicides: isopropalin (Δ), fluchloralin (□) and profluralin (O).

Table II. Photodecomposition Kinetics, Rates of Light Absorption and Quantum
Yields for Dinitroaniline Herbicides

Compound	Half-life (sec)	Trifluralin[a] Half-life (sec)	Experimental Light intensity (microwatts/cm²)	Light Absorption Rate (photons mole-1 sec-1)	Quantum[b] Yield
Fluchloralin	1,752	744	8,077	2.53 E 19	0.0041 (0.0037)
Isopropalin	912	747	8,045	1.43 E 19	0.014 (0.013)
Profluralin	2,658	732	8,210	2.81 E 19	0.0024 (0.0013)

[a] Toluene solutions

[b] The values given in parentheses were derived from simultaneous irradiation of the three pesticides in a single solution. The initial concentration of each compound was 25 ppb and the average light intensity (n = 4) was 7,570 microwatts/cm².

Conclusion

Measurement of wavelength-averaged quantum yields in systems like that described here offers a number of advantages to the environmental photochemist. Determinations are experimentally straightforward, provide an optimum degree of experimental control and yield data which is readily amenable to mathematical modeling. Moreover, since near UV ϕ are generally invariant with wavelength, the wavelength-averaged ϕ should be indistinguishable from single-wavelength ϕ measured at 313 nm or other wavelengths in this portion of the spectrum.

Acknowledgment

Michael Kierski provided assistance in preparation of the computer program. I thank Betty Romani for typing numerous drafts of the chapter. Funding by the National Institute of Environmental Health Sciences (Grant R23ES03524) and the 3M Foundation is gratefully acknowledged.

Literature Cited

1. Zepp, R. G.; Cline, D. M., "Rates of direct photolysis in aquatic environment," *Environ. Sci. Technol.* 1977, 11, 359-366.
2. Zepp, R. G., "Quantum yields for reaction of pollutants in dilute aqueous solution," *Environ. Sci. Technol.* 1978, 12, 327-329.
3. Harris, J. C.; In Handbook of Chemical Property Estimation Methods, Lyman, W.; Reehl, W.; Rosenblatt, D., Eds. McGraw-Hill: New York, 1982; Chapter 8.

4. Calvert, J. G.; Pitts, J. N., Jr. Photochemistry, Wiley; New York, 1966.
5. Moses, F. G.; Liu, R. S. H.; Monroe, B. M., "The merry-go-round quantum yield apparatus," Mol. Photochem. 1969, 1, 245-249.
6. Zepp, R. G.; Baughman, G. L.; Schlotzhauer, P. F.; "Comparison of photochemical behavior of various humic substances in water: I. Sunlight induced reactions of aquatic pollutants photosensitized by humic substances," Chemosphere 10, 119 (1981).
7. Draper, W. M., "Determination of wavelength-averaged, near UV quantum yields for environmental chemicals," Chemosphere, 1985, 14, 1195-1203.
8. Mill, T.; Mabey, W. R.; Lan, B. Y.; Baraze, A., "Photolysis of polycyclic aromatic hydrocarbons in water," Chemosphere, 1981, 10, 1281-1290.
9. Jäger, G., In Chemistry of Pesticides, Büchel, K. H., Ed. John-Wiley: New York, 1983; Chapter 4.
10. Woodrow, J. E.; Crosby, D. G.; Seiber, J. N. "Vapor-phase photochemistry of pesticides," Residue Rev. 1983, 85, 111-125.
11. Sullivan, R. G.; Knoche, H. W.; Markle, J. C., "Photolysis of trifluralin; characterization of azobenzene and azoxybenzene photodegradation products," J. Agric. Food Chem. 1980, 28, 746-755.
12. Plimmer, H. R., "Photolysis of TCDD and trifluralin on silica and soil, "Bull. Environm. Contam. Toxicol. 1978, 20, 87-92.
13. Parochetti, J. V.; Dec, G. W., Jr., "Photodecomposition of eleven dinitroaniline herbicides," Weed Sci., 1978, 26, 153-156.
14. Dureja, P.; Casida, J. E.; Ruzo, L. O., "Dinitroanilines as photostabilizers for pyrethroids," J. Agric. Food Chem. 1984, 32, 246-250.

RECEIVED May 27, 1986

Author Index

Subject Index

281

Production and indexing by Deborah H. Steiner
Jacket design by Pamela Lewis

Elements typeset by Hot Type Ltd., Washington, DC
Printed and bound by Maple Press Company, York, PA